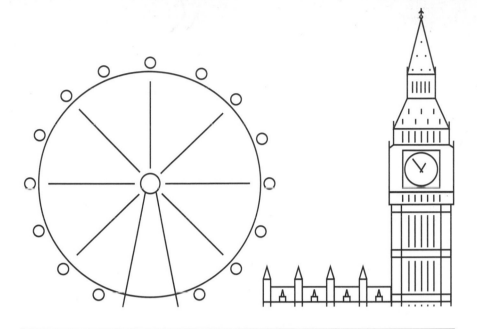

JOHN CATT'S

Which London School? & the South-East

2016/17

27th Edition
Editor: Jonathan Barnes

JOHN CATT
EDUCATIONAL
LIMITED

Published in 2016 by
John Catt Educational Ltd,
12 Deben Mill Business Centre,
Woodbridge, Suffolk IP12 1BL UK
Tel: 01394 389850   Fax: 01394 386893
Email: enquiries@johncatt.com
Website: www.johncatt.com
© 2016 John Catt Educational Ltd

A CIP catalogue record for this book is available from the British Library.

ISBN: 978 1 909 717 73 2

Contacts
Editor
Jonathan Barnes

Advertising & School Profiles
Tel: +44 (0) 1394 389850
Email: sales@johncatt.com

Distribution/Book Sales
Tel: +44 (0) 1394 389863
Email: booksales@johncatt.com

Contents

GDST schools. Where girls can.

Choosing your daughter's school is one of the biggest decisions you, as parents, will make. At the GDST we put girls first, ensuring that everything in their school lives is calibrated and designed to meet their educational and pastoral needs.

The GDST has always been a pioneer of girls' education in the UK. Our network of 26 schools and academies provides unmatched opportunities, connections and resources for girls between the ages of three and 18.

GDST schools in London

Blackheath High School
Bromley High School
Croydon High School
Kensington Prep School
Northwood College for Girls
Notting Hill & Ealing High School

Putney High School
South Hampstead High School
Streatham & Clapham High School
Sutton High School
Sydenham High School
Wimbledon High School

GDST schools and academies outside London

The Belvedere Academy, Liverpool
Birkenhead High School Academy
Brighton & Hove High School
Howell's School, Llandaff
Ipswich High School for Girls
Newcastle High School for Girls
Northampton High School

Norwich High School for Girls
Nottingham Girls' High School
Oxford High School
Portsmouth High School
The Royal High School, Bath
Sheffield High School
Shrewsbury High School

gdst Girls' Day School Trust

A network of Confident, Composed, Courageous, Committed girls.

See www.gdst.net to find your closest GDST school or academy, and arrange a visit.

Great schools where 'heart is the boss' – why London's education sector is thriving

Neil Roskilly, chief executive officer of the Independent Schools Association, says that interest in private schools 'has never been more buoyant'

*"On Waterloo Bridge with the wind in my hair
I am tempted to skip.
You're a fool. I don't care.
the head does its best but
the heart is the boss-
I admit it before I am
halfway across"*
Wendy Cope

Private schools in the capital are in danger of imploding, that's the common message. They have priced themselves out of the market and need desperately to reduce their fees. They're the last refuge of sexism and elitism (and every other -ism, for that matter), perhaps on the same level as membership of the Garrick Club. We hear from the likes of *The Good Schools Guide* that state schools have upped their game and private schools will close as a result.

Yet the real facts behind these very lazy headlines are very different. Interest in private schools has never been more buoyant in London and the South-East. Like-for-like numbers between 2007 and 2015 are up by 7% and schools report growing waiting lists and enquiries. New private schools with excellent backing are being established in the capital and are already providing stiff competition for their more-established brethren.

So why is it that private schools in London are more popular than ever? There can't be that many 'toffs' left in captivity to fill their places, even if their numbers are boosted by overseas aspirants who still rightly regard a British education as the pinnacle? In fact, there are some interesting trends that tend not to get reported. Private education remains a huge aspiration among families who have never accessed the sector. In addition, disposable incomes are once more growing and, at the same time, schools have dramatically increased their bursary provision. That hasn't been limited to charitable trust schools that feel the need to justify public benefit, but also proprietary schools that are also keen to widen access. Incidentally, there's little difference in pupil outcomes between charitable trust schools and their proprietary cousins, so this shouldn't be a deciding factor for parents looking for the best possible outcomes for their children, but that's rather an aside.

However, parents are taking a flexible approach to accessing private education, being more concerned with the quality of education rather than the type of delivery. So if there's a good state primary in the area but secondary options are less appealing, they see it as an opportunity to postpone the cost of private education. But if Early Years prospects aren't strong, then that's the key stage of a child's education where private schools are approached with 'a good start' uppermost in parents' minds. Many new purchasers of independent education are first introduced to the sector via nursery provision, and soon learn that private schools aren't the elite preserves that the media sometimes portrays.

Yet to many there's little doubt that state schools in London have improved. The question is how sustainable that is, especially with Ofsted now finding more requiring improvement and some schools' previously 'good' or 'outstanding' ratings collapsing almost overnight. Snapshot inspection reports aren't everything, of course, and parents should always treat them with some degree of caution. The most important question that any parent can ask of a school remains whether their child will

> The most important question that any parent can ask of a school remains whether their child will be happy there. Nothing else comes close in terms of ensuring success and even very dry academic analysis comes to the same conclusion: a happy child learns. That's where private schools have the edge, even when a state school's headline figures are impressive.

be happy there. Nothing else comes close in terms of ensuring success and even very dry academic analysis comes to the same conclusion: a happy child learns. That's where private schools have the edge, even when a state school's headline figures are impressive. The nurturing approach of private schools in small classes where all children are known – and cannot hide – just isn't replicated in state schools, even the most outwardly successful.

London, more than any other part of the UK, is blessed with ever-changing educational possibilities and parents looking to educate their children privately would do well to explore the market before signing on the dotted admissions line. For every well-known selective school there are many others that also do a fabulous job – they just need hunting down. Parents are discovering these hidden gems and word-of-mouth is of paramount importance in the discovery process. Yet parents need to know their children well in terms of the school environment in which they are likely to thrive. It can't always be assumed that because a school has a growing or ambitious reputation that it will suit every child. Similarly, parents would do well to avoid the views of self-publicists and other gannets that pick on the bones of the sector. When it comes to choosing a school,

there's nothing better than visiting (open days are too orchestrated to be of much use here, but good schools will always open their doors at any time) and for parents to tap into their gut instincts: "It feels right; these are the people that will encourage and nurture my child, allow them to make mistakes and identify their strengths and feed their interests."

And that's where London's education sector shines. Great schools plant the seeds of success at an early age, perhaps only to flower much later in life. They welcome children not just as another number, but as an individual who will contribute to and gain from the community of learners in the school. Many pay lip-service to that, but parents will soon discern the genuine educators from those who seem to believe that the sector owes them a living. Great schools don't put their positions in the league tables above the needs of the children – parents just need to look at the criteria for scholarships to see the underlying values of a school. Great schools allow children to feel the wind in their hair as they cross Waterloo Bridge, and give time to exploring the feelings of exhilaration that result. Great schools allow children of any age to skip and run, particularly through the endless corridors of their own imaginations. For these schools the heart is the boss, and children love it.

Neil Roskilly is Chief Executive Officer of The Independent Schools Association (ISA). For more information about the ISA see page 37

How to use this guide

Are you looking for...

Help and advice?
If so, take a look at our editorial section (pages 5-38). Here you will find articles written by experts in their field covering issues you may well come across when choosing a school for your child.

A school or college in a certain geographical area?
Then you need to go to page D105 to find the directory page reference to a particular area. We suggest that you look first in the directory for basic information about all the schools in each region, complete with contact details, so that you will be better informed about the choices available to you. From this section you will be directed to more detailed information in the profile section, where this is available.

A certain type of school or college in a particular area?
Look in the directories for the area you want (again, you can find the directory page reference on D105). Underneath each school listed you will find icons that denote different types of schools or qualifications that they offer. You can find a key to these icons on the following page; this key is repeated at the front of each section of the directory.

A specific school or college?

If you know the name of the school or college but are unsure of its location, simply go to the index at the back of the guide where you will find all the schools listed alphabetically. You will find that some page numbers are prefixed with the letter D, this denotes that the school appears in the directory section. Schools with page numbers not prefixed by the letter D, denote those that have chosen to include a fuller school profile, which will provide you with much more extensive information.

Maps?

See pp 40, 76 and 88 for maps of London, Greater London, and the South-East. There are also maps within the directory sections on D106 (Central London), D131 (Greater London) and D139 (South-East).

More information on relevant educational organisations and examinations?

Look in the examinations and qualifications section and the useful organisations section, both located towards the back of the guide.

Key to directory

County	**Wherefordshire**
Name of school or college	**College Academy**
Indicates that this school has a profile	*For further details see p. 12*
Address and contact number	Which Street, Whosville, Wherefordshire AB12 3CD
	Tel: 01000 000000
Head's name	**Head Master:** Dr A Person
School type	**Type:** Coeducational day & boarding
Age range	**Age range:** 11–18
Number of pupils. B = boys G = girls	**No. of pupils:** 660 B330 G330
Fees per annum. Day = fees for day pupils. WB = fees for weekly boarders. FB = fees for full boarders.	**Fees:** Day £11,000 WB £16,000 FB £20,000

Key to directory icons (abridged)

Key to symbols:
- Boys' school
- Coeducational school
- Girls' school
- International school

Schools offering:
- A levels
- Boarding accommodation
- £ Bursaries
- Entrance at 16+

- International Baccalaureate
- Learning support
- Tutorial/sixth form college
- Vocational qualifications

Learning lessons From 'The Greatest City on Earth'

Angela Drew, Headmistress of Bromley High School GDST, says making use of close proximity to London helps set a global benchmark for education

Success breeds success. This is no more true than in the competitive educational environment of London and the South-East. The domination of the academic school league tables by schools in what Boris Johnson's Vision for 2020 describes as 'The Greatest City on Earth' is amply demonstrated by the latest *Sunday Times* Parent Power Table. Eight of the top 10 schools might fairly be called London or Greater London schools (including one highly selective state grammar school, Queen Elizabeth's School, Barnet) and the remaining two, Guildford High School and Brighton College, can also be found in the pages of this guide.

A clue to one of the principal reasons for this dominance can be gleaned by scanning further down the top 20 schools; the only schools which break the hegemony of the South-East are schools based in Oxford or Cambridge. The success of the best schools relies on being able to attract the best teachers – teachers whose love of their subject is infectious and inspirational.

Proximity to London, its diversity, nightlife and culture, is often top of the list for bright young people considering their next move after university and London itself offers a vast talent pool of young graduates emerging from the capital's world class universities. University College London's Institute of Education not only trains 1,500 new teachers each year but has 4,000 Masters students and 800 researchers reflecting the unrivalled opportunities for continuing professional development offered by the capital.

Yet, as parents looking for places in the top London academic day schools will be acutely aware, an obvious corollary to their stellar results is the intensively competitive and selective admissions process in the capital. Queen Elizabeth's School, Barnet has 2,000 applicants for its 180 places and numbers attending Open Days at some of the most popular independent day schools can be positively alarming. Small wonder that parental anxiety has fuelled an enormous boom in recent years in tutoring

For highly academic youngsters, bustling London day schools provide an exciting intellectual environment at the heart of one of the world's major cities but these schools offer not only environment in which it is 'cool to be clever' (as Mrs Obama remarked on a visit to a London girls' state school) but also one in which it is 'cool to be cultured.'

for 11+ Entrance examinations for state grammars and independent schools. Intense tutoring of ever younger primary school pupils preparing for multiple entrance examinations is routinely deplored by heads of senior schools as an unnecessary intrusion into the true business of childhood – discovering new things and getting muddy in the process. In selective senior schools, the search goes on for the tutor-resistant test which will identify 'potential', 'problem-solving ability' or 'creativity' – but the march of the tutors continues regardless with new innovations such as Skype and residential tuition extending the reach of preparation for entrance examinations.

For highly academic youngsters, bustling London day schools provide an exciting intellectual environment at the heart of one of the world's major cities but these schools offer not only environment in which it is 'cool to be clever' (as Mrs Obama remarked on a visit to a London girls' state school) but also one in which it is 'cool to be cultured.' London's classrooms reflect its status as an international city immersing children in the rich diversity of cultural influences which their classmates bring to every classroom discussion. Surrounded by the theatres, galleries and concert halls of the West End and South Bank, the capital's schools are in a unique position to develop pupils' appreciation of drama, art and music. Excellence in the creative arts is supported by pupils' access to the best specialist teaching in school but also to external classes at the most prestigious music and drama schools – such as the Junior Guildhall Saturday School. Sport too is often surprisingly strong, despite the obvious lack of rolling acres of playing fields and for one sport in particular, London schools have a distinct natural advantage, the banks of the Thames bristle with school boathouses, a breeding ground for future Olympic rowers.

Outside the capital many of the South-East's schools offer the enticing prospect of an idyllic and healthy childhood spent amongst acres of green space but with the stimulus of the bright lights of London within easy reach.

In many towns across the United Kingdom, choice of independent schools is relatively limited but parents living in the South-East will find that they have a broad choice of schools within a commutable distance from home. Day or boarding, co-educational or single-sex, religious or non-denominational, selective, mixed ability or schools specialising in supporting pupils with learning difficulties. There are also some impressive alternatives in the state sector with several of the Home Counties (Kent, Surrey, Buckinghamshire and Essex) retaining grammar schools, and London state schools have seen a dramatic improvement in results in recent years as a product of increased investment and schemes such as Teach First. Additionally, a distinctive option in the South-East is the 13+ Common Entrance and Scholarship entry to Senior School. Whilst many of those senior schools which used only to admit pupils at 13+ have now shifted to recruiting a proportion of their pupils at 11+, many outstanding prep schools continue to thrive in the Home Counties giving parents the luxury of deciding whether their child would be better suited by beginning senior school as a teenager.

This very breadth of school choice can be daunting. Internet chat rooms encourage parents to agonize over the hunt for the 'perfect' school for their child's unique needs and talents when, in reality, there will be a number of excellent schools in which their child would undoubtedly thrive. All schools value the holistic nature of the education they offer and pride themselves on the excellence of their pastoral care. However, the unusual density of schools in the South-East acts as a driver of quality in education: not only are facilities almost uniformly excellent but schools need to be committed to innovation in order to keep their educational offer distinctive and cutting edge. Schools which use their proximity to London to form creative collaborations – with City firms, Premiership Football Clubs, leading academics and artists – to offer the best career, sporting, intellectual and cultural opportunities will continue to set the global benchmark in education.

For more information about Bromley High School GDST, see 81

Why and how more girls (and boys) should study STEM subjects

Antonia Beary, Headmistress of Mayfield School, says schools need to close a long-standing gender gap

Recent figures reveal a widening divide between the subjects chosen at A level and beyond by girls and boys. While girls are dominating the health sciences like psychology and biology, boys are outnumbering girls by as many as eight to one in subjects like engineering, maths and computer science. Why is this? Is it a problem? And how can we address this issue?

It is well-documented that boys and girls are different. Where boys will take risks easily, girls tend to hang back and weigh up the likelihood of success before committing themselves. Fear of failure can prevent even the brightest girl from challenging herself. Teaching methods and materials for the more mathematical sciences are traditionally biased towards a more-left brain method of learning and understanding, which will typically suit boys better than girls. Coupled with a classroom environment often dominated by male students, it is no surprise that it takes a strong, determined and confident girl, usually with a clear career goal, to opt to enter this environment.

There is no quick fix to this issue, but there are many things that we, as schools, can do to instigate a change. It is not only society's preconceived ideas about science which must be challenged; we need to remove the limits that pupils, particularly girls, are placing on themselves.

Capture her interest

Girls and boys learn in different ways, so in a learning environment it makes sense to give each what they need at each varying stage of development. Girls from single-sex schools like Mayfield are far more likely to opt to study STEM subjects than their peers at co-educational schools. Free from gender stereotyping, our girls enjoy

There is no quick fix to this issue, but there are many things that we, as schools, can do to instigate a change. It is not only society's preconceived ideas about science which must be challenged; we need to remove the limits that pupils, particularly girls, are placing on themselves.

not just equal opportunities, but all the opportunities. Not only that: as specialists in girls' education, we have the expertise to adapt our teaching methods: to contextualise the curriculum with the world around us, in ways that inspire and capture the girls' interest. We find more relevant ways to present scientific principles, and relate what is taught in the classroom to everyday life.

Educate her about the options available
Qualifications in the sciences can lead to careers in all sorts of industries: there are plenty more options than just medicine or laboratory research. We make sure our girls are aware that science degrees can open doors to all sorts of industries, from food production to journalism. We make it our mission to demystify science and to make it accessible to our pupils.

Provide female role models to open doors and share experiences
We invite speakers to talk to our pupils. High flying surgeons and researchers can be very inspiring, but of equal value are former pupils who have recently graduated or embarked upon a career in science: our pupils will relate to and be inspired by a young, female role model, and they will recognise a clear career path, making a sometimes remote goal seem more accessible.

Instil in her the confidence to see that she can do it
We aim to develop within each of our pupils the confidence to succeed in life, not just in science; but they are mutually compatible! We expect girls to be prepared to cope with failure as well as success. We encourage girls to challenge themselves in extra-curricular activities, giving them the confidence to take risks inside the classroom.

Pastoral care is crucial, and this is an area where single-sex schools like Mayfield shine. Individual, focused pastoral care allows girls to develop a positive image of themselves during those turbulent adolescent years, when girls are particularly vulnerable to self-doubt. The right school environment can foster self-belief, developing each girl's confidence in her capabilities, and enabling her to make informed and considered career choices.

Be creative
It is a myth that the sciences and the arts are mutually exclusive. To be a successful as a scientist you need to be creative, and to be a successful artist, you have to have discipline, logic and focus that are usually associate with the scientific. How helpful is it to compartmentalise any child, particularly at the age of 11 or 13 when he or she joins a new school. Schools must encourage their pupils to be creative in all that they do. Rather than be influenced by gender stereotypes, they are encouraged to be themselves, and to be the best that they can be. Consequently, the next generation of girls will grow into mature, independent, confident and well-informed individuals, ready to make their mark on the world.

Antonia Beary has been Headmistress of Mayfield School since 2008.
Fore more information about Mayfield School, see page 94

Developing grit and resilience: Whose responsibility?

Marwan Mikdadi, Deputy Head at Bancroft's School, says schools and families need to work together to help young people cope with life's challenges

Parents rightly expect a lot from schools, especially when they are paying a large chunk of their salary to them, whilst pupils go through their schooling looking for opportunities to learn much along the way; but is it fair, or even right, that schools should be the primary agents for developing grit and resilience in the next generation? Why is it the case that the emphasis on developing resilience has increased in recent years? Clearly parents want to protect their children from the perils in the world outside their comforting school and home environments, deflecting the problems that they may face. But a life without any risk is surely a sorely unfulfilled life? One which is lacking the risks that go hand in hand with the successes. Risk means failure, but it also means rewards; so that without pupils being encouraged to take risks in controlled environments, they are unlikely ever to achieve their full potential.

It is clear that pupils need to develop the skills to cope with the challenges of life that await them in the future.

Successive governments have set out as one of their educational objectives the desire to develop resilience amongst our pupils. Obviously pupils need to be able to cope in the global environment with the difficulties that they will face in trying to find employment, university places and a myriad of other setbacks along the journey that will be their lives; but can schools prepare students for such challenges, especially when we may be trying to develop the skills to cope with the next 50 to 70 years, in other words a world that very few of us can imagine yet? In addition to coping with the potential challenges referred to earlier, pupils also need to be prepared to cope with the challenges posed by technological changes and the potential for failure: failing a driving test, not getting the job hoped for or that university place.

In the current climate, pupils across the developed world are growing up in a very different environment to that which their teachers and parents experienced. Assuming that pupils will respond in the same way

The education of our pupils doesn't start and stop in the academic classroom. All that we embark on is part of the process of developing our pupils' determination to succeed and develop the sort of character that can deal with set-backs.

as we did is clearly not realistic. Pupils are more likely to go through school experiencing cyber-bullying or nomophobia, both of which were not phenomenon that we had to deal with when growing up. I recall growing up in west London and being able to escape a bad day at school; now pupils armed with their smartphones, tablets and laptops are always in communication with their 'friends'; there is nowhere for them to escape to. In addition, young people feel that they need to seek self-affirmation through competing about the number of 'friends' they might have on Facebook, the number of followers on Twitter or the number of likes when they post something. Others will not be able to let go of their smartphone, checking it all through the night and worrying when they do not receive a timely response to their text or instant message. Peer pressure to look a certain way has always existed but usually there was no record, now there is the added pressure of knowing that anything one does in public is almost certain to appear on Instagram or Snapchat in short order and remain there for many years to come.

What can be done by schools to help pupils develop their outer shell, so that they can better cope? At Bancroft's, like many other schools up and down the country, the education of our pupils doesn't start and stop in the academic classroom. All that we embark on is part of the process of developing our pupils' determination to succeed and develop the sort of character that can deal with set-backs. Playing school sport, especially against other schools, gives our children, be they netball, hockey or rugby players, the chance to work as a team, and, importantly, develop the real friendships that allow pupils to share their experiences whilst dealing with adversity. Seeing rugby players calculating the best way to outwit an opposition and working out who they can rely on helps them develop the soft skills that will be necessary in the future. Such experiences are not just confined to the sports' pitches. Many schools like Bancroft's pride themselves on their extensive co-curricular programme, be it in drama, music, Duke of Edinburgh's Award or CCF. All of these give pupils greater opportunities to face a challenge, to deal with it and experience something that doesn't come easily to them whilst requiring them to persevere. The CCF

gives pupils the chance to develop their leadership skills as well as the opportunity to get out of their comfort zone, be it rock climbing in the Lake District or walking across Snowdonia with just a map and your wits to navigate back to base. In music and drama pupils get the chance for rehearsing together, leading, conducting and directing each other, ensuring that they develop the skills necessary to command respect from their peers.

As part of daily life at many independent schools the House and tutor systems play a vital part. Housemasters or Heads of Year look after the progress and welfare of pupils, keeping a close eye on them, using their wealth of experience to keep in touch with parents. Tutors also play a vital role, getting to know the pupil and identifying changes in behaviour as well as pre-empting difficulties and challenges that might arise.

It is absolutely the case that schools play a vital role in developing a young person's resilience and their ability to cope with change and face down the challenges of growing up, but this can only be done in conjunction with parents. Parents have the best chance to get to know their children; they share those special moments, on holidays, at birthday parties and other family moments. Using these special moments can help families work together to ensure that children are better prepared to deal with any setbacks they face, knowing that they have a support mechanism in place and, therefore, giving them the power and confidence to try again and persevere even in the face of difficulties. It is this time and opportunity, when children are open to new ideas, which need to be grasped to ensure that pupils are better prepared to succeed. Parents and schools working hand in hand to set high expectations within a supportive and encouraging environment are probably doing as much as anyone might expect to help the current generation of youngsters develop the skills to cope with the future. But ultimately it is incumbent on parents and schools to remove the scaffolding around pupils over a period of years and allow them to take risks within a controlled environment and so build up the skills necessary for long-term resilience. It will be the children who learn to cope with failure and who pick themselves up after each set-back who are going to most likely succeed in future life.

For more information about Bancroft's School, see page 78

What makes a Steiner education different?

Michael Hall School outlines the focus of its 'rich, broad and balanced curriculum'

Have you ever wondered what life will be like for your child entering adulthood? Modern schooling can sometimes feel as if it is completely dictated by warnings from the future about job markets and job prospects. Little attention is given to the unspoken essence of the child. How do we teach children to navigate through the shifting landscape of this age? Well, for nearly a century, Steiner Waldorf schools have being doing just that, placing the child, rather than the fluctuating impulses of politics and economics, at the centre of the curriculum. It is a system taught on every continent, based solely on a deep understanding of the developmental needs of the growing child.

Michael Hall Steiner School celebrated its 90 years birthday last year and offers a rich, broad and balanced curriculum. Developing 'head, heart and hands', in order that children may develop cognitive, social-emotional

and practical skills in all aspects of life – to the job market and beyond. We can confidently say our school is filled with pupils who have the problem-solving skills required for a sustainable future, in every way. Based on the educational philosophy of Austrian-born Rudolf Steiner (1861-1925), we place high value on play in the Early Years, imagination in the Middle School period and creative thinking in the Upper School. Rather than imposing a model of education on the growing child, subject to the whims of political change, it is a tried and tested model of success, based on a real understanding of the human being. Supporting and guiding children as they take their first footsteps on a path of lifelong learning is our passion. Our disciplined and traditional approach in core subjects is rigorously delivered through a child-centred learning experience.

We understand your concerns as parents. We know

you want your children to be articulate, creative, self-reliant and flexible. We also know you want to develop their capacity to be resourceful, so whatever the future brings, they will be able to find their own way, coming up with new solutions to old problems.

Steiner schools form the largest group of independent, non-denominational private schools in the world, 37 in the UK and over 1,000 worldwide in a total of 64 different countries. Responding to the recognised need from parents for their children to receive truly balanced educational provision, we believe each child has something unique and valuable to contribute to the benefit of the whole. We are not growing children to fit into outdated models of society that no longer work.

We are growing children to be free-thinking and independent individuals. Confident, enthusiastic graduates from Steiner schools contribute to society in a way that is sustainable and respectful of the world in which we live. Engaging with a changing world with flexibility and initiative, pupils are highly sought after both in further education and the workplace, entering a broad spectrum of trades, careers and professions.

What makes our education so different? Seven reasons why Steiner education really works:

1. Childhood is not a race
We take child development seriously. Learning is age-appropriate. Childhood is recognised as a time of wonder. Respecting the power of a young child's imagination in Steiner Early Years' settings offers the foundation for future creativity and adaptability. Similar to Scandinavian countries, reading and writing begins from the age of six, allowing children to develop the right verbal and social skills before formal teaching begins. By age eleven, numeracy, literacy and language skills have normally outpaced those of children in mainstream education.

2. Lifelong love of learning
Subjects are taught using the outdoors, songs, movement and art. OFSTED inspectors, parents and pupils regularly comment on how the teaching methodologies employed in the classroom, alongside traditional teaching of core subjects, enhance a child's experience at school and inspires a curiosity in the world around us.

3. Minimal testing
We monitor progress closely and assess where appropriate, but testing is minimal. In general we do not think regular testing contributes to a love of learning or self-esteem. Having said that; "examination results are well above the national average in relation to GCSE A* to C pass rates and

A*/A grades and at GCE A-level A/A*, which suggests that teaching, learning and achievement are of a good quality overall" Ofsted 2015.

4. World's most exciting curriculum?
Most schools claim preparing children for exams is only part of what they do. With Steiner schools, it is really true. GCSEs and A levels are studied alongside the Waldorf Curriculum, which aims to embrace the wonder and challenge of the world, while achieving academic proficiency. Key subjects are taught in 'Main Lessons', thematic blocks of up to four weeks on the same topic, usually for two hours each morning. This allows for depth, integration and focus on a given subject. Where else can you experience working in a forge, gardening, silver-smithing, basket-weaving, geology and photography alongside studying for exams?

5. Life-changing school trips
School trips offer experiences tailored to the pupils' educational development. These unique trips; walking down to the south coast in Class 4 whilst studying the landscape of the SE in a Main Lesson, or walking Hadrians Wall in Class 6, whilst studying the UK in a Geography; a week-long survival course in Class 9 with the Earths Stewards Partnership, and a three-week artistic pilgrimage to Italy to reflect on masterworks of European art and culture, among many others. Class trips build confidence, deepen friendships and remain treasured memories for life.

6. Respectful relationships
Steiner teaching is a vocation. Children enter the school at six years and ideally have the same class teacher for the next eight years of school life. Entering the Upper School at fourteen years, pupils are supported by a two Guardians, who have both a teaching and pastoral role. The importance of these relationships over the years enables pupils to experience a purposeful progression in their learning.

7. Creativity
Children are encouraged to be open-minded and adaptable, whether involved in complex mathematical solutions, scientific experiments or crafting a bowl on a potter's wheel. Drama and the performing arts form a strong part of the diverse artistic curriculum, where pupils gain confidence for self-expression and deepen their personal maturity.

If you want to help your child grow into a responsible, contributing member of society as they blossom in this fast-changing world, why not consider a Steiner Waldorf education?

For more information on Michael Hall School, see page 98

Striving for excellence

Sarah Gillam, Maple Walk Prep School Head Teacher and an ISI inspector, looks at the value of school inspection reports

Choosing the right school for your child is daunting.

All parents want the best for their children and navigating through reams of glossy brochures and slick presentations is overwhelming.

Add to this the 'word on the street' and it is remarkable that any parent survives school selection without having to retreat into a darkened room.

However, there is a short cut: the Inspection Report. Decode what their language actually means and you could save yourself a fortune in registration fees.

Many parents will be familiar with the Ofsted ratings of 'Outstanding or 'Good' whilst the 'Requires Improvement' rating will have parents decamping to a school within a better catchment.

But most independent schools do not work with Ofsted and instead are regulated by the Independent School Inspectorate. The ISI do not give over-arching grades and instead key areas, such as the 'contribution of teaching' or the 'quality of leadership and management', are judged and scored separately.

Grades are awarded from 'unsatisfactory' at the bottom end, right up to 'excellent' and, in some rare cases, the curriculum can be judged as 'exceptional'. Knowing what these judgements actually mean can be a powerful weapon in a parents' arsenal.

Reports are, according to the ISI, designed to 'provide objective and reliable accounts of the standards of provision within a school.' They also provide signposts for the schools being inspected to assist them in building on their strengths or to encourage them to remedy any weaknesses.

A good school will not arrogantly march forward, ignoring inspectors' recommendations, but instead will genuinely see these as an opportunity to strive to be better.

As the old joke goes: How many inspectors does it

take to change a light bulb? None – it will either change itself, or be failed!

And whilst inspectors (and schools) have an awful lot of boxes to tick, team members have at their hearts a genuine interest in, and concern for, children's education.

Unlike Ofsted inspectors, ISI panels have at least one serving Head Teacher from a member of the Independent Schools' Council Association.

At the 'exceptional' level a school will not only have weighty ambitions for their pupils' achievements, but they will also have fulfilled these to the hilt.

Success is measured not just by what happens in the classroom, but by a school's extra-curricular activities, the attitude of their pupils and their ability to concentrate and to be engaged. It goes without saying that pupil achievement will be way above the national average. All pupils, including those with special educational needs (SEND) or English as an additional language (EAL), will be judged on their individual progress and their approach to learning. For SEND and EAL pupils, this will be gauged by how rapidly they improve from their starting point, or in accordance with their Individual Education, Care and Health Plans.

In effect, there is nowhere to hide for schools that blame poor results on an unusually high number of 'challenging' pupils.

Conversely, a highly selective school that sits back on its laurels may not achieve as well as a non-selective school that recognises the need to challenge all pupils according to their individual ability.

To this aim, marking and feedback to pupils and parents should be consistent and focused on assessing progress and guiding development.

A lot of red marks will only demoralise, rather than encourage pupils to identify the areas they need to improve and children themselves need to be seen to be engaged in the assessment and marking process.

The curriculum should be stimulating: creative and expressive subjects 'strongly represented in regular work', a foreign language taught from an early age and the computing and library learning integrated within the curriculum.

It is easy to be wowed by impressive and expansive facilities, and these certainly help a school on the road toward 'excellent', but even small schools with limited budgets should compensate by making sure facilities nearby are utilised or that school trips make the best use of their surrounding environment.

Regular outings on foot to the local swimming pool should not, therefore, be rejected in favour of an underused Olympic-sized facility on site. Similarly, rows of brand new iPads are only as good as their integration and use within the whole curriculum.

The spiritual, moral, social and cultural development of pupils is also scrutinised. According to ISI criteria a school graded 'excellent' in this area will have pupils that 'show a keen sense of fair play' and also an awareness of those less fortunate than themselves.

Alongside this, schools should regularly engage with the local community and fundraise for a range of charities, in order to develop pupils' social and moral responsibility.

Fierce debate is encouraged, whilst appreciating pupils from all social backgrounds and nationalities.

This is underpinned by the topic of the day, 'fundamental British values'.

In the course of their inspection, the ISI team will look at pupils' work, talk to management, question pupils and parents and, perhaps crucially, observe lessons.

Excellent teaching needs to be nurtured.

This means that teachers should be supported, encouraged, well managed and given regular opportunities to keep up-to-date with their specialist subjects.

A lack of investment in staff development can lead to stagnated teaching and a high staff turnover, so look for a school that provides ongoing opportunities for training.

Inspections should be detailed, rigorous and unbiased.

And whilst they can cause a wave of panic to ripple through a school (typically only three day's notice of an imminent inspection is given), a good school should have an attitude of 'bring it on'.

A school will be under regulatory scrutiny too – safe recruitment, health and safety, governance, policies and procedures.

These essential aspects and their associated documentation of school life cannot be conjured up overnight and so there is a good chance that if the ship is not in order on the big day … it probably hasn't been for a while.

This year the inspection process is set to have a big shake up, in line with the Government's desire to bring independent schools to heel like Ofsted inspected schools, but in the interim, existing reports can offer enormous insight.

Parents should, however, trust their own instincts and no amount of reading or decoding can replace actually visiting a school.

And what a report cannot tell you is whether a particular school is the right school for your child.

For more information about Maple Walk Prep School, see page 62

Overseeing a 'sixth form revolution'

Babington House School aims to give its pupils an edge by combining work experience with study. Helen Balfour reports...

There is a quiet revolution happening in Chislehurst, radiating from Babington House School, which provides an education from 3-18 years in Grange Drive, just next to Elmstead Woods railway station. The new Sixth Form there is very much at the head of the educational curve.

The Sixth Formers start at 9.15am and have a very full day of intensive A Level tuition in small sets; often with no more than three in a group. All their 'free periods' are put together onto one day – Wednesday – when the students go off to work; mainly in the City, on properly organised internships, something the school arranges and monitors. This gives the pupils the edge on the fiercely competitive university application process and later on in the world of work. As Tate, who is in Year 13 and studying Law, Politics and Business Studies says: "While my friends in other schools are frittering their free periods away

in Nandos, I've travelled into the City to work in a multi-national company, building up proper work experience and making real contacts; it's not an easy option by any means, but it's really exciting." This is echoed by Ed in Year 12, who is studying History, English, Government & Politics and German, who says: "The move to a co-educational Sixth Form has enabled me to adapt to different situations and is preparing me for life at University and beyond. The work experience is a massive bonus and makes you learn faster and grow in confidence."

The rest of the week is busy studying very hard for the A Levels; as Rachel in Year 13, who has just received an unconditional offer from the University of Roehampton to study Business Management, comments: "The teachers get to know you really well and work you really hard; when you are in a small group with tutorial style teaching, there is no escape! You just have to do the work. The teachers have a rule that they hand back your written assignments by the next lesson, which is great because you get immediate feedback on how to improve. I'm very ambitious and focused on the next step after school; Babington totally gets this and helps me to find a way to make it a reality."

Jess, who has offers from Brighton, Manchester and Liverpool Universities to study Accountancy and Business, endorses this view by saying: "Don't come to Babington unless you are committed to doing well and ambitious to succeed after school, at Uni or in the world of work. I won't lie; it is hard and there is no let up, but it is great to be with others who share this drive."

> "Don't come to Babington unless you are committed to doing well and ambitious to succeed after school, at Uni or in the world of work. I won't lie; it is hard and there is no let up, but it is great to be with others who share this drive."

Full written reports from each subject every three weeks help to give the students and their parents useful feedback and it is never 'sugar coated' as the Headmaster, Tim Lello comments: "We use A Level examination mark schemes to assess the students work, so clear, accurate and meaningful feedback is very much at the heart of the A Level teaching; it's all geared to the exam really; we are hungry for them to succeed; the world outside school is unforgiving when it comes to weak exam results."

Mr Lello draws on his experience as the Senior Tutor at Queen's College London, to give the Babington Sixth Form students the best possible chance when it comes to University applications and he is also a specialist on applications to American Universities. He has appointed several A Level specialists, including the previous Head of Maths and Director of Studies from Bromley High School, another Maths teacher from St Olave's Grammar School, a Biochemist from Wilmington Grammar, History and Government & Politics teacher from Watford Grammar School for Girls, and a Business Studies teacher from Blackfen School for Girls. As Tim Lello says: "I'll not compromise on getting quality teachers; our pupils deserve the best and they will get it. I'll also not tolerate anything mediocre; from the students, the staff and the school in general. We are an outstanding school and will remain so."

Although they have a full programme of study and work experience, the Sixth Formers also have access to all the resources of a fully equipped, major academic day school, including a wide sporting programme, state of the art climbing wall, extensive playing fields, music, drama, art and languages. Sixth Formers are given whole-school responsibilities as 'Ambassadors' on an area of their choice, such as fund raising for local and global charities, local politics or environmental projects.

Places are available for entry to the Babington Sixth Form in September 2016. Come for a tour of the School with the Headmaster during a normal working day and see this unique Sixth Form for yourself. Contact Mrs Lee, Admissions Registrar, on Tel: 020 8467 5537 for an appointment.

For more information about Babington House School, see page 80

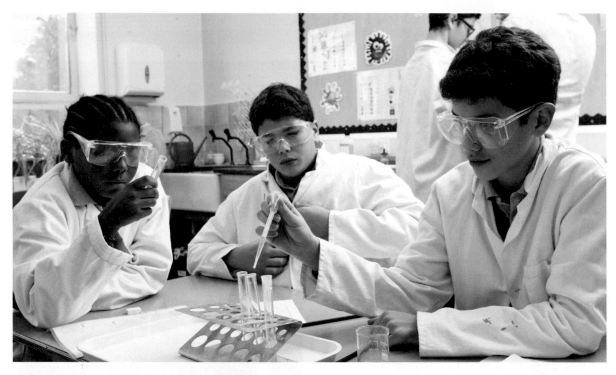

The silent struggle

Ronda Fogel, founder of The Moat School, on why children with minor learning difficulties often face the biggest challenges

We all dream of our children excelling at school – in maths, English, sport or music, but for some children, just getting through the normal school day can be challenging enough.

With a bit of luck, a pupil's school will flag up any learning difficulties around Year 2 and suggest an assessment, although many children with specific learning difficulties (SpLD) can remain undiagnosed for much longer. Parents may have suspected their child was not keeping up even though his or her intelligence appeared 'normal' otherwise it could come as a bolt out of the blue. It is at this stage that parents usually wonder what they should be doing.

A good school will probably recommend an educational psychologist (EP) and this will be the next step to finding out what the difficulties are and how serious. You can access a good list of EPs through the BDA. An EP will assess the child by performing a series of tests designed to calculate verbal and non-verbal reasoning as well as general cognitive ability. Parents will receive a report with the results of the administered tests and a recommendation on how to address the child's

needs. The sort of difficulties identified by an educational psychologist cover a broad range from Dsylexia, Dyspraxia, Discalcula, Aspergers or ADHD/ADD (Attention Deficit Hyperactivity Disorder/Attention Deficit Disorder), all on the SpLD spectrum.

There are many independent schools that offer specialist teaching outside of the classroom, but for children with moderate to severe difficulties this minimal intervention is like 'papering over the cracks'. In many cases, there are children unable to cope in a mainstream school environment and who need something more specialist. For parents in the expat community this will be a particular concern, not only will their child have to cope with a completely new home environment and new friends, but also a new school. If confidence levels are low due to previous poor achievement, then this will add to the family's anxieties at an already stressful time.

Much of the difficult part of the transition can be avoided by transferring a child to a school that specialises in the teaching of children who require more individual learning support. This is where the child will get a complete and individual programme of the help they need including occupational and speech and language therapy, as well as counselling where necessary, all incorporated into their school day.

Specialist schools like the Moat School in London provides children diagnosed with a SpLD the opportunity of receiving an academic education in a safe and supportive learning environment up to GCSE for children between the ages of 11 to 16 years. CReSTeD produces a useful handbook and their website gives a list of accredited schools.

It comes as no surprise to parents that their children often possess extraordinary talents and creativity and it is an important goal for these schools to identify and foster this by providing additional courses in non-traditional subjects such as creative and performing arts, food technology, computer technology, art and design, media studies and design technology. Pupils will need

individual timetables that address their needs and classes must be small with a high teacher/pupil ratio. Look for a school that offers an enrichment program that enhances the pupils' skills academically, emotionally and socially.

It is well known that progress of pupils at these type of holistic specialist schools are typically outstanding. This reinforces the belief that, given the opportunity and resources at the right age, despite their difficulties, these children can make meaningful improvements to the quality of their lives and their contributions to society.

Helping parents find their way through the minefield of special education is not easy, but follow these steps and you could put them on the right track:

1. Do some research, this will pay enormous dividends.
2. Get free advice from the numerous agencies there to help. In the UK this will be the British Dyslexia Association, CReSTeD, and the Helen Arkell centre.
3. Make sure there is an up to date assessment of the child's special needs.
4. Encourage research in possible schools in the country the families are relocating to.
5. Speak to professionals such as educational psychologists, therapists and specialist tutors.
6. Consider an educational consultant who will know and understand schools in the destination area of relocation and who will be able to follow a particular brief. Especially useful if there is no time for research.

There are many alternative therapies and treatments around, but it is the view of many professionals that repetitive and intensive teaching from qualified teachers experienced in the teaching of children with SpLD pays the best educational dividends. With proper diagnosis and tailored educational practises, children with SpLD can go on to achieve academically, reach their full potential and have successful careers and future lives.

The Moat School was established by the Constable Educational Trust, an incorporated charitable company limited by guarantee in 1998 and is London's first secondary day school for children with dyslexia and related specific learning difficulties.

For more information about The Moat School, see page 74

Giving students the Advantage

Christine Cunniffe, Principal at LVS Ascot, offers guidance on what benefits a good school should provide sixth form students with along with top A level grades.

For all good schools there should be more to years 12 and 13 than just exams. It is very easy for schools to be drawn in to focusing on these at the expense of everything else, but we believe that there is far more to preparing students for university and work that can be done alongside providing the vital qualifications.

The world of work, and to a lesser extent university, have the potential to take young adults out of their comfort zone, and whilst the qualifications are what will get them there, how do you ensure they are confident and equipped to deal with the new challenges they will face?

We are committed to ensuring that once in work or further education, LVS Ascot has provided them with the necessary tools to go on and excel, by helping them develop that 'X Factor' they will need to shine in a rapidly changing and demanding workplace.

That's why LVS Ascot has created our LVS Advantage programme, giving students the opportunity to experience an enriching course outside of the academic arena in business management. Working with a business development consultancy, the programme consists of six modules and students from years 12 and 13 are encouraged to apply. By its conclusion, they are equipped with negotiation skills and knowledge of how to deal with conflict management, effective communication and strategic decision making, as well as learning key concepts of competitive advantage and marketing and operations.

This type of programme is just one of the ways a school can help sixth formers develop additional skills to complement their academic studies. In December a group of LVS Ascot sixth formers celebrated receiving unique awards thanks to our rare position as the only school in the country able to offer pupils an Institute in Leadership & Management course.

LVS Ascot is owned and managed by the Licensed

We are committed to ensuring that once in work or further education, LVS Ascot has provided sixth formers with the necessary tools to go on and excel, by helping them develop that 'X Factor' they will need to shine in a rapidly changing and demanding workplace.

Trade Charity, which became an approved ILM centre in 2011. This has given us the ability to not only provide valuable in-house training to staff, but also offer sixth formers the opportunity to get ahead via a qualification unavailable in schools anywhere else in the UK.

The ILM Level 2 Award in Effective Team Member Skills gives students the chance to learn the importance of communication, adapt their own styles of learning and communication, improve negotiation skills and learn how to adapt in a business environment. The facilities at LVS Ascot allow course leaders to create a business environment on site separate from the school, and students have access to support from staff who have experienced the ILM process, allowing greater direction and support on the assignment which follows an intensive two day course.

Five students in Year 13 saw their achievements celebrated at a special assembly where they received their certificates for the ILM Level 2 Award in Effective Team Member Skills, something which course trainer Jackie Green says will be an important advantage to them in future: "The ILM qualification is recognised worldwide, and for students having it on their CV is a definite plus when applying for universities and jobs. It helps so much in the transition from education to business by enhancing communication, negotiation and team work".

The Institute of Leadership & Management offers the UK's widest range of leadership and management qualifications, and with 35,000 managers members of ILM, LVS Ascot is keen to ensure its pupils have the best possible start to life and leave fully equipped for successful careers. We always seek to attain greater academic achievement and enhance career prospects,

helping students to aim for, and reach, new heights. The ILM qualification is a great way of doing this as it is such a unique qualification that it sets our students apart and gives them a boost going into university and careers.

Besides additional courses such as LVS Advantage and the ILM award, which enrich and build on the knowledge and interpersonal skills students gather during their time at school, there are also other ways schools can be innovative to help students prepare for life beyond the school and learn valuable interpersonal skills.

We are really focused on helping our students build personal attributes such as communication and leadership. The Duke of Edinburgh's Award is a perfect way to achieve that, and our students are gaining so much valuable experience from it. We are an accredited training centre and so committed to the benefits students receive from the scheme that we now have a dedicated Head and Assistant of Outdoor Pursuits, which is rare for a school.

The scheme is thriving – over 100 students started on it last year with their Bronze Award – and in February several of our students went to St James's Palace to be presented with Gold Awards in the presence of the Duke of Edinburgh himself, following others who achieved the same feat the previous year. This was a particularly notable achievement as it is rare to complete the award whilst still at school and highlighted our ability to guide students successfully through the various sections to be completed.

LVS Ascot aims to develop caring, confident citizens for the future. With excellent teaching supported by building additional skills to prepare students for life beyond the school, we are able to achieve this.

For more information about LVS Ascot, see page 93

A practical guide to the London school run

Transport for London offers guidance and support for parents and children travelling in the capital

Transport for London (TfL), wants to keep London working, growing and to make life in the capital better. Young people are significant users of the capital's transport network; whether it is for their journey to school or college, meeting friends or family or going to work. Therefore TfL recognise using the transport network is incredibly important to young people and to enable them to get the most of London, we have an important role to ensure travelling in London is a happy, healthy and safe experience.

We offer a wide range of programmes to schools and colleges, with the support of partners. These are aimed at young people, their families and teachers to promote safer, responsible travel. We also help young people learn about careers in the transport sector. The programmes and resources highlighted here fit into the National Curriculum, and are available for use within schools and colleges, as well as at home.

The majority of TfLs work with schools and young people can be found at **www.tfl.gov.uk/younglondon**

What mode of travel?
Choosing one mode of travel to school over another mode can bring about different benefits to both the parent and child. TfL and the boroughs are keen to promote active travel (walking and cycling) as the modes of travel that should be considered first for all journeys. The majority of schools in London have a travel plan in place to promote active modes of travel to parents, pupils and staff, with the vast majority of schools now offering cycle parking facilities and sheltered waiting space for parents who choose to walk.

Where a trip cannot be done wholly by an active mode, then public transport should be considered especially for children aged 11+ who can travel independently. If parents decide to drive their child to and from school then they should also consider car sharing and/or parking in a safe, secure and legal location or where possible a distance of around 500m from the school site to avoid congestion in the schools vicinity and feel the benefit of a short walk.

Planning a journey
TfL offer an integrated online journey planner **http://journeyplanner.tfl.gov.uk**. The journey planner helps the viewer plan a route on several modes of transport for any set time and day. You can print out maps, routes to school by foot and timetables.

Travelling on public transport
Children and young people up to the age of 25 are entitled to special concessionary discounts and benefits on London's transport system. Children aged 10 and under can travel for free on London buses, Underground, DLR, tram and some national rail services. Young people aged 11-15 are entitled to apply for an Oyster card and this grants free travel on London buses and tram with discounted travel on the underground, DLR and selected national rail services. Young people aged 16+ who continue to attend an educational establishment can apply for an Oyster card that gives them reduced travel on all modes – for more information and how to apply visit **www.tfl.gov.uk/tickets**.

More information
For information about travelling in London by different modes as well as links to update travel services **visit www.tfl.gov.uk**.

BEING BROAD-MINDED WIDENS HORIZONS.

QUILTER CHEVIOT
INVESTMENT MANAGEMENT

WE'RE THINKING BEYOND THE OBVIOUS TO GET THE BEST FOR YOUR INVESTMENTS. FIND OUT MORE.

CALL TIM HEALY
EXECUTIVE DIRECTOR
TEL. 020 7150 4298 OR VISIT
WWW.QUILTERCHEVIOT.COM

Belfast   Birmingham   Bristol   Dublin   Edinburgh   Glasgow   Jersey   Leicester   Liverpool   London   Manchester   North Wales   Salisbury

Managing the cost of independent schooling

Tim Healy, executive director at Quilter Cheviot Investment Management, offers some advice on managing the cost of school fees

Putting your children through independent schooling does not always come easy, financially speaking. Although a recent census by the Independent Schools Council found that between 2014 and 2015 private school fees were subject to the lowest annual increase since 1994, they still rose by an average of 3.6%. So costs remain on the up and, over the course of a child's education, they represent a substantial sum.

As with any major financial outlay, early stage planning can make a big difference. By using a combination of cost spreading, savvy saving and various tax efficiencies parents can make the sometimes daunting costs of private schooling far more manageable.

Once you've decided to go down the independent school route, it is important to start planning for the associated costs at the earliest opportunity. Obviously, planning for independent schooling at secondary level will allow more time to study the options and it will also mean more time for saving. Whether looking at primary or secondary schooling though, the following approaches can be considered when it comes to easing the school fees burden.

Take full advantage of tax efficiencies

There are a number of tax efficient means to help with the cost of independent school fees. Parents should know, for example, that any income from gifts given directly to their children is regarded as a child's own income. As such, a child's personal allowance of £10,000 is available to use.

An increasing number of people are sourcing support from grandparents when it comes to covering school fees and tax efficiencies can come into play here too. Advantage can be taken of a grandparent's £3,000 annual gifts exemption from inheritance tax, on a yearly basis where individuals are wanting to make a regular contribution to their grandchildren's schooling.

Tailor your investments

Having efficient investments in place can be very helpful when it comes to building a fees pot. Investing in UK gilts can be very tax efficient, for example, as any capital gain is tax exempt.

Another strategy to consider is investing in funds. The UK equity market is currently expected to yield roughly 4% for the current year and when compared against the very low interest rates offered by banks at present stock market investment clearly leads the pack in terms of value.

Of course, it is important to remember that stock markets are notorious for exaggerating fundamental economic trends and understanding how this can impact upon your financial investment over the short, medium and long term is essential. By nurturing returns though, efficient investments could enable you to withdraw money when needed while continuing to save once education has started.

Elsewhere, the tax free advantages of an ISA make it an ideal choice for parents planning and saving to pay for private schooling too. If both parents use their full ISA annual allowance, in eight years a family could have a tax free investment pot of about £300,000. This can then be used as a tax free supplement to an existing income when a family starts paying school fees, or it can simply be drawn upon to pay the school fees.

Seek solutions with schools

Beyond investment and tax efficiency strategies parents may also look to lessen the pressure of costs by spreading them over a longer period of time. Many private schools are open to individual payment schemes, so it's advisable to strike up an open dialogue with the school as soon as you identify it as a preferred choice. In some cases it will be possible for agreements to be put in place that enable parents to begin payments several years before a child joins their chosen school and finish payments after the child has left.

Whichever methods are utilised, expert advice and planning at the earliest opportunity helps to pay for the education you have chosen. At Quilter Cheviot we understand the needs of clients who are looking to develop investments that will support the cost of their childrens' education. Our aim is to help our clients fulfil their objectives over the long term and our investment process is central to achieving this goal. By combining the in-depth analysis of our dedicated research teams and the talents of our experienced investment managers, we can provide clients with a truly unique resource. It allows us to generate an investment process that is sufficiently agile to keep ahead of today's constantly changing markets, and flexible enough to incorporate the investment requirements of our clients. We choose from among the best and most suitable investments to meet your objectives, whether the priority is growth, income or capital preservation. In the case of being able to raise school fee funds, we will work hard to help you achieve that objective.

Getting fit as a family – in St Lucia

The BodyHoliday presents an active family holiday with a difference

WellFit Families at The BodyHoliday is a family based fitness week for teenagers and their parents. Beach Boot Camps instructed by visiting Olympians, abseiling down a waterfall and even a Quadrathlon are all part of this active Caribbean family holiday. The WellFit Families programme runs weekly, during the school summer holidays between 3rd July and 28th August, 2016. Families will thrive on this adventurous experience on the beautiful Caribbean island of Saint Lucia.

WellFit Families at The BodyHoliday combines a comprehensive list of adventures, life changing experiences and plentiful activities all in the Caribbean sunshine. Rappelling, bike rides along coastal trails, BeachFit classes, sailing racing boats and a generous helping of fun all come as standard. Our visiting Olympic hosts are on hand to deliver motivation, encourage involvement in beach sports and host fitness classes as well as teach you and your teenager's new skills.

WellFit Families promises a wholesome family experience that motivates teenagers and adults alike towards family bonding though the pursuit of wellbeing and fitness. The programme also encompasses all aspects of the BodyHoliday- an award-winning 5* health and wellbeing resort where your accommodation, all meals, watersports and a daily spa treatment are included in the price.

Your teenagers can expect to develop their physical fitness, strength and stamina with our unique BeachFit Boot Camps, gain mental focus and clarity through Yoga presented by International teachers and learn new skills such as first aid, CPR, basic sailing and even healthy cooking. Encourage them to take a walk on the wild side and challenge themselves on the obstacles of our outdoor 'WellFit' trail or even take the ultimate challenge of The BodyHoliday 'Quadrathlon'. Families work together during their weeks' training and combine their competitive spirit with the final event; the Saturday afternoon family versus staff beach tournament.

Well-Fit Families has it all! This fun packed week will bring a sense of cohesion and family spirit felt by everyone who attends. This year's 2016 WellFit Families programme is hosted by Olympic legends Jamie Baulch and Danny Crates, Jamie won 11 medals at Olympic Games, World and European Championships and Commonwealth Games. Paralympic gold medalist Danny Crates was the face of Channel 4's athletics coverage at the London 2012 Paralympic games. Returning again for WellFit Families 2016, our guest presenters are always well received.

New for 2016, led by our 'BodyGuards' our WellFit Champs programme is designed to give teenagers their own space and to take time out from the adults on holiday with a series of dedicated activities just for the teens. Champs Dinners are hosted in The Clubhouse Restaurant. There's a pre-dinner get together at the pool table and after dinner there are more activities to keep everyone entertained.

Our adventure programme for families provides an opportunity for the whole family to take in the spectacular sights of Saint Lucia and at the same time embark on some exciting adventures. Rappelling down rock faces, jumping through waterfalls and hiking through the rain forest are there to challenge every enterprising family team.

If you are looking for an active family holiday with a difference, WellFit Families at The BodyHoliday is a must.

For more information: www.thebodyholiday.com.

Choosing a school – the key questions

However much a school may appeal at first sight, you still need sound information to form your judgement.

Schools attract pupils by their reputations, so most go to considerable lengths to ensure that parents are presented with an attractive image. Modern marketing techniques try to promote good points and play down (without totally obscuring) bad ones. But every Head knows that, however good the school prospectus is, it only serves to attract parents through the school gates. Thereafter the decision depends on what they see and hear. Research we have carried out over the years suggests that in many cases the most important factor in choosing a school is the impression given by the Head. As well as finding out what goes on in a school, parents need to be reassured by the aura of confidence that they expect from a Head. How they judge the latter may help them form their opinion of the former. In other words, how a Head answers questions is important in itself and, to get you started, we have drawn up a list of points that you may like to consider. Some can be posed as questions and some are points you'll only want to check in your mind. They are not listed in any particular order and their significance will vary from family to family, but they should be useful in helping you to form an opinion.

Before visiting and asking questions, **check the facts** – such as which association the school belongs to, how big it is, how many staff *etc*. Is there any form of financial pie chart showing how the school's resources are used? The answers to questions like these should be in the promotional material you've been sent. If they aren't, you've already got a good question to ask!

Check the website. Is it up-to-date? Almost certainly not 100% because that's just about impossible, but it shouldn't be obsolete. And that first impression is very important.

When you get to the school you will want to judge the overall atmosphere and decide whether it will suit you and your child. Are any other members of the family going to help to pay the fees? If so, their views are important and the school's attitude towards them may be instructive.

When you make it to the inner sanctum, **what do you make of the Head as a person?** Age? Family? Staying? Moving on? Retiring? Busted flush? Accessible to children, parents and staff? If you never get to see the Head, but deal with an admissions person of some sort, it may not mean you should rule the school out, but it certainly tells you something about the school's view of pupil recruitment.

Academic priorities – attitude towards league tables? This is a forked question. If the answer is 'We're most concerned with doing the best for the child', you pitch them a late-developer; if the answer is, 'Well, frankly, we have a very high entry threshold', then you say 'So we have to give you a foolproof academic winner, do we?'

Supplementary questions:

- What is the ratio of teachers to pupils?
- What are the professional qualifications of the teaching staff?
- What is the school's retention rate? In prep schools this means how many pupils do they lose at 11 when the school goes on to 13.
- How long is the school day – and week?
- What are the school's exam results?
- What are the criteria for presenting them?
- Were they consistent over the years?
- Is progress accelerated for the academically bright?
- How does the school cope with pupils who do not work?
- Where do pupils go when they leave?
- How important and well resourced are sports, extracurricular and after school activities, music and drama?
- What cultural or other visits are arranged away from the school?

Other topics to cover:

- What is the school's mission?
- What is its attitude to religion?
- How well is the school integrated into the local community?
- How have they responded to the Charities Act initiatives?
- What are the responsibilities and obligations at weekends for parents, pupils and the school?
- Does the school keep a watching brief or reserve the option to get involved after a weekend incident?

Choosing a school – the key questions

- What is the school's attitude to discipline?

- Have there been problems with drugs, drink or sex? How have they been dealt with?

- What is the school's policy on bullying?

- How does the school cope with pupils' problems?

- What sort of academic and pastoral advice is available?

- What positive steps are taken to encourage good manners, behaviour and sportsmanship?

- What is the uniform?

- What steps are taken to ensure that pupils take pride in their personal appearance?

- How often does the school communicate with parents through reports, parent/teacher meetings or other visits?

- What level of parental involvement is encouraged both in terms of keeping in touch with staff about your own child and more generally, eg a Parents' Association?

- Is it possible to have the names and addresses of parents with children at the school to approach them for an opinion?

And finally – and perhaps most importantly – what does your child make of the school, the adults met, the other children met, pupils at the school in other contexts, and the website?

Initial advice

Educational institutions often belong to organisations that encourage high standards. Here we give a brief guide to what some of the initials mean.

BSA

The Boarding Schools' Association

Since its foundation in 1966, the Boarding Schools' Association (BSA) has had the twin objectives of the promotion of boarding education and the development of quality boarding through high standards of pastoral care and boarding accommodation. Parents and prospective pupils choosing a boarding school can, therefore, be assured that the 500 schools in membership of the BSA are committed to providing the best possible boarding environment for their pupils.

A school can only join the BSA if it is in membership of one of the ISC (Independent Schools Council) constituent associations or in membership of SBSA (State Boarding Schools' Association). These two bodies require member schools to be regularly inspected by the Independent Schools' Inspectorate (ISI) or Ofsted. Between April 2007 and August 2011, all boarding inspections, in both independent and state schools, were carried out by Ofsted, whose reports can be found on their website. Boarding inspection of independent schools has been conducted by ISI since September 2012. Ofsted retains responsibility for the inspection of boarding in state schools. Boarding inspections must be conducted every three years. Boarding is judged against the National Minimum Standards for Boarding Schools (revised 2011) with considerable input from the BSA.

Relationship with government

The BSA is in regular communication with the Department for Education (DfE) on all boarding matters. The Children Act (1989) and the Care Standards Act (2001) require boarding schools to conform to national legislation and the promotion of this legislation and the training required to carry it out are matters on which the DfE and the BSA work closely. The key area is in training.

Boarding training

The programme of training for boarding staff whose schools are in membership of the BSA has been supported and sponsored in the past by the DfE. The BSA maintains the high standards expected as a consequence of that support. The Utting Report on the Safeguards for Children Living Away from Home highlighted the importance of the development of 'policy, practice and training for services for children who live away from home'. It focuses on the right of parents to expect that staff looking after children are competent to do so, and points out the responsibility of central government to secure consistent national standards in promoting the welfare of children away from home. The Singleton Review (March 2009) reiterated the importance of rigorous safeguarding of such children.

In addition the BSA organises five conferences and more than 50 seminars a year for governors, Heads, deputies, housemasters and housemistresses, and matrons and medical staff where further training takes place in formal sessions and in sharing good practice. The BSA provides the following range of training and information:

- Professional qualifications for both teaching and non-teaching staff in boarding schools. The BSA has been responsible for the development of courses leading to university validated Certificates of Professional Practice in Boarding Education. These certificates, the result of at least two years' study, are awarded by the University of Roehampton.

- A rolling programme of day seminars on current boarding legislation and good practice.

State Boarding Schools Association

The BSA issues information on the 38 state boarding schools in England and Wales and the BSA should be contacted for details of these schools. In these schools parents pay for boarding but not for education, so fees are substantially lower than in an independent boarding school.

National Director: Robin Fletcher MBA, MPhil, FRSA
Director of Training: Alex Thomson OBE, BSc(Hons), PGCE, DipEd, FCIPD
Boarding Schools' Association
4th Floor
134-136 Buckingham Palace Road
London SW1W 9SA
Tel: 020 7798 1580
Fax: 020 7798 1581
Email: bsa@boarding.org.uk
Website: www.boarding.org.uk

GSA

The Girls' Schools Association, to which Heads of leading girls' schools belong

The Girls' Schools Association represents the heads of many of the top performing day and boarding schools in the UK independent schools sector and is a member of the Independent Schools Council.

Many of the schools in GSA membership were founded in the nineteenth century when a national movement to provide better education for girls and women gathered momentum. Campaigners founded new schools in which girls studied similar subjects to boys – a far cry from the superficial curriculum they had previously been given.

Today, 21st century girls' schools come in many different shapes and sizes. Some cater for 100% girls, others provide a predominantly girls-only environment with boys in the nursery and/or sixth form. Some follow a diamond model, with equal numbers of boys but separate classrooms between the ages of 11 to 16. Educational provision across the Association offers a choice of day, boarding, weekly, and flexi-boarding education. Schools range in type from large urban schools of 1000 pupils to small rural schools of around 200. Many schools have junior and pre-prep departments, and can offer a complete education from three/four to 18. A significant proportion of schools also have religious affiliations. Heads of schools in the Girls' Day School Trust (GDST) are members of the GSA.

The GSA encourages high standards of education for girls and promotes the benefits of being taught in a largely girls-only environment. As a whole, GSA schools punch well above their weight when it comes to academic achievement; analysis of A Level statistics shows they are more likely to study and do well in STEM (science, technology, engineering, maths) subjects than girls in other schools. Approximately 94% go on to higher education.

The Association aims to inform and influence national educational debate and is a powerful and well-respected voice within the educational establishment, advising and lobbying educational policy makers on core education issues as well as those relating to girls' schools and the education of girls. The Association liaises with the Department for Education, the Office for Standards in Education, the Qualifications and Curriculum Authority and other bodies.

The GSA also provides its members and their staff with professional development courses, conferences, advice and opportunities to debate and share best practice, ensuring that they have every opportunity to remain fully up-to-date with all aspects of their profession.

As the GSA is one of the constituent bodies of the Independent Schools' Council (ISC), its schools are required to undergo a regular cycle of inspections to ensure that these rigorous standards are being maintained. GSA schools must also belong to the Association of Governing Bodies of Independent Schools, and Heads must be in membership of the Association of School and College Leaders (ASCL).

The Association's secretariat is based in Leicester.

Suite 105, 108 New Walk, Leicester LE1 7EA
Tel: 0116 254 1619
Email: office@gsa.uk.com
Website: www.gsa.uk.com
Twitter: @GSAUK

President 2015: Caroline Jones, Headington
Vice President:
Alun Jones,
St Gabriel's (Newbury)
Executive Director:
Charlotte Vere

HMC

The Headmasters' and Headmistresses' Conference, to which the Heads of leading independent schools belong

Founded in 1869 the HMC exists to enable members to discuss matters of common interest and to influence important developments in education. It looks after the professional interests of members, central to which is their wish to provide the best possible educational opportunities for their pupils.

The Heads of some 269 leading independent schools are members of The Headmasters' and Headmistresses' Conference, whose membership now includes Heads of boys', girls' and coeducational schools. International membership includes the Heads of around 60 schools throughout the world.

The great variety of these schools is one of the strengths of HMC but all must exhibit high quality in the education provided. While day schools are the largest group, about a quarter of HMC schools consist mainly of boarders and others have a smaller boarding element including weekly and flexible boarders.

All schools are noted for their academic excellence and achieve good results, including those with pupils from a broad ability band. Members believe that good education consists of more than academic results and schools provide pupils with a wide range of educational co-curricular activities and with strong pastoral support.

Only those schools that meet with the rigorous membership criteria are admitted and this helps ensure that HMC is synonymous with high quality in education. There is a set of membership requirements and a Code of Practice to which members must subscribe. Those who want the intimate atmosphere of a small school will find some with around 350 pupils. Others who want a wide range of facilities and specialisations will find these offered in large day or boarding schools. Many have over 1000 pupils. About 50 schools are for boys only, others are coeducational throughout or only in the sixth form. The first girls-only schools joined HMC in 2006. There are now about 20 girls-only schools.

Within HMC there are schools with continuous histories as long as any in the world and many others trace their origins to Tudor times, but HMC continues to admit to membership recently-founded schools that have achieved great success. The facilities in all HMC schools will be good but some have magnificent buildings and grounds that are the result of the generosity of benefactors over many years. Some have attractive rural settings, others are sited in the centres of cities.

Pupils come from all sorts of backgrounds. Bursaries and scholarships provided by the schools give about a third of the 215,000 pupils in HMC schools help with their fees. These average about £30,000 per annum for boarding schools and £12,000 for day schools. About 170,000 are day pupils and 43,000 boarders.

Entry into some schools is highly selective but others are well-suited to a wide ability range. Senior boarding schools usually admit pupils after the Common Entrance examination taken when they are 13.

Most day schools select their pupils by 11+ examination. Many HMC schools have junior schools, some with nursery and pre-prep departments. The growing number of boarders from overseas is evidence of the high reputation of the schools worldwide.

The independent sector has always been fortunate in attracting very good teachers. Higher salary scales, excellent conditions of employment, exciting educational opportunities and good pupil/teacher ratios bring rewards commensurate with the demanding expectations. Schools expect teachers to have a good education culminating in a good honours degree and a professional qualification, though some do not insist on the latter especially if relevant experience is offered. Willingness to participate in the whole life of the school is essential.

Parents expect the school to provide not only good teaching that helps their children achieve the best possible examination results, but also the dedicated pastoral care and valuable educational experiences outside the classroom in music, drama, games, outdoor pursuits and community service. Over 90% of pupils go on to higher education, many of them winning places on the most highly-subscribed university courses.

All members attend the Annual Conference, usually held in a large conference centre in September/October. There are ten divisions covering England, Wales, Scotland and Ireland where members meet once a term on a regional basis, and a distinctive international division.

The chairman and committee, with the advice of the general secretary and membership secretary, make decisions on matters referred by membership-led sub-committees, steering groups and working parties. Close links are maintained with other professional associations in membership of the Independent Schools Council and with the Association of School and College Leaders.

Membership Secretary: Ian Power.
Tel: 01858 465260
General Secretary: Dr William Richardson.
Tel: 01858 469059
12 The Point
Rockingham Road
Market Harborough
Leicestershire LE16 7QU
Email: gensec@hmc.org.uk
Website: www.hmc.org.uk

Leading Independent Schools

IAPS

The Independent Association of Preparatory Schools (IAPS) is the membership association for the headteachers of leading prep and junior schools in the UK and overseas

With more than 600 members, IAPS schools represent a multi-billion pound enterprise, educating more than 160,000 children and employing more than 20,000 staff.

Schools are spread throughout cities, towns and the countryside and offer pupils the choice of day, boarding, weekly and flexible boarding, in both single sex and coeducational settings. Sizes vary from 100 to more than 800 per school, with the majority between 150 and 400. Most schools are charitable trusts, some are limited companies and a few are proprietary. There are also junior schools attached to senior schools, choir schools, those with a particular religious affiliation and those that offer specialist provision as well as some schools with an age range extending to age 16 or above.

IAPS only accredits those schools that can demonstrate that they provide the highest standards of education and care. Member schools offer an all-round, values-led, broad education, which produces confident, adaptable, motivated children with a lifelong passion for learning. In order to be elected to membership, a Head must be suitably qualified and schools must be accredited through a satisfactory inspection. IAPS offers its members and their staff a comprehensive and up-to-date programme of professional development courses to ensure that high professional standards are maintained.

Pupils are offered a rich and varied school life. The targets of the National Curriculum are regarded as a basic foundation, which is greatly extended by the wider programmes of study offered. Specialist subject teaching begins at an early age and pupils are offered a range of cultural and sporting opportunities. Together with more than 30 recreational games, music, art and drama form part of curricular and extracurricular activities. In addition, IAPS organises holiday and term-time sporting competitions for pupils to take part in, including skiing, sailing, judo, swimming, golf, fencing and squash, amongst many others.

IAPS has well-established links with senior independent schools, and experience in methods of transfer and entry to them. As the voice of independent prep school education, it has national influence and actively defends and promotes the interests of its members. It lobbies the government on their behalf and promotes prep school issues on a national and international stage. IAPS works directly with ministers and national policy advisers to ensure that the needs of the prep school sector are met.

IAPS, 11 Waterloo Place,
Leamington Spa,
Warwickshire CV32 5LA
Tel: 01926 887833
Fax: 01926 888014
Email: iaps@iaps.uk
Website: www.iaps.uk

ISA

The Independent Schools Association, with membership across all types of school

The Independent Schools Association (ISA), established in 1879, is one of the oldest of the Headteachers' associations of independent schools that make up the Independent Schools' Council (ISC). It began life as the Association of Principals of Private Schools, which was created to encourage high standards and foster friendliness and cooperation among Heads who had previously worked in isolation. In 1895 it was incorporated as The Private Schools Association and in 1927 the word 'private' was replaced by 'independent'. The recently published history of the association, *Pro Liberis*, demonstrates the strong links ISA has with proprietorial schools, which is still the case today, even though boards of governors now run the majority of schools.

Membership is open to any independent school Head or proprietor provided they meet the necessary criteria, which includes the accreditation standards of the Independent Schools Inspectorate (ISI). ISA's executive council is elected by members and supports all developments of the Association through its committee structure and the strong regional network of co-ordinators and area committees. Each of ISA's seven areas in turn supports members through regular training events and meetings.

ISA celebrates a wide ranging membership, not confined to any one type of school, but including all: nursery, pre-preparatory, junior and senior, all-through schools, coeducational, single-sex, boarding, day and performing arts and special schools.

Promoting best practice and fellowship remains at the core of the ISA, as it did when it began 130 years ago. The association is growing, and its 367 members and their schools enjoy high quality national conferences and courses that foster excellence in independent education. ISA's central office also supports members and provides advice, and represents the views of its membership at national and governmental levels. Pupils in ISA schools enjoy a wide variety of competitions, in particular the wealth of sporting, artistic and academic activities at area and national level.

President : Lord Lexden
Chief Executive: Neil Roskilly, BA PGCE NPQH FRSA FRGS

ISA, 1 Boys' British School
East Street, Saffron Walden,
Essex CB10 1LS
Tel: 01799 523619
Fax: 01799 524892
Email: isa@isaschools.org.uk
Website: www.isaschools.org.uk

ISA
INDEPENDENT
SCHOOLS
ASSOCIATION

The Society of Heads

The Society of Heads of Independent Schools represents the interests of the smaller independent secondary schools.

The Society of Heads represents the interests of the smaller, independent, secondary schools. The Society celebrated its 50th Anniversary in 2011. The Society has as its members over 110 Heads of well-established secondary schools, many with a boarding element, meeting a wide range of educational needs. All member schools provide education up to 18, with sixth forms offering both A and AS levels and/or the International Baccalaureate. Also some offer vocational courses. Many have junior schools attached to their foundation. A number cater for pupils with special educational needs, whilst others offer places to gifted dancers and musicians. All the schools provide education appropriate to their pupils' individual requirements together with the best in pastoral care.

The average size of the schools is about 350, and all aim to provide small classes ensuring favourable pupil:teacher ratios. The majority are coeducational and offer facilities for both boarding and day pupils. Many of the schools are non-denominational, whilst others have specific religious foundations.

The Society believes that independent schools are an important part of Britain's national education system. Given their independence, the schools can either introduce new developments ahead of the maintained sector or offer certain courses specifically appropriate to the pupils in their schools. They are able to respond quickly to the needs of parents and pupils alike.

Schools are admitted to membership of the Society only after a strict inspection procedure carried out by the Independent Schools Inspectorate. Regular inspection visits thereafter ensure that standards are maintained.

The Society is a constituent member of the Independent Schools Council and every full member in the Society has been accredited to it. All the Society's Heads belong to the Association of School and College Leaders (ASCL) (or another recognised union for school leaders) and their schools are members of AGBIS.

The Society's policy is: to maintain high standards of education, acting as a guarantee of quality to parents who choose a Society school for their children; to ensure the genuine independence of member schools; to provide an opportunity for Heads to share ideas and common concerns for the benefit of the children in their care; to provide training opportunities for Heads and staff in order to keep them abreast of new educational initiatives; to promote links with higher and further education and the professions, so that pupils leaving the Society's schools are given the best advice and opportunities for their future careers; and to help Heads strengthen relations with their local communities.

The Society of Heads' Office,
12 The Point, Rockingham Road,
Market Harborough,
Leicestershire LE16 7QU
Tel: 01858 433760
Fax: 01858 461413
Email: gensec@
thesocietyofheads.org.uk
Website: www.thesocietyofheads.org.uk

THE
Society
OF
Heads

The Independent Schools Council

The Independent Schools Council (ISC) works with its members to promote and preserve the quality, diversity and excellence of UK independent education both at home and abroad

What is the ISC?
ISC brings eight associations together to represent over 1,250 independent schools in the UK. These schools are ranked among the best in the world and educate more than half a million children each year, around 80% of independently educated pupils. ISC also represents 130 British International schools in more than 50 countries worldwide.

ISC schools
ISC schools are at the forefront of educational achievement in every way and offer great choice to parents looking for the right school to suit their child. There are schools to suit every need, whether you want a day or boarding school, single sex or co-education, a large or a small school, or schools offering specialisms, such as in the Arts. They are the most academically successful schools, offering excellent teaching and pastoral care, an astonishing breadth of co-curricular activities and outstanding facilities.

Our schools are very diverse: some of our schools are selective and highly academic, offering a chance to stretch the bright child. Others have very strong drama or music departments full of creative opportunities in plays, orchestras and choirs. For children with special needs such as dyslexia or autism there are many outstanding independent schools that offer the best provision in the country.

And of course, our schools have very strong track records of high achievement at sport, offering superb facilities, excellent coaches and a full fixture list. Independent schools excel at the traditional sports like football and rugby, but also offer more unusual sports like rowing, fencing and even rock climbing.

There is also a wealth of co-curricular opportunity available. Whether your child is into debating, sailing, the Model United Nations or is interested in army training in the Combined Cadet Force, most schools offer numerous clubs and activities. It all adds up to an exciting, broad and stimulating all-round education.

Academic results
ISC schools achieve excellent academic results. At A level, 51% of entries from pupils at ISC schools were awarded at least an A grade, compared to over 26% nationally. Independent schools account for 14% of A level entries, but 27% of A/A* grades and 32% of A* grades. Just over 8% of GCSE entries come from ISC schools, but pupils achieve 29% of A* grades. ISC schools continue to be strong in traditional subject areas such as maths, science and modern foreign languages.

Fee Assistance
ISC schools are sympathetic to the financial challenges facing many parents and the amount of bursaries and scholarships available has grown to reflect this, with £660million available in fee assistance. Over one third of ISC pupils receive help with their fees.

ISC associations
There are eight member associations of ISC each with its own distinctive ethos reflected in their entrance criteria and quality assurance:

Girls' Schools Association (GSA) – see page 34

Headmasters' and Headmistresses' Conference (HMC) – see page 34

Independent Association of Prep Schools (IAPS) – see page 36

Independent Schools Association (ISA) – see page 36

The Society of Heads – see page 37

Association of Governing Bodies of Independent Schools (AGBIS)
www.agbis.org

Independent Schools' Bursars Association (ISBA)
www.isba.org.uk

Council of British International Schools (COBIS)
www.cobis.org.uk

Two further organisations are affiliated to ISC: **Boarding Schools Association (BSA)** and **Scottish Council of Independent Schools (SCIS)**

The Independent Schools Council can be contacted at:
First Floor,
27 Queen Anne's Gate,
London,
SW1H 9BU
Telephone: 020 7766 7070
Fax: 020 7766 7071
Website: www.isc.co.uk

independent schools council

Profiles

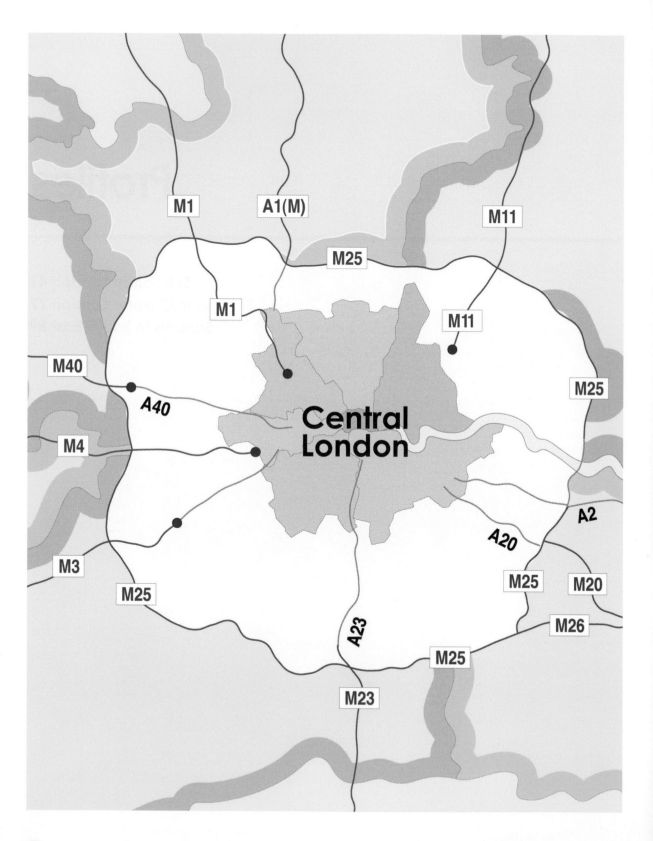

Schools in Central London

Bassett House School

Bassett House
School

(Founded 1947)

60 Bassett Road, London, W10 6JP
Tel: 020 8969 0313
Email: info@bassetths.org.uk
Website: www.bassetths.org.uk
Headmistress:
Mrs Philippa Cawthorne MA (Soton) PGCE
Appointed: January 2014

School type: Co-educational Day
Age range of pupils: 3–11
No. of pupils enrolled as at 01/01/2016: 190
Fees per annum as at 01/01/2016:
Day: £7,890–£16,440
Average class size: 20
Teacher/pupil ratio: 1:7

Bassett House School, a highly successful co-educational IAPS school for children aged 3-11 situated in North Kensington, combines an extraordinarily happy atmosphere with first class academic results. It enjoys an enviable reputation, as evidenced by its ISI inspection in which in all areas assessed it was judged to be 'outstanding' or 'excellent', the highest grades they awarded. The school participates in the Minimum Funding Entitlement Scheme, which reduces the fees charged for children aged under five years old.

Bassett House is a member of House Schools Group and has as sister independent preparatory schools Orchard House School in Chiswick and Prospect House School in Putney. There will be approximately 190 children on roll in September 2013 at Bassett House School.

It is our aim that all pupils should enjoy coming to Bassett House each morning. They take full advantage of a broad-based curriculum, as well as numerous extracurricular activities. Our objective is for all pupils to be happy and fulfilled, so that they may reach their full potential

across all areas of the curriculum thereby becoming confident, creative and independent learners. Teaching is supportive yet challenging and always takes into account the individual needs of the children. We also strive to develop self-respect along with a strong sense of moral values, thus enabling our pupils to become responsible and involved members of society. Underpinning all aspects of school life is an ethos that requires mutual respect and concern for all members of the school community and fosters close relationships between school

S.R. Binney-King
1.11.00

and home. Good manners and courteous behaviour are encouraged at all times.

Girls continue at Bassett House until the age of eleven, when they move to their senior schools. Boys are prepared for 7+ and 8+ assessment but increasingly continue at the school until the age of 11. Whilst the Nursery and Reception entry years are almost invariably fully subscribed (early registration is advised), the school occasionally has places for children from Year 3 upwards.

Bassett House provides a thorough grounding in the usual educational subjects and the children are prepared for the entrance examinations to leading day and boarding schools.

In recent years the entrance examination results to these schools have been excellent with the children regularly being offered places at, amongst other schools, The City of London, Colet Court, Francis Holland (Clarence Gate and Graham Terrace), Godolphin & Latymer, The Hall, The Harrodian, Highgate, Latymer, More House, Notting Hill and Ealing High, Queen's College, Queen's Gate, South Hampstead, St Benedict's, St Paul's Girls', Sussex House, University College, Westminster Cathedral Choir School and Westminster Under School.

As at its sister schools and via the House Schools Trust, Bassett House occasionally offers scholarships for gifted children aged 7+ which contribute to or cover fees in full. The scholarships are restricted to children currently attending a maintained school who show significant promise and for whom an education in the private sector would represent a major opportunity. To learn more about the trust please visit the website www.houseschoolstrust.org.

To find out more about Bassett House, please look at the school's website www. bassetths.org.uk. Alternatively, please telephone 020 8969 0313 to order a prospectus or to join one of our regular tours. In addition, there are occasional Open Days which give an even greater opportunity to speak to our strongest supporters, namely the children!

Blackheath High School GDST

BLACKHEATH
HIGH SCHOOL GDST

(Founded 1880)
Vanbrugh Park, Blackheath, London, SE3 7AG
Tel: 020 8853 2929
Fax: 020 8853 3663

Email: info@bla.gdst.net
Website:
www.blackheathhighschool.gdst.net
Head: Mrs Carol Chandler-Thompson BA (Hons) Exeter, PGCE Exeter
Appointed: 2014
School type: Girls' Day

Age range of girls: 3–18
No. of pupils enrolled as at 01/01/2016: 780
Fees per annum as at 01/01/2016:
Senior School (11-18): £4,693 per term
Junior Department: £3,861 per term
Nursery: £3,005 per term
Teacher/pupil ratio: 1:12

Blackheath High School (which opened in 1880) is a selective, independent day school for girls aged 3-18.

Situated in Blackheath, South East London, it is a member of the Girls' Day School Trust (GDST) and a registered charity (no. 306983) aimed to advance the education of girls and young women.

Rated 'excellent' in the latest ISI inspection, academic success is at the heart of what is offered at Blackheath High School. Fuelled by our aspirational culture, students make exceptional progress, with excellent public examination results and a range of ambitious and interesting university destinations. This is achieved through the provision of an innovative and interesting curriculum that challenges and inspires students and nurtures a love of learning. Alongside our core curriculum there are unique opportunities such as Astronomy GCSE at the Planetarium and our bespoke academic enrichment programme: The Wollstonecraft. Optional courses are designed to engage and inspire, covering topics as diverse as: the culture and history of Tibet; an introduction to architecture and designing a radio programme for Radio 4 Women's hour. Within the core curriculum, girls are able to choose two languages from Mandarin, German, French and Spanish and study these all through to year 13 and great value is placed upon the girls broadening their horizons beyond the school with a range of exciting trips and work experience opportunities. A strong focus on science and technology subjects ensures that our students defy the national trends in terms of numbers of girls applying for science and technology subjects. Strong role models and a curriculum that is well supported by the latest technology, including iPads, digital radio stations and 3D printing, inspire

ever-growing numbers of girls to pursue ambitions related to computing, science and design. This is a school where girls are encouraged to discover their passions and teachers support and challenge girls in pursuing their aims.

Fortunately situated in-between beautiful Greenwich Park and stunning Blackheath, our school is located over three sites: separate Junior and Senior Schools and a dedicated sporting facility in Kidbrooke Grove that enables us to ring-fence curriculum time for the girls' sporting activity. With a multi-million pound investment in our Senior School facilities this year, the opportunities available to the girls will continue to grow. A dedicated sixth form centre is being added to our historic Senior School site and a state-of-the-art library, creative arts centre, science labs and entrance building will enhance the opportunities already on offer through our theatre, dance and drama studios, language lab, science suite and teaching rooms.

Our students benefit from a long-established harmonious and diverse school

community. Teachers pride themselves on their superb knowledge of the girls and the positive relationships that are fostered in the school. This is a community where older girls mix readily with younger and the atmosphere of open-mindedness and tolerance is genuine and tangible. These excellent relationships are founded upon the staff's willingness and desire to provide a superb and wide-ranging extra-curricular programme. From overseas trips to exotic destinations like Peru and Beijing, to clubs designed to appeal to every girl, like 'crochet collective', 'Samba Band' or 'Iron Woman running club', the extra-curricular programme builds vital life-skills and cements positive and productive relationships. Our strong focus on 'girls first' as part of our founding mission, ensures that this is a school where girls take pride in their talents and ability and there is no truck with gender stereotypes.

As described in the ISI report, the school provides an educational experience that is "stimulating and extraordinarily supportive, conducive to the highest standards of teaching and learning".

Cameron House

(Founded 1980)
4 The Vale, Chelsea, London, SW3 6AH

Tel: 020 7352 4040
Fax: 020 7352 2349
Email: info@cameronhouseschool.org
Website: www.cameronhouseschool.org
Headmistress: Mrs Lucie Moore BEd(Hons)
Principal: Miss Josie
Cameron Ashcroft BSc(Hons), DipEd
School type: Coeducational Day

Religious Denomination: Church of England, all denominations welcome
Age range of pupils: 4–11
No. of pupils enrolled as at 01/01/2016: 120
Boys: 55 **Girls:** 65
Fees per annum as at 01/01/2016:
Day: £16,875

The curriculum
'The school fully meets its aim of maintaining high academic standards and helping each pupil to do their best.' (ISI Inspection 2010). Our academic curriculum prepares all our children for Common Entrance exams. The children study a comprehensive range of subjects using techniques that encourage them to explore, work co-operatively and be creative.

Setup and atmosphere
Cameron House has a nurturing environment that gives children a strong sense of belonging and purpose. With the guidance of the highly qualified staff, children of all abilities achieve excellent standards.

Games and the arts
Essential to life at Cameron House is sport, as well as music, drama and specialist art lessons. These are all integral to the curriculum.

Pastoral care
We encourage all our children to consider and care for others. 'Exemplary pastoral care is a strong feature of the school and staff are united in their approach to the promotion of pupils' well-being and development.' (ISI Inspection 2010).

Outstanding characteristics
Cameron House is a vibrant school well-known for maintaining high academic standards while encouraging individual creativity. Children leave Cameron House as independent thinkers, brimming with intellectual curiosity. Children move on to St Paul's, Godolphin & Latymer, Wycombe Abbey, Benenden, Alleyn's, Latymer Upper, Emanuel, City of London, Francis Holland and many more.

'The headteacher is highly skilled at moulding the staff into a unified team who work with a shared goal of a positive and caring approach towards each individual pupil, that has produced the outstanding response in the attitudes of pupils towards learning and to school' (ISI Report, 2010).

City of London School
A rounded education in the Square Mile

CITY OF LONDON SCHOOL

(Founded 1442)

Queen Victoria Street, London, EC4V 3AL
Tel: 020 7489 0291
Fax: 020 7329 6887
Email: admissions@clsb.org.uk
Website: www.clsb.org.uk
Head: Mrs S Fletcher MA
Appointed: 2014

School type: Boys' Day
Age range of boys: 10–18
No. of pupils enrolled as at 01/01/2016: 940
Sixth Form: 250
Fees per annum as at 01/09/2016:
Day: £15,633

"There is no such thing as a typical City boy. What characterises the education offered is a true preparation for life."

City of London School is a truly unique independent school not least because of its unrivalled location on the banks of the Thames, between St. Paul's Cathedral and the Tate Modern. We are at the heart of the capital and our pupils benefit enormously from all that is on offer on our doorstep.

We are a modern and forward-looking institution drawing on clever boys from all social, economic and ethnic backgrounds and in so doing truly reflect the diversity of the capital in the 21st century. Boys travel

to City from all over London and come from a huge number of both state primary and independent preparatory schools and, once here, receive an academic yet liberal education.

Our examination results are excellent, but, more importantly, boys leave us with a sense of identity and an independence of thought and action which are rare among leavers from private schools; it is significant that the vast majority of boys go on to their first choice of university.

Facilities are outstanding (the school moved downstream to its new buildings in 1986) and are continually updated.

Access to the school is not restricted by money and we are generously endowed with academic, music and sport scholarships and also bursaries for families who may not be able to afford the full fees. In addition, the bursary campaign has raised significant funding for several full-fee places to be awarded each year to those who could not otherwise afford even a proportion of fees. In this way, the school seeks to maintain the socio-economic mix which has always been its tradition and strength.

For more information, please refer to our website, or contact the Registrar.

Devonshire House Preparatory School

(Founded 1989)
2 Arkwright Road, Hampstead,
London, NW3 6AE

Tel: 020 7435 1916
Email: enquiries@
devonshirehouseprepschool.co.uk
Website:
www.devonshirehouseschool.co.uk
Headmistress: Mrs S. Piper BA(Hons)
School type: Preparatory, Pre-preparatory
& Nursery Day School

Religious Denomination:
Non-denominational
Age range of boys: 2½ –13
Age range of girls: 2½ –11
No. of pupils enrolled as at 01/01/2016: 620
Boys: 340 *Girls:* 280
Fees per annum as at 01/01/2016:
Day: £9,060–£16,635

Academic & leisure facilities

The school is situated in fine premises in the heart of Hampstead with its own walled grounds. The aim is to achieve high academic standards whilst developing enthusiasm and initiative throughout a wide range of interests. It is considered essential to encourage pupils to develop their own individual interests and a good sense of personal responsibility.

Curriculum

Early literacy and numeracy are very important and the traditional academic subjects form the core curriculum. The younger children all have a class teacher and classroom assistant and their day consists of a mixture of formal lessons and learning through play. Whilst children of all ages continue to have a form teacher, as they grow older an increasing part of the curriculum is delivered by subject specialists. The combined sciences form an increasingly important part of the timetable as the children mature. The use of computers is introduced from an early stage, both as its own skill and as an integrated part of the pupils' education.

Expression in all forms of communication is encouraged, with classes having lessons in art, music, drama and French. Physical exercise and games also play a key part of the curriculum. Much encouragement is given to pupils to help widen their horizons and broaden their interests. The school fosters a sense of responsibility amongst the pupils, and individuality and personal attention for each pupil is considered essential to make progress in the modern world.

The principal areas of the National Curriculum are covered, though subjects may be taken at a higher level, or at a quicker pace. For the girls approaching the eleven plus senior schools' entry examinations, special emphasis is given to the requirements for these, and in the top two years for the boys, Common Entrance curriculum is taught. The pupils achieve great success in these examinations and a number also sit successfully for senior school scholarships.

The school has its own nursery, The Oak Tree Nursery, which takes children from two-and-a-half years of age.

Entry requirements

The Oak Tree Nursery: For children entering the Oak Tree Nursery, places are offered on the basis on an informal assessment made at the nursery. Children in The Oak Tree Nursery transfer directly to the Junior School.

The Junior School: For children entering the junior school from the ages of three to five, places are offered on the basis of assessment made at the school. From the age of six places are usually subject to a written test taken at school. At eight, children transfer directly into the upper school. Parents and their children are welcome to visit for interview and to see around the school.

The Upper School: Entry to the upper school is principally from the junior school. For pupils seeking to join the school from elsewhere places are normally subject to a written entrance test.

DLD College

DLD COLLEGE LONDON

(Founded 1931)

199 Westminster Bridge Road, London,

SE1 7FX

Tel: 020 7935 8411

Fax: 020 7935 0755

Email: dld@dld.org

Website: www.dldcollege.co.uk

Principal: Ms. Rachel Borland MA

Appointed: May 2013

School type: Coeducational Day & Boarding

No. of pupils enrolled as at 01/01/2016: 485

Boys: 263 **Girls:** 222

No. of boarders: 220

Fees per annum as at 01/01/2016:

Day: £17,800–£19,900

Full Boarding: £15,000–£21,000

Average class size: 10-12

Teacher/pupil ratio: 1:6

DLD College is a leading independent boarding school that offers over 500 students a wide-ranging curriculum in superb learning environment, delivered by tutors who are selected both for their academic strength, enthusiasm and their ability to relate positively to young people. We are helping students achieve grades they often didn't believe possible and preparing them to access the university courses and destinations of their choice. DLD College is a dynamic place to study providing high quality GCSE, A Level & BTEC courses.

Our lessons are lively and encourage students to discuss ideas, ask questions and actively learn. We recognise that choosing the most appropriate programme of study is a very important part of the application process and we therefore invite all those interested in enrolling at DLD to interview to discuss your subjects.

We believe small class sizes encourage a more purposeful learning and allow for a greater measure of individual attention, helping students to be more focused on their studies and building their confidence. Students learn important study skills including note taking, essay writing, time management, revision and exam technique. On average, class sizes at DLD are around 8 students. Each student is allocated a Personal Tutor who monitors his or her progress as they move through the course. The welfare of students is paramount and the personal tutors are backed up by a team of Directors of Studies.

In September 2015, DLD College relocated to brand new, purpose-built premises in the heart of London overlooking Westminster and the River Thames. DLD College London is a truly unique college

campus, with facilities including:

- 55 classrooms – 60 touch screens
- 70 seat theatre with state of the art LED lighting. The theatre is also equipped with a cinema screen and surround sound.
- Two 1st floor music rooms fully equipped with the latest iMacs and software, a studio complex in the basement with three rooms. The music technology lab comprises state of the art iMac computers with the latest versions of Logic and Sibelius software on them, In addition we have three practice rooms equipped with a top end acoustic and digital pianos as well as a drum kit.
- Three art studios, graphic suite and a photography studio and classrooms.
- Separate laboratories for Biology, Chemistry and Physics equipped with interactive touch screens.
- Four dedicated learning zones with quiet booths and water fountains.
- Learning centre equipped with state

of the art technology.

- Under 16's Study areas equipped with computers (supervised) and open space learning.
- 5 private tuition rooms for one on one learning.
- The Refectory provides a multifunctional space for eating, studying and socialising, and has a mixture of long bench style tables and booths. In addition, students also have access to a Starbucks Café from 8am.
- Atrium with film projectors and surround sound.
- Gallery with seating for student group work.
- College nurse with onsite medical facilities.
- Students under the age of 16 can access a dedicated terrace on the third floor of the College. All students can benefit from an enclosed, safe and secure landscaped garden area just outside the College.

Dolphin School
(incorporating Noah's Ark Nursery Schools)

(Founded 1986)

106 Northcote Road, London, SW11 6QW

Tel: 020 7924 3472

Email: admissions@dolphinschool.org.uk

Website: www.dolphinschool.org.uk

Principal: Mr J Schmidt BA(Hons), BEd, BPE

Appointed: September 2015

School type:

Coeducational Day and Nursery

Age range of pupils: 2–11

No. of pupils enrolled as at 01/01/2016: 317

Fees per annum as at 01/01/2016:

Day: £10,785–£11,895

Average class size:

18 in school: 8 in Nursery

Teacher/pupil ratio: 1:8 Nursery,

1:9 (Lower School), 1:18 (Upper School)

Curriculum

Our small class sizes enable us to get to know your child extremely well so that we can not only set specific individualised academic targets, but also discover how he or she learns best. We give priority to English and maths as well as hands-on science, colourful geography, history (with outings to the real thing) and whole-school Spanish.

Games and the arts

We train pupils in the arts with fantastic specialist teaching and a plethora of performing and exhibiting opportunities. We also coach children in a wide range of sports through dynamic teaching and a superb fixture list.

Pastoral care

We are committed to giving both time and care to grow your child's character on his or her journey from Reception to Year 6. Our Christian ethos leads us to believe that personal growth ultimately matters more than anything. So while we are thrilled that our leavers win academic or sporting scholarships to a range of excellent secondary schools, we are even more excited about who they are – and pleased that they enjoyed the journey.

Entry requirements

Reception class: appointment with the Principal. Years 1-6: interview, assessment day and past school reports.

Principal's philosophy

If we want children to be the best they can be, academically, artistically, in sport or as people, we must start by valuing them for who they are.

Outstanding characteristics

The combination of nurture and dynamism. The passionate commitment of the staff. A fantastic all-round education.

Examinations offered

11+ entry examinations.

Senior exit schools: Alleyn's, City of London Schools, Downe House, Ibstock Place, Royal Russell, Dulwich College, JAGS, Streatham & Clapham High, Oakham, Emanuel, TCC, Lady Margaret, Putney High School, Croydon High School, Francis Holland, Frensham Heights.

Dolphin School Trust is a registered charity (No. 1145113) and exists to promote a high quality of education for all its children based upon Christian principles.

École Jeannine Manuel – London

(Founded 2015)

43-45 Bedford Square, London WC1B 3DN

Tel: 020 3829 5970

Email: contact@jmanuel.uk.net

Website:

www.ecolejeanninemanuel.org.uk

Principal: Pauline Prévot

School type: Coeducational Day

Age range of pupils: 3–14 years

No. of pupils enrolled as at 01/01/2016: 190

Fees per annum as at 01/01/2016:

£16,410

Average class size: 16

Teacher/pupil ratio: 1:8

École Jeannine Manuel in London is a French, bilingual, international school which opened its doors in September 2015 in three contiguous mansions on Bedford Square, steps from the British Museum in the heart of Bloomsbury. In its first year, our school opened with 190 Reception - Year 8 pupils from all nationalities and cultural background. 130 new pupils will join us in September 2016, from Nursery to Year 9, the next step towards a primary and secondary school of 1,100 pupils leading to the French and the International Baccalaureates.

École Jeannine Manuel is the young sister school of its Paris namesake, a UNESCO associated school founded in 1954 and one of France's most prestigious schools, ranked first among French high schools (public and independent) for overall academic performance in 2013, 2014 and 2015. As is the case in France, the mission of the London school is "to promote international understanding through the bilingual education of a multicultural community of students, the fostering of pedagogical innovation, and the constant exploration of best practices in the context of an ever-changing global environment."

A bilingual education

École Jeannine Manuel offers an enriched, bilingual adaptation of the French national curriculum, including English, Science and Chinese programmes developed by its Paris sister school. In History, the French national curriculum is complemented to help pupils gain a coherent knowledge and understanding of Britain's past and that of the wider world. Co-curricular activities include sports – with walking access to outdoor facilities – as well as a broad range of after-school clubs.

English and French are used equally in class. Our aim is to bring pupils to a native proficiency – oral and written – in both languages. We welcome non French-speaking students at all levels and help them adapt to the demands of a bilingual curriculum. With respect to English, the school accommodates

beginners up to Year 7. Experience shows that studying in French and in English yields a strong and mutually reinforced command of both languages as well as a deep understanding of the cultures they express. A bilingual education enhances pupils' capacity for abstract, conceptual thinking and develops a sense of nuance, nurtured by exposure to multiple perspectives.

A multicultural community of students
Looking beyond French and bi-national families, the school welcomes pupils from all nationalities, cultural traditions and native languages. École Jeannine Manuel in London is positioned, as is the case in Paris, as a unique, truly bicultural institution with a multicultural student body representing almost 40 nationalities. We attract international and internationally

minded families deeply invested in the education and well being of their children. Living this cultural melting pot every day yields a special consciousness of one's place in the world, an appreciation for the broad landscape of culture and civilizations, which we learn to understand and value together.

The fostering of pedagogical innovation
The key drivers of our school's pedagogy are coherence and innovation. Whether inspired by current research in the cognitive sciences, by best practices from around the world or home-grown, our teaching methods are constantly evolving. Our international teams of teachers stimulate new ideas that lead to a creative, pioneering education. Hands-on manipulations in math, inquiry-based learning in the sciences, and teamwork are among the practices that foster pupil engagement and growth. Our aim is to have pupils think, do and share. The school's pedagogical principles are founded on four pillars: the early mastery of core academic skills; the development of autonomy; the encouragement of collaborative work; and the nurturing of curiosity, creativity and a lifelong appetite for culture.

Dwight School London

DWIGHT SCHOOL LONDON
Igniting the spark of genius in every child
PERSONALISED LEARNING • COMMUNITY • GLOBAL VISION

(Founded 1885)
6 Friern Barnet Lane, London, N11 3LX

Tel: +44 (0)20 8920 0600
Email: admissions@dwightlondon.org
Website: www.dwightlondon.org
Head: Mrs Alison Cobbin BA, Dip Ed, MBA
IB coordinator: Paul Johnson
School type: Coeducational Day

Age range of pupils: 2–18+
No. of pupils enrolled as at 01/09/2015:
Fees per annum as at 01/01/2016:
May vary upon application
Average class size: max 20

Dwight School London has its roots firmly embedded in north London where it has been serving local and international families for generations. As part of the Dwight family network of schools around the globe in New York, Vancouver, Shanghai, and Seoul, Dwight School London has an established reputation as one of the UK's early International Baccalaureate (IB) World Schools. It is one of the few UK schools authorised to offer the International Baccalaureate Primary Years Programme (IBPYP); Middle Years Programme (IBMYP) as well as the more widely known rigorous and prestigious Diploma (IBDP). Dwight was also selected to pilot the IB online courses.

The School's philosophy and IB curriculum place an emphasis on understanding international perspectives, encouraging global thinkers and developing global citizens. This is enhanced when experienced by a diverse community of students representing nearly 50 nationalities. The school offers students an exciting opportunity to discover an authentic global experience through our Dwight network of schools, exchange programmes, and curriculum-based excursions both in the UK and abroad. The holistic nature of the IB programmes encourages students to develop through a full range of sports, arts and service-learning endeavours, as well as through their academic studies.

Dwight School London has a positive and stimulating learning environment that aims to nurture individual progress by *'igniting the spark of genius'* in each student. Dwight School is guided by a belief that effective learning is best achieved in a supportive community where self-respect and responsibility for others are key characteristics. These ingredients and a world-class IB curriculum serve to prepare students for university and life beyond.

Faraday School

Old Gate House, 7 Trinity Buoy Wharf,
London, E14 0FH
Tel: 020 8965 7374
Email: info@newmodelschool.co.uk
Website: www.faradayschool.co.uk
Head Teacher: Miss S Stark

School type: Coeducational Day
Age range of pupils: 4–11
No. of pupils enrolled as at 01/01/2016: 100
Fees per term as at 01/01/2016:
Day: £2,930

Faraday is a small, independent prep school situated at the historic setting of Trinity Buoy Wharf, close to the City and Canary Wharf.

Faraday School is committed to giving every child a first-class education in the arts and sciences, drawing as a resource upon the Core Knowledge approach, which imparts knowledge through traditional academic subjects.

Although we believe in a traditional approach, our lessons reflect modern thinking on how children learn most effectively and our small classes and quality staff allow for a very personal approach to learning.

We feel literacy and numeracy are important, however, our curriculum is broad and stimulating, including specialist teaching in French, Music and Physical Education. Our aim is to educate the whole child through a rich curriculum with many stimuli, in order to support an atmosphere of life-long learning.

We also provide a wide range of after school clubs and, to help working parents, a private school bus runs before and after school from 17 different locations, including south of the river.

We were founded in 2009 and maintain strong links with our sister school, Maple Walk, in North West London. Our setting beside the River Thames, opposite the iconic O2 arena and beside the Trinity Lighthouse, gives our pupils an inspirational location in which to learn. We are fortunate enough to be surrounded by creative industries and we make the best of all that London has to offer, with regular trips to museums, historic attractions and galleries.

Our June 2014 ISI Inspection found Faraday School pupil attainment to be *"well-above national age-rated expectations."*

Herne Hill School

(Founded 1976)

The Old Vicarage, 127 Herne Hill,
London, SE24 9LY
Tel: 020 7274 6336
Fax: 020 7924 9510
Email: enquiries@hernehillschool.co.uk
Website: www.hernehillschool.co.uk
Headteacher: Mrs Ngaire Telford

Director: Mr Dominik Magyar
School type: Coeducational Day
Age range of pupils: 2+ to–7
No. of pupils enrolled as at 01/01/2016: 275
Fees per term as at 01/01/2016:
Day: £1,790–£4,435

Herne Hill School has much to offer – caring and enthusiastic staff, happy and confident children, and excellent results at 7+ years.

In the UK, it is the largest independent pre-school and pre-prep focusing exclusively on 2+ to 7 year olds. In South London, it is well known as an oasis of happy learning and as the largest feeder into the reputable Dulwich schools. Children join the Kindergarten in the autumn term of the year in which they become three years old, Pre-Reception in the autumn of the year they become four or then Reception. Chance vacancies are occasionally available in Years 1 and 2.

The school lies tucked away behind St Paul's Church on Herne Hill. Its grounds and facilities provide a 'homely', safe and nurturing feel while at the same time being open, green and deceptively large – the perfect environment for young children to blossom and enjoy discovering how to learn. Since January 2016, a new hall and Kindergarten has become fully operational and enabled a number of additional benefits:

- the provision of healthy hot lunches freshly cooked on site daily;
- a large, state-of-the-art Kindergarten with free-flow access to a covered outdoor play area;

- a modern, multi-purpose hall for sports, drama, dance, assemblies, lunches, *etc*; and
- upgraded playground facilities with a new, enlarged all-weather surface and a trim trail in the nature area.

By focusing on Early Years and Key Stage 1, Herne Hill School has developed a strong expertise in making the critical transition from 'nursery' to 'school' seamless. Children joining the Kindergarten and Pre-Reception can avoid the disruption of a 4+ change and have continuity for up to five years in what are arguably their most important formative years. Children joining in Reception also benefit from the

smooth progression from a play-based learning approach to more structured lessons.

"*Love • Care • Excellence*" encapsulates the school philosophy that love, nurture and a caring environment foster the children's self-confidence, sense of achievement and happiness, thereby stimulating their curiosity and desire to learn. The school's atmosphere lives this philosophy. It is a caring, friendly and fun place, and at the same time there is an air of achievement, respect and discipline.

The proprietary curriculum is finely balanced to take account of each child's individual needs as well as the requirements of the 7+ entry tests – and to make learning fun! It is designed to develop the skills of independent learning and to sustain the children's innate joy of learning. Music, drama, gym, dancing and French are emphasised and taught by specialists. Wrap-around care is available from 8am to 6pm through a broad offering of attractive clubs aimed at satisfying the children's various interests and enabling earlier drop-off and later pick-up for parents.

The latest ISI inspection report delivered a strong endorsement of the school's ethos, staff, curriculum, modus operandi and infrastructure by giving the highest possible rating of 'excellent' or 'outstanding' to every aspect of the school. The inspectors deemed overall achievement to be excellent and that pupils are very well educated and achieve very high standards in both their learning and personal development. The full report can be found on www.isi.net.

The school holds two open mornings a year, typically in March and September. Prospective parents may also see the school 'in action' by joining one of the regular tours held during school hours. The school's website contains relevant information about life at the school, its curriculum and the destination of its leavers.

Hawkesdown House School Kensington

Hawkesdown House School
Endeavour • Courage • Truth

27 Edge Street, Kensington, London, W8 7PN

Tel: 020 7727 9090
Email: admin@hawkesdown.co.uk
Website: www.hawkesdown.co.uk
Head: Mrs C Bourne MA(Cantab)
Appointed: January 2010
School type:
Boys' Independent Pre-Prep Day

Religious Denomination: Non-denominational
Age range of boys: 3–8
No. of pupils enrolled as at 01/01/2016: 141
Fees per annum as at 01/01/2016:
Day: £14,550–£16,725
Average class size: 18-21
Teacher/pupil ratio: 1:9

Hawkesdown House is an independent school for boys from the age of four to eight with a Nursery Class for boys of three years old. It is housed in a fine building in Edge Street, off Kensington Church Street, and most of the boys live within walking distance. Founded in 2001, the School's reputation has spread by word of mouth and it is an important part of the community.

The Headmistress, Mrs Claire Bourne, a Cambridge Classics graduate, is a firm believer in single sex education for this age group. "Boys learn in such a different way from girls and we understand that completely here and cater to their needs."

She leads a young and enthusiastic staff who all have high expectations of the boys. "Our main curriculum focus is on literacy and numeracy but our syllabus is wonderfully broad. We want the boys to leave Hawkesdown House with a joy of learning so we ensure that their education is enriched in every way. Music, chess, judo, fencing and Mandarin are just some of the subjects on offer." After school clubs, School Council and a House system offer the boys many opportunities to contribute to school life. The Friday assembly for parents, where the boys' achievements

are celebrated, is always packed. "Hawkesdown House is a big family," says Mrs Bourne, "we are immensely proud of our boys and everyone here is valued for their contribution and effort."

The School is dedicated to providing an outstanding early education for the boys, who are prepared for examinations at eight years old to London's most selective Prep Schools including Westminster Under, Colet Court and Sussex House.

Parents who would like further information or to visit the School and meet the Head, should contact the School Office for a prospectus or an appointment.

International Community School

ICS
INTERNATIONAL
COMMUNITY
SCHOOL
(Founded 1979)

4 York Terrace East, Regents Park,
London, NW1 4PT
Tel: +44 20 7935 1206
Email: admissions@ics.uk.net
Website: www.icschool.co.uk
Head of School: Ms Rose Threlfall
Principal of Secondary: Ms Brenda Murray

Principal of Primary: Ms Elizabeth McLaughlin
School type: Coeducational Day
Age range of pupils: 3–18
No. of pupils enrolled as at 01/01/2016: 260
Fees per annum as at 01/01/2016:
Day: £16,650–£22,100
Average class size: 16

The International Community School is the independent, International Baccalaureate World School, located in central London. This year marks our 35th anniversary. The School is accredited by the IB, the British Council, NAS and is also a member of the European Council of International Schools and the Council of International Schools.

ICS offers the IB Primary Years, Middle Years and Diploma programmes. Our class sizes are small, and there is a strong focus on personalised learning highly tailored to each student's needs and interests. This allows all students, regardless of their academic background, to thrive and excel in our rigorous but supportive environment.

Our school community of approximately 260 students represents 45 different nationalities, giving each member of the school a truly international perspective and a broad global horizon, as well as an unmatched inter-cultural understanding and solid academic base preparing them for university and life beyond.

All our 2015 IB Diploma graduates were successful in entering the university of their choice.

We use Information Communication Technology in a variety of innovative ways to engage and encourage our students to become lifelong learners. In addition we ensure curriculum enrichment through the 'Outdoor Classroom'. This entails frequent educational visits within London, spending time at our Outdoor Education Centres in Suffolk and Chorleywood, and our unique 'Travel and Learn' opportunities.

There are lunchtime and after school clubs and activities for students ranging from football and basketball to rock climbing, capoeira and cooking clubs.

The School also provides a door-to-door minibus service that serves most of central London.

For more information please contact the Admissions Office – admissions@ics.uk.net

L'Ecole de Battersea

Trott Street, Battersea, London SW11 3DS

Founded in 1977

Director: Mrs F Brisset

Head: Mr L Balerdi

Principal: Mrs M Otten

School type: Independent Bilingual Pre-Primary and Primary (Ecole Homologuée)

Age range of pupils:
3–11 years, boys and girls

No of pupils enrolled as at 1.9.15:
252 pupils

Fees per annum as at 1.9.15:
£10,515–£10,710

Religious denomination:
All denominations welcome

Entry requirements:
Interview with parents and school tour

L'Ecole de Battersea opened in 2005 following on from the success of its sister school, L'Ecole des Petits. The school is unique in that it offers a **continuous bilingual education from age three through until age eleven** at the end of primary, where both the French and English educational systems operate together. The teaching emphasis throughout the school is fundamentally based on the French system, into which aspects of the English curriculum and methodology are integrated.

The highly motivated bilingual team of teachers are qualified in both the English and French educational systems.

This bilingual facility enables children and parents to choose to progress on to either the English private school system or on to the French Lycée system, and is also ideal for the increasingly popular International Baccalaureate.

The school welcomes bilingual pupils from a range of cultures, and so aims to generate a **truly international atmosphere**.

Partnership with the family is paramount in the school's ethos, and the school successfully seeks **to develop confident and balanced children** with experience of a wide range of activities, an appreciation of artistic and cultural heritage and a thoughtful and considerate attitude towards others.

Class sizes are small and the school occupies a recently refurbished building with **top quality facilities**, and with good outside spaces for a Central London school. The school is only **five minutes drive from Chelsea** and operates a twice daily school bus service between South Kensington and Battersea, as well as a link to its sister school in Fulham, ten minutes distance.

The school is inspected by both the French Inspectorate and Ofsted and achieves excellent academic results. **Ofsted 2012 report said the school was "*Outstanding in all categories*"** and it has been selected as one of the top 225 private schools in the country in *The Tatler Education Guides 2009–2015*.

TEL 020 7371 8350   admin@lecoledespetits.co.uk   www.lecoledespetits.co.uk

Founded in 1977

L'Ecole des Petits

2 Hazlebury Road, Fulham, London SW6 2NB

Director: Mrs F Brisset
Deputy Head: Mrs F Tailfer
Principal: Mrs M Otten
School type: Independent Bilingual Pre-Primary (Ecole Homologuée)
Age range of pupils:
3–6 years, boys and girls
No of pupils enrolled as at 1.9.15:
136 pupils
Fees per annum as at 1.9.15:
Full day £10,320–£10,620
Religious denomination:
All denominations welcome
Entry requirements:
Interview with parents and school tour

L'Ecole des Petits is a flourishing pre-primary school situated in Fulham, just **ten minutes from Chelsea**, with easy access by public transport. The school also runs its own daily morning and afternoon **bus service between South Kensington and Fulham**, and between its sister school in Battersea.

The school was founded in 1977 to cater for English and French families who want their children to **grow up in a bilingual environment**. By combining the Early Years curriculum with the French National curriculum, the school provides all aspects of education in both French and English, and today has a wonderfully **international flavour with children from 22 different countries** attending.

Children are taught by qualified and highly-motivated bilingual teachers. The school aims to provide **an education that enhances early learning skills in the controlled environment of small classes**.

The school has a warm and friendly atmosphere which encourages children to express themselves whilst following the structured bilingual curriculum. We consider maintaining **traditional family values** a very important aspect of our approach.

Our philosophy is to develop confident and happy children by providing **the best possible all-round education and care**, with an abundance of sports, drama, clubs, school outings and events as well as academic lessons.

We prepare our children to move onto both English and French schools, and many also continue their primary education at our sister school, L'Ecole de Battersea.

According to one of our parents, *"This is an exceptional school that provides a nurturing environment, as well as good discipline and a wonderful education, and my child could not be happier and more confident about going to school."*

OFSTED 2009: *"Outstanding School"*.

TEL 020 7371 8350   **admin@lecoledespetits.co.uk**   **www.lecoledespetits.co.uk**

Lyndhurst House Prep School

LYNDHURST HOUSE
PREPARATORY SCHOOL

(Founded 1952)

24 Lyndhurst Gardens, Hampstead,
London, NW3 5NW
Tel: 020 7435 4936
Email: pmg@lyndhursthouse.co.uk
Website: www.lyndhursthouse.co.uk
Headmaster: Andrew Reid MA(Oxon)
Appointed: September 2008

School type: Boys' Day
Age range of boys: 4–13
No. of pupils enrolled as at 01/01/2016: 165
Fees per annum as at 01/01/2016:
Day: £5,515–£6,160
Average class size: 18
Teacher/pupil ratio: 1:8

Lyndhurst House Pre-Prep & Prep School for boys was founded by Vernon Davies in 1952, in a tall, handsome Willett-style building in leafy Lyndhurst Gardens, Hampstead.

For over 60 years Lyndhurst has played a full part in the range of local independent educational provision, sending on its thirteen year olds to the many renowned senior schools in London, and some to boarding further afield with an excellent record of academic success and achievement, matched by a strong participation in sports, music and art.

Pupils develop a good knowledge of their own and other cultures and traditions. Visits to theatres, museums and art galleries feature prominently throughout the year. A significant strength of the school is the way pupils from a wide range of cultural backgrounds work and play together harmoniously.

One of the smaller prep schools in the area, Lyndhurst provides a structured but individually responsive education from reception at four-plus up to Common Entrance and scholarship at 13, delivered by an experienced, well-qualified, and stable staff team, and the abiding characteristics of its pupils seem to be a lively enthusiasm and sense of engagement and belonging. Lyndhurst House is a non-denominational school.

For all enquiries, please contact
Mrs P M Green
Lyndhurst House Preparatory
24 Lyndhurst Gardens
Hampstead
London NW3 5NW
Tel: 020 7435 4936
Email: pmg@lyndhursthouse.co.uk
Website: www.lyndhursthouse.co.uk
We look forward to meeting you.

Mander Portman Woodward – London

M|P|W

Mander Portman Woodward

(Founded 1973)

90-92 Queen's Gate, London, SW7 5AB
Tel: 020 7835 1355
Fax: 020 7259 2705
Email: london@mpw.ac.uk
Website: www.mpw.ac.uk
Principal: Mr Steven Boyes BA MSc PGCE
Appointed: August 2006

School type: Coeducational Day
Age range of pupils: 14–19
No. of pupils enrolled as at 01/01/2016: 620
Fees per annum as at 01/01/2016:
Day: £8,247–£8,928
Average class size: 6
Teacher/pupil ratio: 1:6

MPW London was founded in 1973 by three Cambridge graduates. The academic experience for students is modelled on the Oxford and Cambridge tutorial, with lessons being more relaxed and informal than those of a typical school, but also academically stimulating and demanding. With a maximum number of eight students in any class, lessons are intensive but rewarding with plenty of opportunity for individual attention and personalised learning.

Over 40 subjects are offered at A level and 25 at GCSE. As well as expert tuition, students receive past paper practice, coaching in examination techniques and detailed advice on university entrance. Parents are invited to the college regularly to discuss progress with their child's Director of Studies and also for events such as our Art Show, Principal's lecture series or UCAS week, where we provide advice on university applications.

Our academic programme aims not only to enable students to achieve their best in their GCSE and A level examinations but also to prepare them for life at university and beyond. We prepare students for a range of universities, including Oxford and Cambridge, University of the Arts, and competitive degree specialisms such as Medicine or Law.

In addition to the academic side of life at MPW, the college prides itself on maintaining a relatively informal, personalised and supportive atmosphere. As well as the small class sizes, which provide a nurturing environment for students, pastoral care has gone from strength to strength. Our Director of Studies team monitors each student's progress and wellbeing. We endeavour to foster community and offer a broad range of experience for all our students, including a comprehensive PHSE programme for GCSE and General Studies activities for Year 12 upwards.

Maple Walk School

62A Crownhill Road, London, NW10 4EB

Tel: 020 8963 3890

Email: admin@maplewalkschool.co.uk

Website: www.maplewalkschool.co.uk

Head Teacher: Mrs S Gillam

School type: Coeducational Day

Age range of pupils: 4–11

No. of pupils enrolled as at 01/01/2016: 200

Fees per term as at 01/01/2016:

Day: £2,846

Average class size: 20

Maple Walk is a small, independent prep school in North West London.

Maple Walk School is committed to giving every child a first-class education in the arts and sciences, drawing as a resource upon the Core Knowledge approach, which imparts knowledge through traditional academic subjects.

Although we believe in a traditional approach, our lessons reflect modern thinking on how children learn most effectively and our small classes and quality staff allow for a very personal approach to learning.

We feel literacy and numeracy are important, however, our curriculum is broad and stimulating, including specialist teaching in French, Music, Drama, Dance and Physical Education. Our aim is to educate the whole child through a rich curriculum with many stimuli, in order to support an atmosphere of life-long learning.

Our sports teams compete in a range of competitions and have seen growing success, particularly at Cross Country, Football and Gymnastics. We also provide a wide range of after school clubs and care.

Maple Walk was founded in 2004 and we maintain strong links with our sister school, Faraday School, in East London. We are easily accessible by road and public transport and make use of the local facilities, including the Green-Flag awarded Roundwood Park for PE and Willesden Sports Centre for swimming lessons. We take full advantage of the extensive cultural opportunities London has to offer, with termly trips to a wide range of museums, galleries, theatres and places of scientific, historical and religious interest.

Our March 2012 ISI Inspection found that *"the personal development of pupils is excellent"*.

More House School

MORE HOUSE
SCHOOL
KNIGHTSBRIDGE

(Founded 1953)
22-24 Pont Street, Knightsbridge,
London, SW1X 0AA

Tel: 020 7235 2855
Fax: 020 7259 6782
Email: office@morehouse.org.uk
Website: www.morehouse.org.uk
Headmistress: Mrs. Amanda Leach
Appointed: April 2014
School type: Independent Girls' Day

Age range of girls: 11–18
No. of pupils enrolled as at 01/01/2016: 211
Fees per annum as at 01/01/2016:
Day: £17,160
Average class size: 16
Teacher/pupil ratio: 1:6

More House School provides an environment where pupils and staff are valued and supported as individuals and where their rights and dignity are maintained. Our School fosters an ethos of spiritual growth, not only for those within the Roman Catholic Church but also for those who adhere to other Christian traditions and other faiths.

Founded in 1953, by the Canonesses of St Augustine, at the request of a group of parents determined to send their daughters to a Catholic London day school. The school occupies two interconnecting townhouses in the heart of Knightsbridge. Pupils of all faiths and none are welcome and the school has a broad cultural mix. Girls are provided with a rounded education, designed to allow individual strengths to shine through.

Academic results are good, balanced by a wide range of extra-curricular activities. Music, drama and art are well supported and pupils regularly achieve local success in sports such as netball and running. The Duke of Edinburgh's Award is popular, and there is an active commitment to fundraising for charity.

Our mission at More House, is to provide an environment for pupils to not only gain the qualifications they need to pursue the courses and careers of their choice, but also the confidence and self assurance to meet the challenges that lie ahead in an ever changing world.

Academic, music, drama and art scholarships are available at 11+ entry and sixth form. Bursaries are also available.

Orchard House School

Orchard House
School

(Founded 1993)
16 Newton Grove, Bedford Park, London,

W4 1LB
Tel: 020 8742 8544 Registrar: 020 8987 9886
Email: registrar@orchardhs.org.uk
Website: www.orchardhs.org.uk
Headmistress: Mrs M V Edwards BEd
(Bedford), CertEd (Man)
Appointed: September 2015

School type: Co-educational Day
Age range of pupils: 3–11
No. of pupils enrolled as at 01/01/2016: 290
Fees per annum as at 01/01/2016:
Day: £7,890–£16,440
Average class size: 20
Teacher/pupil ratio: 1:7

Orchard House School, a highly successful co-educational IAPS school for children aged 3-11 situated in Chiswick, combines an extraordinarily happy atmosphere with first class academic results. It enjoys an enviable reputation, as evidenced by its ISI inspection in which in all areas assessed it was judged to be 'outstanding' or 'excellent', the highest grades that are awarded. The school participates in the Minimum Funding Entitlement Scheme,

which reduces the fees charged for children aged under five years old.

Orchard House is a member of House Schools Group and has as sister independent preparatory schools Bassett House School in North Kensington and Prospect House School in Putney. There will be approximately 290 children on roll in September 2013 at Orchard House School.

It is our aim that all pupils should enjoy coming to Orchard House each morning. They take full advantage of

a broad-based curriculum, as well as numerous extracurricular activities. Our objective is for all pupils to be happy and fulfilled, so that they may reach their full potential across all areas of the curriculum thereby becoming confident, creative and independent learners. Teaching is supportive yet challenging and always takes into account the individual needs of the children. We also strive to develop self-respect along with a strong sense of moral values, thus enabling our pupils

to become responsible and involved members of society. Underpinning all aspects of school life is an ethos that requires mutual respect and concern for all members of the school community and fosters close relationships between school and home. Good manners and courteous behaviour are encouraged at all times.

Girls continue at Orchard House until the age of eleven, when they move to their senior schools. Boys are prepared for 7+ and 8+ assessment but increasingly continue at the school until the age of 11. Whilst the Nursery and Reception entry years are almost invariably fully subscribed (early registration is advised), the school occasionally has places for children from Year 3 upwards.

Orchard House provides a thorough grounding in the usual educational subjects and the children are prepared for the entrance examinations to leading day and boarding schools.

In recent years the entrance examination results to these schools have been excellent with the children regularly being offered places at, amongst other schools, Colet Court, Caldicott, Godolphin & Latymer, King's House, The Harrodian, The Lady Eleanor Holles School, Latymer Preparatory and Upper, Ludgrove, Notting Hill and Ealing High, St Paul's Girls', Sussex House, University College, Westminster Cathedral Choir School and Westminster Under School.

As at its sister schools and via the House Schools Trust, Orchard House occasionally offers scholarships for gifted children aged 7+ which contribute to or cover fees in full. The scholarships are restricted to children currently attending a maintained school who show significant promise and for whom an education in the private sector would represent a major opportunity. To learn more about the trust please visit the website www.houseschoolstrust.org.

To find out more about Orchard House, please look at the school's website www. orchardhs.org.uk. Alternatively, please telephone 020 8742 8544 to order a prospectus or to join one of our regular tours. In addition, there are occasional Open Days which give an even greater opportunity to speak to our strongest supporters, namely the children!

Prospect House School

Prospect House
School

QUISQUE PRO SUA PARTE

(Founded 1991)

75 Putney Hill, London, SW15 3NT

Tel: 020 8780 0456 Registrar: 020 8246 4897

Email: registrar@prospecths.org.uk

Website: www.prospecths.org.uk

Headmistress: Mrs Dianne Barratt MEd

(Newcastle-upon-Tyne)

Appointed: 2004

School type: Co-educational Day

Age range of pupils: 3–11

No. of pupils enrolled as at 01/01/2016: 300

Fees per annum as at 01/01/2016:

Day: £7,890–£16,440

Average class size: 20

Teacher/pupil ratio: 1:7

Prospect House School, a highly successful co-educational IAPS school for children aged 3-11 situated in Putney, combines an extraordinarily happy atmosphere with first class academic results. It enjoys an enviable reputation, as evidenced by its ISI school inspection this year in which in all areas assessed it was judged to be 'excellent', the highest grade that is awarded. The school participates in the Minimum Funding Entitlement Scheme, which reduces the fees charged for children aged under five years old.

Prospect House is a member of House Schools Group and has as sister independent preparatory schools Bassett House School in North Kensington and Orchard House School in Chiswick. There will be approximately 290 children on roll in September 2013 at Prospect House School.

It is our aim that all pupils should enjoy coming to Prospect House each morning. They take full advantage of a broad-based curriculum, as well as numerous extracurricular activities. Our objective is for all pupils to be happy and fulfilled, so that they may reach their full potential across all areas of the curriculum thereby becoming confident, creative and independent learners. Teaching is supportive yet challenging and always takes into account the individual needs of the children. We also strive to develop self-respect along with a strong sense of

moral values, thus enabling our pupils to become responsible and involved members of society. Underpinning all aspects of school life is an ethos that requires mutual respect and concern for all members of the school community and fosters close relationships between school and home. Good manners and courteous behaviour are encouraged at all times.

Boys and girls continue at Prospect House until the age of eleven, when they move to their senior schools. Whilst the Nursery and Reception entry years are almost invariably fully subscribed (early registration is advised), the school occasionally has places for children from Year 3 upwards.

Prospect House provides a thorough grounding in the usual educational subjects and the children are prepared for the entrance examinations to leading day and boarding schools.

In recent years the entrance examination results to these schools have been excellent with the children regularly being offered places at, amongst other schools, Benenden, City of London Freemen's, Colet Court, Downe House, Emanuel, Francis Holland (both Regent's Park and Sloane Square), Godolphin & Latymer, Hampton, The Harrodian, The Lady Eleanor Holles, Ibstock Place, King's College, Kew House, Latymer Upper, Notre Dame, Putney High, Radnor House, Reed's, St Paul's Girls', Surbiton High, Tiffin, Westminster Under School, Wimbledon High and Wycombe Abbey.

As at its sister schools and via the House Schools Trust, Prospect House occasionally offers scholarships for gifted children aged 7+ which contribute to or cover fees in full. The scholarships are restricted to children currently attending a maintained school who show significant promise and for whom an education in the private sector would represent a major opportunity. To learn more about the trust please visit the website www.houseschoolstrust.org.

To find out more about Prospect House, please look at the school's website www.prospecths.org.uk. Alternatively, please telephone 020 8780 0456 to order a prospectus or to join one of our regular tours. In addition, there are occasional Open Days which give an even greater opportunity to speak to our strongest supporters, namely the children!

North Bridge House School

(Founded 1939)

Hampstead, Regent's Park, Canonbury

Tel: 020 7267 6266

Email:

admissions@northbridgehouse.com

Website: www.northbridgehouse.com

Head of Nursery & Pre-Prep School:
Mrs. Christine McLelland

Head of Prep School: Mr. Brodie Bibby

Head of Senior School – Hampstead:
Mrs. Georgina Masefield

Head of Senior School & Sixth Form –
Canonbury: Mr. Jonathan Taylor

School type: Co-educational Day

Age range of pupils:
2 years 9 months–18 years

No. of pupils enrolled as at 01/09/2015:

Nursery: 220 *Pre-Prep:* 210 *Prep:* 486

Senior – Hampstead: 320

Senior & Sixth Form – Canonbury: 110

Fees per annum as at 01/01/2016:

Nursery: £6,309 (half day)–£12,615 (full time)

Pre-Reception & Reception: £14,715

Pre-Prep – Prep: £15,285 –£15,585

Senior – Hampstead: £15,615

Senior & Sixth: £15,615 –£16,860

Average class size: 20

At North Bridge House we provide an individually tailored education for boys and girls, aged from 2 years 9 months to 18 years. We know, support and inspire every pupil to achieve their full potential and provide a solid foundation for a successful academic career and adult life.

Pupils can join us from Nursery and stay until Sixth Form without the added pressure of entrance exams, or we can prepare them for other key schools. To ensure each individual flourishes we work closely with the parents to choose the right educational environment for their child and help many win much sought after scholarships. Our Senior and Sixth Form schools in turn prepare pupils for university life and the world of work through careers events, industry speakers, job experience and mock interviews. Plus, to maximize the potential of our Sixth Formers, they start lessons later in the day as research has shown that their sleeping patterns make them less likely to absorb teaching early in the morning.

At the heart of the school is a highly qualified and inspirational team of teachers who deliver a rich and varied range of academic and extra-curricular activities, tailor-made to challenge, stimulate and reward our pupils. This, together with our outstanding pastoral support, allows them to grow in confidence and independence. Through PE and games we develop the individual's physical and emotional wellbeing as well as essential team working skills which are enhanced further in the latter years through the Duke of Edinburgh Awards, civic engagements and leadership programmes such as form captain and peer mentoring.

North Bridge House celebrates each individual, develops their character and nurtures their aspirations, providing a platform to success and a gateway to the top universities.

To find out more, join us at an open day or book a private tour at northbridgehouse. com/open.

Rosemead Preparatory School, Dulwich

ROSEMEAD
PREPARATORY SCHOOL
inspirans flammas posteritatis DULWICH

(Founded 1942)
70 Thurlow Park Road, London, SE21 8HZ

Tel: 020 8670 5865
Fax: 020 8761 9159
Email:
admin@rosemeadprepschool.org.uk
Website:
www.rosemeadprepschool.org.uk
Headmaster: Arthur Bray CertEd

School type: Coeducational Day
Age range of pupils: 3–11
No. of pupils enrolled as at 01/01/2016: 349
Boys: 172 **Girls:** 177
Fees per annum as at 01/01/2016:
Day: £10,272–£11,286
Average class size: 18-20

Rosemead Preparatory School is a coeducational independent school in Dulwich, which caters for just under 370 pupils.

Rosemead prepares its pupils for private and maintained schools in the Dulwich area and elsewhere, giving them a thorough understanding of learning and a competitive edge that helps the vast majority secure places at their first choice schools. Each year, a high percentage of pupils are given academic, sports, music and art scholarships, exhibitions, bursaries and other awards at a wide range of schools.

Arthur Bray, who joined the school in 2012 as Headmaster, has overseen an expansion of the school's extracurricular sports and clubs, which now number just under 70 per week, as well as taking on additional space locally for sports activities.

The opening of new classrooms in the Pre-Prep department, an additional floor for Year 6, a new library and a new art studio in the Prep department and significant investment in laptops and other new technology would, Mr Bray said, be a model for further refurbishments elsewhere in the school.

What has not changed, however, is Rosemead's renowned family feel and sense of community, and the high standards of behaviour expected of its pupils. Rosemead produces kind, caring individuals who are ready to take on the challenges of life in the classroom and beyond. Friendships are forged that last well beyond Key Stage 2 – and that includes among the parents. It is the kind of place where pupils cry when they leave, not when they arrive.

There is no doubt that Rosemead does things a bit differently, as its hugely successful annual family skiing trip to Switzerland and camping weekends, demonstrate. To find out more about the difference that Rosemead makes, please email admissions@rosemeadprepschool.org.uk.

St Benedict's School

(Founded 1902)

54 Eaton Rise, Ealing, London, W5 2ES

Tel: 020 8862 2254

Fax: 020 8862 2199

Email: enquiries@stbenedicts.org.uk

Website: www.stbenedicts.org.uk

Headmaster: Mr C J Cleugh BSc, MSc

Appointed: January 2002

Headmaster from September 2016:
Mr A Johnson BA

School type: Coeducational Day

Age range of pupils: 3–18

No. of pupils enrolled as at 01/01/2016: 1106

Boys: 733 *Girls:* 373 *Sixth Form:* 212

Fees per annum as at 01/01/2016:

Day: £11,520–£14,550

Average class size: Junior School, Max 23;
Senior School, Max 24; Sixth Form, Max 14

Teacher/pupil ratio: 1:10

St Benedict's is London's leading independent Catholic co-educational school. Our Mission of 'Teaching a way of living' is at the core of the holistic education that is provided throughout the School from Nursery to Sixth Form.

St Benedict's is committed to supporting all children to develop their full potential and has a distinguished academic record. In August 2015, *The Telegraph* included St Benedict's among its list of 'ten best value private schools in the UK', the only London school to be included. The school welcomes children of other Christian denominations and other faiths.

The Junior School and Nursery provide a supportive, friendly and vibrant co-educational environment. Sharing excellent facilities with the Senior School and participating in cross-curricular activities helps ease the transition at 11+ to the Senior School. Older pupils are encouraged to think and express themselves creatively, to work independently and to take pride in their achievements. In the Sixth Form students are encouraged to take on leadership roles and all contribute to a variety of projects, which raise funds for communities across the world.

The school is committed to providing the best possible facilities for teaching and learning. The latest development, the Sixth Form Centre and Art & Design building, was opened in January 2016.

St Benedict's is renowned for its sporting tradition and has a national reputation for rugby. Whilst promoting the highest sporting aspirations, the school is committed to sport for all. A wide range of co-curricular activities is offered including music, drama and opportunities for Christian service.

St Benedict's School is unique. We are an extended family in which pupils can thrive and we are proud of our cohesive community. Come and visit and see what we have to offer. You can be sure of a warm Benedictine welcome.

St Mary's School Hampstead

st mary's hampstead

(Founded 1926)
47 Fitzjohn's Avenue, Hampstead,
London, NW3 6PG
Tel: 020 7435 1868

Fax: 020 7794 7922
Email: enquiries@stmh.co.uk
Website: www.stmh.co.uk
Head Teacher: Miss Angela Rawlinson BA,
MA(1st Class Honours), DipTchng, NPQH
Appointed: April 2003
School type: Coeducational Day
Religious Denomination: CISC

Age range of boys: 2 years 9 months–7 years
Age range of girls: 2 years 9 months–11 years
No. of pupils enrolled as at 01/01/2016: 300
Boys: 17 **Girls:** 283
Fees per annum as at 01/01/2016:
Day: £6,975–£12,915
Average class size: Max 20
Teacher/pupil ratio: 1:9.5

St Mary's School seeks to blend and balance the best of traditional educational practices with contemporary teaching, supported by the latest classroom technology.

Each pupil is encouraged as an individual to attain a high standard of personal excellence and is taught to appreciate the value of being a member of a community.

St Mary's is a Roman Catholic school with approximately 70% Catholic parents. Children experience a programme based on common spiritual themes that enables and supports their faith development. From Nursery they attend services in the School's chapel and study Catholic Christianity, along with an awareness of other faiths.

St Mary's is very much a family orientated school, promoting the Christian values of love and understanding, and believing that the school environment is an extension of a child's family home.

Boys are welcomed in the Early Years Foundation Stage and there is a thriving co-educational Nursery, where they are are prepared for transfer to popular London boys' preparatory schools. Girls are prepared for the entrance examinations for London senior schools at the age of 11 and achieve excellent results each year, including a number of academic scholarships.

There is no formal assessment for entry to the School before Year 3.

The School is fortunate to have an attractive learning environment, with airy classrooms, IT suites and large halls for sports, drama and choral performances, as well as a wonderful outdoor open space for play and relaxation. Joy and laughter are encouraged and there is a great enthusiasm for life and learning, while the School buzzes with energy and excitement.

St Mary's is proud that pupils not only achieve academic success, but that they also develop as caring, thoughtful individuals who respect each other and the values that the School strives to embody – kindness, curiosity and excellence.

SINGING FROM THE HEART

Being a chorister at St Paul's Cathedral is the experience of a lifetime.

— 100% tuition fees for all choristers
— Assistance with boarding fees available
— One of the top preparatory schools in the country
— The finest musical education
— An amazing start to life

Entry is in Year 3 or Year 4. If your son shows musical promise, he could become one of the next generation of choristers at St Paul's.

For more information please contact:
Clare Morgan, Registrar, St Paul's Cathedral School
020 7248 5156 · admissions@spcs.london.sch.uk

St PAUL'S CATHEDRAL SCHOOL

72

The Lloyd Williamson School

LLOYD WILLIAMSON
SCHOOLS

(Founded 1999)

12 Telford Road, London, W10 5SH
Tel: 020 8962 0345
Fax: 020 8962 0345
Email: admin@lws.org.uk
Website: lloydwilliamson.co.uk
Co-Principals:
Ms Lucy Meyer & Mr Aaron Williams

Appointed: December 1999
School type: Coeducational Day
Age range of pupils: 4 months–14 years
Fees per annum as at 01/01/2016:
Day: £13,050
Average class size: 12-16
Teacher/pupil ratio: 1:12

Over the past twelve years, the Lloyd Williamson School has built an excellent reputation for being a school with high academic standards, personalised learning for individual children and a friendly, happy environment in which to learn. We foster initiative and a love for learning. 'Outstanding' (Ofsted).

We are pleased to offer parents important extras:

- Breakfast and after-school club at NO extra cost (the school and nurseries are open 7.30am – 6pm).
- Holiday clubs (we are open 50 weeks of the year).
- Small classes (maximum of 16).
- Competitive fees.
- Home cooked meals freshly prepared every day by our in-house chefs.

We boast an outstanding playground with excellent facilities, a homely atmosphere with school pets, and dedicated teachers who support the children to be focused, positive and enthusiastic.

'Throughout the school, relationships between staff and children are excellent, which gives the pupils security and confidence to succeed.' (Ofsted)

In the words of our children:

"I'm really happy here – the teachers really listen and if I get stuck they help!"

"There is always someone who listens to me."

"I like the way the big children look after the little children."

And the parents:

"You always know a Lloyd Williamson child – they're so polite!"

"I think the school is, beyond doubt, the best I could wish for."

"The best-kept secret in London!"

To visit the school or nurseries, please contact the school administrator, Emma Cole on: 020 8962 0345.

The Moat School

The
MOATSCHOOL

(Founded 1998)

Bishops Avenue, Fulham, London, SW6 6EG

Tel: 020 7610 9018

Email: office@moatschool.org.uk
Website: www.moatschool.org.uk
Head: Ms Clare King
Appointed: January 2013
School type: Coeducational Day
Age range of pupils: 9–16

No. of pupils enrolled as at 01/01/2016:
Boys: 54 *Girls:* 13
Fees per annum as at 01/01/2016:
Day: £28,800
Average class size: 10
Teacher/pupil ratio: 1:4

Founded in 1998 The Moat School is London's first independent secondary day school for children with dyslexia (SpLD). It offers an intensive and structured learning programme teaching the National Curriculum, enabling success in public examinations, in a safe and supportive learning environment.

Mainstream schools can disadvantage the SpLD child as they are unable to understand what is being taught and without specialist help they fall rapidly behind their year group and underachieve. Children at The Moat School receive a totally inclusive education, they understand their difficulties, but thrive academically, emotionally and socially in spite of them.

The school identifies and fosters the extraordinary talents and creativity that these children often possess, by providing courses in non-traditional subjects such as performing arts, food technology, computer technology, art and design and design technology. Pupils have individual timetables that address their needs and classes are small and coeducational for children of average to above average ability. Subjects are taught by highly qualified specialist teaching staff, with learning support assistants, and there is a wide range of sporting and extracurricular activities.

The Moat School has recently been re-inspected by CReSTeD and their report is on the School's website.

The Moat School has been described as the 'Gold Standard' in SpLD education and the *Good Schools Guide* says:

'Something special. Not for children wanting to be cosseted and comforted, but a hard-working haven for bright, determined dyslexics and dyspraxics who know what they want from life and will achieve when given a chance.'

The Moat is opening a prep department taking pupils in year 5 and year 6 this September. For further details on visiting please call or email the School office.

The Moat School is managed by the Constable Educational Trust, a Registered Charity No. 1068445 and is committed to the education of children disadvantaged by SpLD.

This is the aim of the Trust: "to advance the education of children but particularly those disadvantaged by SpLD".

The Roche School

(Founded 1988)
11 Frogmore, London, SW18 1HW
Tel: 020 8877 0823
Fax: 020 8875 1156
Email: office@therocheschool.co.uk
Website: www.therocheschool.co.uk

Headmistress: Mrs V Adams BA(Hons), PGCE, MA
Appointed: September 2010
School type: Co-educational Day
Religious Denomination:
Non-denominational

Age range of pupils: 2–11 years
No. of pupils enrolled as at 01/01/2016: 239
Boys: 153 **Girls:** 152
Fees per annum as at 01/01/2016:
Day: £12,090–£13,050
Average class size: 18
Teacher/pupil ratio: 1:9

Curriculum

The Roche School aims to offer children outstanding teaching and a wide variety of opportunities, academic, artistic and sporting, in a pleasant, homely atmosphere in which children feel valued and secure. We take care that the styles of teaching should match the children's different levels of understanding and stimulate each child to make the best possible progress. The school is proud of its academic reputation and seeks to build on it. Art, Music, French and Sport are taught by specialist teachers.

Entry requirements

Prospective pupils spend a morning in class during which their work is assessed. There is no testing at nursery and reception entry.

Examinations offered

Children are prepared for 7+, 8+ and 11+ examinations to other schools.

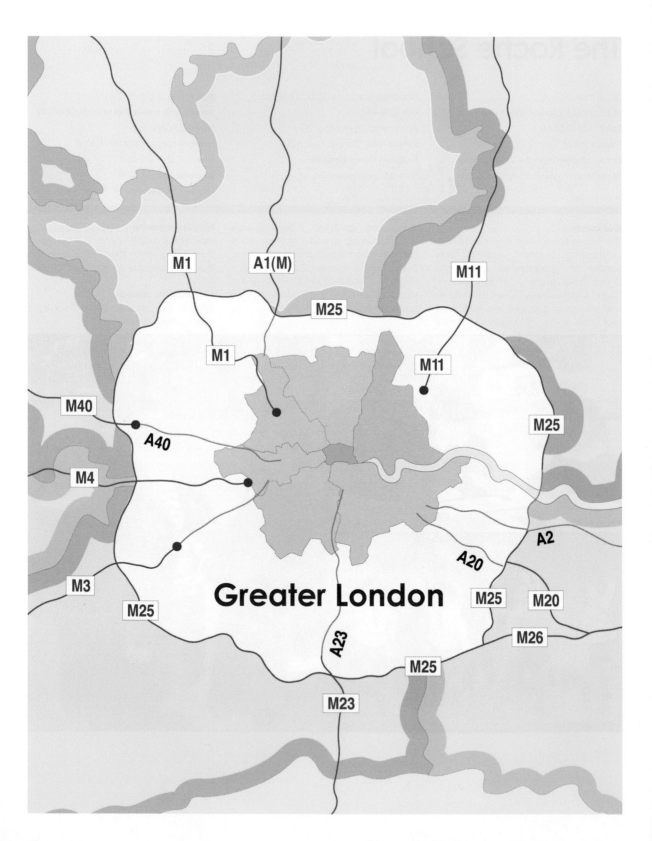

M1 A1(M) M11

M25

M1 M11

M40

A40

M25

M4

A2

A20

M3

M25 M20

M25

M26

Greater London

A23

M25

M23

Schools in Greater London

Bancroft's School

(Founded 1737)

High Road, Woodford Green, Essex IG8 0RF

Tel: 020 8505 4821

Email: office@bancrofts.org

Website: www.bancrofts.org

Head:

Mrs Mary Ireland BSc, DipEd, CBiol, MBS

Appointed: January 2008

Head from September 2016:

Mr Simon Marshall MA, PGCE (Cantab), MA, MPhil (Oxon)

Head of Prep: Mr Joe Layburn MA

School type: Coeducational Day

Age range of pupils: 7–18

No. of pupils enrolled as at 01/09/2015: 1123

Sixth Form: 240

Prep: 257

Fees per annum as at 01/09/2015:

Prep: £4,228 per term

Senior: £5,192 per term

Average class size: 22

Teacher/pupil ratio: 1:8

Situated in north east London, adjacent to Epping Forest, Bancroft's School is London's best kept educational secret. We feel we have got a lot to shout about and want to share what makes Bancroft's so special.

Pupils initially join us at the age of 7 into Bancroft's Prep. Prep pupils are marked out by their enthusiasm, their friendliness and their confidence. The latest technology, a stimulating curriculum and the contemporary buildings of the Prep all provide an ideal learning environment. The Prep is a secure and caring environment, where the importance of cultural and moral values is emphasised.

There is a real 'buzz' in the Prep School – a sense of fun and enjoyment from pupils and teachers alike.

The majority of Prep pupils stay with us at 11, crossing the playing field to the Senior School; here they are joined by another 60 children from a wide range of independents and state schools.

Academic results at Bancroft's are fantastic. Summer 2015 saw 93% of GCSEs awarded either grade A*or A, with 64% at A*. Our leavers' A Levels were equally impressive: 36% of all exams at A* and 92% of A Levels graded A* to B. Each year 99% of Bancroftians progress to university, the majority to Russell Group

institutions; last year Cambridge, Durham, Exeter, Nottingham and London colleges were popular. Many Bancroftians are keen to pursue careers in medicine; in 2015 a phenomenal 21 went on to read Medicine or Dentistry. In addition, pupils took up places at art schools, music conservatoires and drama colleges. Our results place Bancroft's firmly amongst the very top of co-educational schools in the London area.

Life here isn't just about exams. This is a busy, energetic and diverse community. Our pupils are eager to take part in a multitude of clubs and societies catering for all interests and abilities.

The Duke of Edinburgh Award scheme is particularly popular; every year over 200 pupils work towards their Awards. A recent highlight was having 37 former pupils presented with their Gold DofE Awards at the same ceremony, even the Earl of Wessex was surprised to see so many Gold Award holders from the same school! In 2015 Bancroft's was presented with a special award, acknowledging that we had more pupils enrolled on the DofE scheme than any other school in the London region.

Prep pupils can join our lively and large Cub pack and we offer a Sea Scout Troop for older children. Our Sea Scouts are Royal Navy recognised which means that they have the opportunities to use the facilities at Royal Navy bases as well as enjoying an exciting programme both on and off the water.

Our thriving Combined Cadet Force, with both Army and RAF sections, is another popular co-curricular option. The CCF offers leadership opportunities as well as encouraging teamwork. In addition to weekly training sessions, CCF members enjoy field days, an annual camp and adventurous training.

Drama productions at Bancroft's are ambitious; 2015 saw a much praised *Les Misèrables* and a technically daring production of *Fahrenheit 451* and

the Bancroft's Players have become regular performers at the Edinburgh Fringe. Musicians are well catered for too, with a whole variety of ensembles and choirs giving frequent chances for performances.

As you might expect, our sports facilities are first class: a huge multi-purpose sports hall, an indoor pool, a state of the art fitness suite and acres of pitches and courts for rugby, tennis, cricket, netball, soccer and athletics. Hockey takes place on local Olympic standard pitches. All teams have a busy programme of fixtures and enjoy success in national competitions. By expanding the number of teams we field, we encourage participation from everyone. We have extended the range of sporting activities on offer, so that senior pupils can now participate in indoor climbing, mountain biking and shooting, while badminton and fencing are increasingly popular.

Underpinning all we do is our pastoral system, which is a tremendous strength of the whole School. It enables pupils to flourish and make the most of opportunities. We work hard to foster a friendly, supportive and caring environment where each pupil is nurtured and their individual needs addressed. Relationships between staff and pupils are extremely important, as are those between parents and the School. At the heart of this is our traditional House system, with the tutor and house staff being key points of contact for pupils and parents throughout their time here.

The best way of getting to know about a school is to visit. Please join us on one of our Open Days, which are held in the autumn and summer terms. Details can be found on our website: www.bancrofts.org.

Babington House School

(Founded 1887)

Grange Drive, Chislehurst, Kent BR7 5ES

Tel: 020 8467 5537

Fax: 020 8295 1175

Email: enquiries@babingtonhouse.com

Website: www.babingtonhouse.com

Headmaster: Mr Tim Lello MA, FRSA, NPQH

Appointed: 2013

School type: Coeducational Day

Age range of boys: 3-11 & 16–18

Age range of girls: 3–18

No. of pupils enrolled as at 01/01/2016: 354

Fees per annum as at 01/09/2015:

Nursery: £2,880 per term
(inclusive of lunches)

Preparatory (Reception to Year 6):
£3,925 per term (inclusive of lunches)

Seniors (11 to 18):
£4,888 per term (inclusive of lunches)

Teacher/pupil ratio: 1:20

Babington House School is an independent day school from 3 to 18 years, situated in a beautiful group of buildings on Grange Drive in Chislehurst, near Bromley.

We are co-educational up to 11 years old; girls only from 11 to 16 and have a mixed Sixth Form.

This is a really exciting time for Babington House School with the arrival of a lot of new children. Our commitment is to provide an academic and well-rounded education with small class sizes which is tailored to the needs of our pupils, believing that bright children benefit from carefully monitored and well directed learning, where self-discipline is highly prized and where

each pupil is known as an individual. This helps Babington House pupils grow into confident, accomplished, creative young people with emotional intelligence and high standards.

The years at school are precious; the lessons learned can last a lifetime. That is why it is so important to find the school that is right for your son or daughter; the school where they will be happy and love learning from the outset.

Babington is an academic school. Our academic, social and sporting endeavours are underpinned by core Christian values which include a respect for others and an awareness of a purpose greater than ourselves. There is a strong

sense of community at Babington House.

The girls Senior School is academically selective with an Entrance Examination for Year 7 entry. Babington recently opened (September 2014) a co-educational Sixth Form, with the focus very much on A-level study in small sets whilst at the same time providing work experience, something that will help their university applications stand out and provide them with great self-confidence.

Headmaster, Mr Tim Lello says "I am immensely proud to lead such a vibrant community. Babington House is an outstanding school in every way. The boys and girls receive a first class education in a supportive and academic environment."

Bromley High School GDST
A GDST School

FIDES et OPERA

(Founded 1883)

Blackbrook Lane, Bickley, Bromley,

Kent BR1 2TW

Tel: 020 8781 7000/1

Fax: 020 8781 7002/3

Email: bhs@bro.gdst.net

Website: www.bromleyhigh.gdst.net

Head: Mrs A M Drew BA(Hons), MBA (Dunelm)

Appointed: September 2014

Head of Junior School:

Mrs Claire Dickerson BA(Anglia)

School type: Independent Selective Day

School for Girls

Age range of girls: 4–18

No. of pupils enrolled as at 01/01/2016: 912

Sixth Form: 125

Senior School (ages 11-18): 912 *Junior School (ages 4-11):* 312

Fees per annum as at 01/01/2016:

Day: £12,423–£15,405

Average class size: 20-25

Set in leafy parkland and benefitting from first rate facilities, Bromley High School provides a beautiful and buzzy environment where bright girls will flourish.

In the classroom, each girl's intellectual potential is challenged and developed by inspirational teachers whose concern for your daughter ranges infinitely beyond her performance in examinations; teachers who have a capacity to develop a love of learning, a spirit of enquiry and an independence of mind. Our girls learn to collaborate and to compete; to be creative and intellectually curious and their learning is underpinned by the school's ethos of achievement for all and by the subject passion, enthusiasm and expertise of their teachers.

Results are consistently superb. This year, 88% of A level results were A*-B and Bromley High was placed 79th in the *Sunday Times* Parent Power Independent School League Tables. Whilst we celebrate exceptional individual academic achievement – for example, one of our A level Chemists receiving the Salters' Award for achieving the second highest mark in the UK in this summer's A level examinations – we are most proud of the school's consistently impressive Value Added results at GCSE and A level which demonstrate the care taken to bring out the best in every girl.

However, outstanding success at Bromley High School is not purely academic. Bromley High girls are resilient and well-rounded young women participating with enthusiasm and commitment in Music, Drama, Sport, Duke of Edinburgh and an overabundant range of activities – and where they have interest or talent or enthusiasm, it is nurtured so that they learn to excel. Sport is exceptional: with 25 acres of top class facilities, Bromley High hosts England Netball's Regional Performance Academy. Our U16 hockey team are the reigning Kent County Champions – both indoors and out – and one of this year's Leavers has taken up a Sports Scholarship to Princeton.

Our pastoral care is thoughtful and developmental, actively encouraging girls to develop key attributes: Confidence, Composure, Courage, Compassion and Commitment. Every class takes on the responsibility of supporting its own individual charity and the school has a highly valued tradition of volunteering and charitable activity.

We welcome you very warmly to our Open Events and Taster Days. We hope that you will like what you see – confident, cheerful, considerate girls enthusiastic about the myriad of opportunities their school has to offer.

For 4+, 7+, 11+ and 16+ Entry in September 2017 please visit us at our Open Events on Tuesday May 17th and Saturday October 1st 2016. Booking is Essential.

Please contact the school via our website: www.bromleyhigh.gdst.net or our admissions office on admissions@bro.gdst.net or Tel 020 8781 7066 to arrange a visit.

Lyonsdown School

LYONSDOWN
SCHOOL

(Founded 1906)
3 Richmond Road, New Barnet, Barnet,
Hertfordshire EN5 1SA

Tel: 020 8449 0225
Fax: 020 8441 4690
Email: enquiries@lyonsdownschool.co.uk
Website: www.lyonsdownschool.co.uk
Head: Mrs L Maggs-Wellings BEd
Appointed: September 2005
School type:
Independent Coeducational Day

Age range of boys: 3–7
Age range of girls: 3–11
No. of pupils enrolled as at 01/01/2016: 205
Boys: 39 *Girls:* 166
Fees per annum as at 01/01/2016:
Day: £3,612–£9,186
Average class size: 16-22
Teacher/pupil ratio: 1:10

Situated in the leafy suburb of New Barnet, Lyonsdown School provides a happy, secure environment in which children can thrive and achieve personal excellence.

Lyonsdown has the facilities for high quality teaching and learning, yet is small enough for each child to be nurtured as an individual. Class sizes allow the caring well qualified staff to help pupils achieve high standards, not only academically, but creatively, physically and aesthetically in an atmosphere of relaxed purposefulness.

Founded in 1906, the school has built on traditional values to create a curriculum and environment to prepare children to take their place in the 21st century.

Our philosophy is that a child's education is a shared responsibility between school and home. We positively encourage the support of parents, offering a partnership that embraces regular contact and communication.

The Early Years Foundation Stage creates the basis on which future building blocks of learning can be developed. Great care is given to the development of social skills, confidence and enthusiasm for learning, both in the classroom and in the outdoor learning areas. Children are encouraged to progress and develop their skills, knowledge and understanding across seven areas of learning. Reception children are introduced to specialist teachers for computing, music, French, PE, art and science.

Pupils continue their learning in the Lower School under the pastoral care of their class teachers. Specialist teaching extends to include design and technology.

Lyonsdown education continues for girls in the Upper School. Throughout years 3 to 6, eight to 11-year-olds extend their knowledge of subjects, studying them in greater depth. They begin to develop the disposition needed to become self-motivated learners. Pupils are encouraged to develop independent critical thinking, to express thoughts and feelings, to write creatively and use their imagination. They enjoy using their numeracy skills, interpreting and using data and applying their knowledge to problem solving situations. Computing, including coding, is an integral part of work across the curriculum and specialist teaching extends to maths and English from Year 4.

Pupils' education is supplemented through a wide variety of educational visits and visitors from the community, such as theatre groups and interactive workshops. Year 5 and 6 participate in residential trips during the Summer Term.

During Year 6, many girls sit entrance examinations for leading independent and selective maintained schools. External test results continue to be excellent.

We place a high priority on personal development. Growth in moral, spiritual and cultural values is encouraged as part of the everyday ethos of the school. Daily collective worship is broadly Christian in character in accordance with the school's foundation. Assemblies provide an opportunity for the school community to gather together to consider spiritual and moral issues irrespective of individual religious commitment. Pupils are encouraged to develop their physical skills through a variety of activities. Physical education is considered to be an important ingredient in the development of confidence and team work. In addition, it contributes towards healthy growth and is taught in a large purpose built gymnasium from an early age. The Upper School girls also use off site facilities for sport and games. Healthy competition is embraced and children's achievements – in and out of school – are celebrated. As pupils move through the school, foundations are laid in the sports of netball, hockey, football, athletics, rounders and tennis.

Lyonsdown School Trust Ltd, a registered charity (No. 312591), aims to keep fees low in order to make independent education available to a wider community.

Marymount International School London

(Founded 1955)
George Road, Kingston upon Thames,
Surrey KT2 7PE

Tel: +44 (0)20 8949 0571
Fax: +44 (0)20 8336 2485
Email:
admissions@marymountlondon.com
Website: www.marymountlondon.com
Headmistress: Ms Sarah Gallagher MA,
HDip in Ed
School type: Girls' Day & Boarding
Age range of girls: 11–18

No. of pupils enrolled as at 01/01/2016: 252
Sixth Form: 115
No. of boarders: 90
Fees per annum as at 01/01/2016:
Day: £19,260–£22,035
Weekly Boarding: £33,020–£35,765
Full Boarding: £34,615–£37,360
Average class size: 12
Teacher/pupil ratio: 1:6

Marymount International School is an independent Catholic day and boarding school – welcoming girls of all faiths, aged 11-18.

A small school with only 250 pupils, Marymount offers a supportive, nurturing environment which prepares the students for life in a global setting. Part of an international network of schools, Marymount has an inclusive ethos which achieves a common purpose for young women from over 40 nationalities.

In 1979 Marymount was the first girls' school in the UK to adopt the IB Diploma programme in the belief that it provides the most challenging and stimulating educational offering to the Sixth Former. The IB programme sets out to develop inquiring, critical minds, enabling pupils to become independent thinkers and "active, lifelong learners". In concert with Marymount's Catholic values the IB also sets out "to develop caring young people who help to create a better and more peaceful world through intercultural understanding and respect." Graduates attest that they feel they have been stretched academically, spiritually and socially: they are fully prepared for university and for life.

The School has a proud history of excellent academic results, consistently ranking within the top 5% of IB schools globally. Typically 25% of our graduates achieve more than 40 points (achieved by only 4% worldwide) and over 50% graduate with a Bilingual Diploma. Although the largest single national group is British, additional languages taught include Spanish, German, French, Japanese, Korean and Mandarin for native speakers. In preparation for the IB, the school offers the Middle Years Programme: stretching students without the need for incessant testing.

Set in a leafy campus close to the London South West postcodes, school buses cover routes from amongst others Sloane Square, South Kensington and Fulham.

The School has a rolling admissions programme and students go on to top universities worldwide.

St Helen's School

(Founded 1899)
Eastbury Road, Northwood, Middlesex

HA6 3AS
Tel: +44 (0)1923 843210
Fax: +44 (0)1923 843211
Email: admissions@sthelens.london
Website: www.sthelens.london
Headmistress: Dr Mary Short BA, PhD
Appointed: September 2011
School type: Girls' Day

Age range of girls: 3–18
No. of pupils enrolled as at 01/01/2016: 1145
Sixth Form: 165
Fees per annum as at 01/01/2016:
Senior School: £15,438
Junior School: £12,129
Little St Helen's: £11,586
Nursery: £10,623 –

St Helen's School is committed to academic excellence and is dedicated to equipping pupils with the skills which will enable them to take their places as leaders in a rapidly changing world. The culture of our School is deeply-rooted in its fine history but is also forward-looking and innovative.

We provide a first-class academic education for able girls aged 3 to 18, developing their personal integrity while encouraging their intellectual, creative and sporting talents, and providing the supportive and nurturing pastoral care which enables every girl to achieve her full potential. Our spacious and beautiful 21-acre site is conveniently located adjacent to Northwood Underground station on the Metropolitan Line, approximately 30 minutes by Underground from Central London.

The School's development plan reflects the Headmistress's Vision for the School's journey from providing an excellent academic education to becoming exceptional in all that we do. Dr Short launched her Vision for St Helen's in Spring 2014; this is an ambitious and exciting long-term plan for the development of the School, to fulfil our aim of being nationally recognised as north London's exceptional independent school for girls.

Since then we have been working tirelessly to turn her vision into reality, The 20-year Estates Masterplan has been completed, and we are now embarking on the most significant development to the School estate in over a decade.

As part of our ongoing development plans, a new Junior School building is being built on the School site and is scheduled to open in September 2016. This building will contain a spacious assembly hall (fully-equipped with sound and lighting facilities and capable of staging concerts, plays and lectures), and dedicated Drama, Art and DT studios.

Our Futures Programme provides cutting-edge advice on external examinations, entry to top universities, student life, the best intelligence on the quality of courses available, work experience, careers advice and mentoring, and enables our students to stand out from the crowd at interviews and at work. Teaching is rigorous and stimulating throughout, and the school

and public examination results are outstanding. From the start, our girls are encouraged to take an active involvement in their learning and to question things both inside and outside the classroom. We support the aims of the National Curriculum, but offer a wider range of subjects and teach to greater depth. The staff are specialists who aim to inspire a love of their subjects.

We offer excellent specialist facilities for Science, Design and Technology, Art, Drama, Music and Computer Science, in addition to a modern Sports Complex with 25m swimming pool, fully equipped gymnasium and a climbing wall; a digital multi-media language laboratory; an excellent library; and well-equipped teaching rooms.

St Helen's provides each girl with a broad and balanced education which enables her to explore her individual strengths and interests.

The girls in our pre-preparatory section, Little St Helen's, make use of the School's superb on-site facilities as well as the extensive grounds in their learning. These pupils from Nursery through to Year 2 have specialist teachers for PE, Music, Speech and Drama, Ballet and French. Our girls are taught by well-qualified primary specialists with outstanding subject expertise. Each class in Little St Helen's enjoys the support of a full-time teaching assistant. There is also a full-time Welfare Assistant who is part of the Nursing Team.

Within our Junior School, class teachers in Years 3 and 4 each have a substantial teaching commitment with their own class, although the pupils are also introduced to some specialist teaching. By Years 5 and 6 the girls receive more specialist teaching from selected subject-based staff; they are streamed for Mathematics from Year 4 onwards. In Year 6 all girls take the entrance examination for Senior School, set by the North London Independent Schools Consortium, in order to show that they have reached an appropriate standard.

In Year 7 all girls study Art, Computer Science, Design & Technology, Drama, English, Geography, History; Latin, Mathematics, two Modern Languages from a choice of French, German, Mandarin and Spanish, Music, Physical Education, Personal, Social, Health & Citizenship Education (PSHCE), Religious Studies and Science. Science is taught separately as Biology, Chemistry and Physics from Year 8.

Music, art, drama and sport are an integral part of school life for every girl at St Helen's. Many also take extra music, ballet and speech and drama lessons, and benefit from specialist sports coaching. Social and elite sportswomen are equally welcome in our wide range of team and individual games, and will find a sport which fires their competitive spirit! Those who enjoy music and the performing arts will find a wealth of opportunities in our many orchestras, choirs and bands, plays and musicals – or can work backstage in

our technical and production teams.

Lunchtime and after school clubs include art, photography, book clubs, language clubs, our famous Heath Robinson Inventors' Club and many more.

Girls are able to develop their leadership and teamwork skills through the Duke of Edinburgh's Award Scheme. St Helen's is also one of the few girls' schools to offer a Combined Cadet Force, which is run jointly with Merchant Taylors' School.

Debating is a highly successful activity from Years 6 to 13, with girls competing both in school and up to national level.

St Helen's Sixth Form is a flourishing community of over 150 girls who take an active role in the life of the school. Each year we welcome new students who join us from other schools. The Sixth Form is in many ways a new beginning and often the most enjoyable and challenging time of school life. Academic examination courses are complemented by a programme of enrichment and fortnightly lectures intended to stretch students intellectually and to develop a range of skills. All students leave the Sixth Form with the St Helen's Portfolio and go on to study at Oxford, Cambridge and other leading universities.

A St Helen's girl enjoys learning, has intellectual curiosity and thinks independently and creatively. Above all, our girls are exceptional. We build the girls' confidence and encourage them to fulfil their ambitions, ready to become leaders in their chosen fields, professions and communities.

Old Palace of John Whitgift School

(Founded 1889)

Old Palace Road, Croydon, Surrey CR0 1AX
Tel: 020 8686 7347
Fax: 020 8680 5877
Email: info@oldpalace.croydon.sch.uk
Website: www.oldpalace.croydon.sch.uk
Head: Mrs. C Jewell
Appointed: September 2011

School type: Girls' Day
Age range of boys: 3 months–4 years
Age range of girls: 3 months–19 years
No. of pupils enrolled as at 01/01/2016: 740
Sixth Form: 120
Fees per annum as at 01/01/2016:
Day: £10,086–£13,497

At Old Palace every student enjoys a first class academic education. We promote a broader values-based education embracing four dimensions: service, skills and knowledge, courage and emotional intelligence. With this approach, students from a very young age start to learn about who they are and what they stand for.

Old Palace is blessed with magnificent historical buildings, excellent facilities and an enthusiastic, highly motivated staff. For all who embrace the many opportunities presented, Old Palace will reward them with a happy, memorable and empowering education.

All students at Preparatory are fully prepared for the 10+ and 11+. We also embrace a highly challenging curriculum at Seniors that prepares students for their GCSE, AS and A-Level examinations.

There are a large number of financial awards carrying substantial remission which are offered to Old Palace Preparatory students who demonstrate outstanding merit and potential as they head into Seniors. These include:

- The Whitgift Scholarship, the highest ranking Academic Scholarship, worth 50% of the school fees
- The Ayckbowm Scholarship, the second highest ranking Academic Scholarship, worth 50% of the school fees
- Academic Scholarship, worth 25% of the school fees for Year 7 and up to 50% for Year 12
- Music Scholarship, worth 25% of the school fees
- Mathematics Award, worth 18.5% of the school fees
- English Award, worth 18.5% of the school fees
- Reasoning Award, worth 18.5% of the School fees

- Head's Award, worth 12.5% of the school fees
- Exhibitions, worth up to 50% of the school fees
- Music Awards, worth the equivalent of instrumental lessons taken at school
- Choral Scholarships, worth 10% of school fees

The Whitgift Scholarship, Ayckbowm Scholarship, Music Scholarship, Mathematics, English, Reasoning and

Head's Awards and Music Awards are awarded for entry into Year 7 only.

Academic Scholarships are awarded for entry into Year 7 and Year 12.

Exhibitions are available for entry into Year 12 only.

Choral Scholarships are awarded for Year 3 only.

Old Palace also offers a generous means-tested bursary scheme from Year 7.

Woodford Green Preparatory School

(Founded 1932)

Glengall Road, Woodford Green,
Essex IG8 0BZ
Tel: 020 8504 5045
Email: admin@wgprep.co.uk
Website: www.wgprep.co.uk
Headmaster: Mr J P Wadge
Appointed: September 2015

School type: Co-educational Day
Age range of pupils: 3–11
No. of pupils enrolled as at 01/01/2016: 375
Fees per term as at 01/01/2016:
Day: £2,995
Average class size: 24
Teacher/pupil ratio: 1:12

Known locally as the "Red School" because of the scarlet uniforms, Woodford Green Preparatory School was founded in 1932 to provide a non-denominational Christian education for boys and girls, a tradition that has been maintained throughout and is now enriched by a vibrant, multi-cultural environment. The School is highly regarded by parents as successful in terms of ensuring children are safe, happy and well prepared for achieving excellent results in 11+ entrance examinations. We aim to provide a learning community that lights the flame within and empowers all children to reach their educational and personal potential.

Our latest independent school inspection report highlights our outstanding work. Our school ensures that 'pupils' personal development is excellent' and that 'the quality of pupils' achievements and learning is excellent and reflects the school's aims'. It was also noted by the Inspectors that our children 'are confident, self-aware and have high esteem. Pupils have a keen moral sense, awareness of others and accept responsibility willingly'.

The friendly, supportive environment, in which excellent work and behaviour fosters interest and independence, encourages all children to do their very best. We have purpose-built areas for Science, Sport, Art, Music, Computing and French, complemented by specialist teachers. We have excellent teachers and modern facilities throughout the school, including a fabulous Library which is regularly used by the whole school to foster a love of reading. In the Early Years, fully qualified staff ensure that children have an outstanding foundation for the rest of the school to build on. Excellent governance, leadership and management gives strong support and challenge, setting strategic priorities and building excellent teamwork, to ensure all children's needs are met. Our links with parents are very good as we strive to give parents excellent opportunities to be involved in school life and their children's progress.

We look forward to welcoming you to our very happy and successful school.

© Redcoat Photography

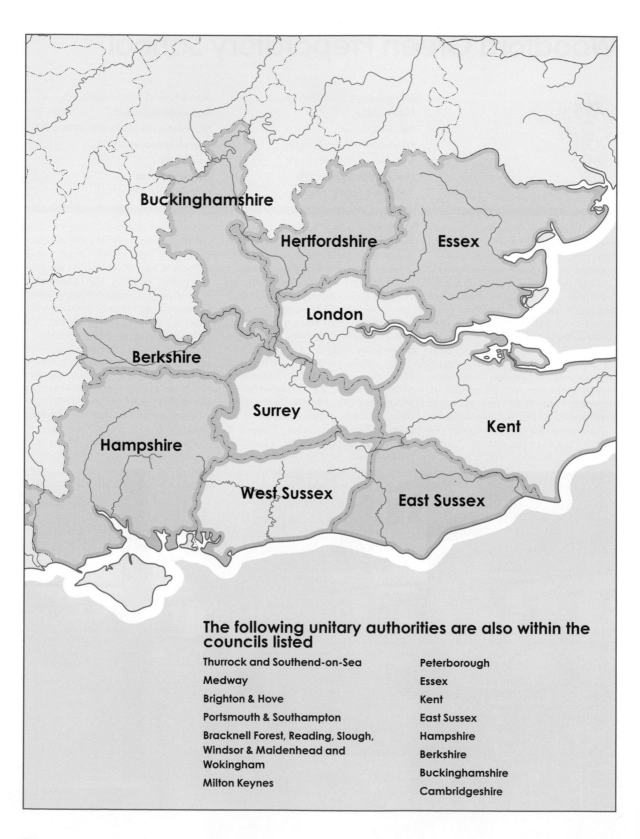

Buckinghamshire

Hertfordshire

Essex

London

Berkshire

Surrey

Kent

Hampshire

West Sussex

East Sussex

The following unitary authorities are also within the councils listed

Thurrock and Southend-on-Sea

Medway

Brighton & Hove

Portsmouth & Southampton

Bracknell Forest, Reading, Slough, Windsor & Maidenhead and Wokingham

Milton Keynes

Peterborough

Essex

Kent

East Sussex

Hampshire

Berkshire

Buckinghamshire

Cambridgeshire

Schools in the South-East

Ardingly College

(Founded 1858)

College Road, Ardingly, Haywards Heath,
West Sussex RH17 6SQ
Tel: +44 (0)1444 893000
Fax: +44 (0)1444 893001
Email: registrar@ardingly.com
Website: www.ardingly.com
Headmaster: Mr Ben Figgis
Appointed: September 2014

School type: Coeducational Boarding
Age range of pupils: 13–18
No. of pupils enrolled as at 01/01/2016: 548
Fees per annum as at 01/01/2016:
Day: £21,960–£23,160
Full Boarding: £29,715–£31,425
Average class size: 12-20
Teacher/pupil ratio: 1:12

Ardingly College is increasingly the school of choice for families from London as well as the wider south-east. More and more children are hopping on the school's weekly buses between Clapham and our Sussex campus, situated midway between London Victoria and Brighton. We are finding that the capital's students (and their parents) are taking action to forego the frenzy of finding a school in the city in favour of a first-rate education further afield and yet easy to reach.

We think their decision is absolutely spot-on, bearing in mind Ardingly's spectacular academic results, boarding ethos, winning programmes of sport, music, the arts and vast array of activities. In the Sixth Form, around half the year group study A Levels and the other half the International Baccalaureate Diploma Programme. The IB students achieved an average of 37 points, the equivalent of A*A*A* A at A Level, and placing us in the UK's top 10 IB schools. Using UCAS points, If you combine our IB scores with our A Level grades, Ardingly's overall showing is an excellent 74% A*-B. Our GCSE candidates also achieved a laudable 65% A*- A.

Of course, there is much more to an Ardingly education than great grades. Open, international-mindedness is a key characteristic. Our pupils aspire to build greater understanding of their own and others' cultural backgrounds; we help develop leadership skills through deep thinking, questioning and communication, enabling every individual to become confident, global citizens. We promote social responsibility towards communities beyond the confines of the College and an awareness of environmental stewardship; we encourage international exchanges, dialogue and co-operation.

In Sport, we have produced the national Independent Schools Football Association (ISFA) champions two years running and have created a Football Academy that enables the brightest minds to be top performers not only on the sports field but also in the classroom. We are a quintessentially British school with a proudly international dimension - and we expect every student to become the best possible version of themselves.

Combe Bank School

Combe Bank
— A RADNOR HOUSE SCHOOL —
celebrating every individual

(Founded 1924)
Combe Bank Drive, Sevenoaks, Kent

TN14 6AE
Tel: 01959 563720
Fax: 01959 561997
Email: enquiries@combebank.co.uk
Website: www.combebank.co.uk
Head: Mr David Paton BComm (Hons)
PGCE MA
Appointed: April 2016

School type: Independent
Coeducational Day
Age range of pupils: 2½–18
No. of pupils enrolled as at 01/01/2016: 250
Fees per annum as at 01/01/2016:
Prep: £9,045–£11,850
Senior & Sixth Form: £15,825 –£16,305
Average class size: 18

Combe Bank School is the perfect environment for children to achieve academic excellence whilst developing their individual characters, abilities and interests.

We are an independent school in Sevenoaks and take boys and girls from 2½yrs to 18yrs.

Life at Combe Bank is shaped by our commitment to providing an active learning environment for limitless minds. We firmly believe that all pupils are capable of great things if effectively taught, motivated and inspired by their school environment. This vision is underpinned by four key values which are central to school life: Excellence, Perseverance, Courage, and Respect.

A rich, broad and challenging curriculum delivered through innovative teaching in small classes gives pupils the skills they need to succeed in their studies. This approach lets us truly understand each individual and to care for their personal needs, guaranteeing excellent results for each child, year after year.

Currently Head at Radnor House School in Twickenham, David Paton takes over as Head at Combe Bank in April 2016, part of an ambitious plan of improvements and growth. David has a proven track record and is a passionate and visionary schools leader.

Last year £9.5m was invested by Radnor House Schools Group in Combe Bank and its ambitious plans include increasing the roll, innovations in teaching and learning, raising academic aspirations and results, as well as building on the school's strong reputation for excellent pastoral care, family values and community links.

David Paton, Head commented: *"This is a hugely exciting time for us all. There are very few independent schools offering tailored teaching, state of the art sporting facilities and an extensive extra-curricular programme that can match Combe Bank. As a committed believer in the power of aspirational teaching and celebrating every individual child, I look forward to working with the school community to take Combe Bank to new heights and ensure it fulfils its true potential."*

Haileybury

Haileybury

(Founded 1862)

Haileybury, Hertford, Hertfordshire SG13 7NU

Tel: +44 (0)1992 706353

Fax: +44 (0)1992 470663

Email: registrar@haileybury.com

Website: www.haileybury.com

The Master: J S Davies MA(Cantab)

Appointed: September 2009

School type: Coeducational Boarding & Day

Age range of pupils: 11–18 (entry at 11+, 13+ and 16+)

No. of pupils enrolled as at 01/01/2016: 759

Boys: 439 **Girls:** 320 **Sixth Form:** 301

Fees per annum as at 01/01/2016:

Day: £15,435–£23,220

Full Boarding: £19,605–£30,900

Teacher/pupil ratio: 1:7

Haileybury is a co-educational boarding and day school situated in 500 acres of beautiful rural Hertfordshire yet only 20 miles from central London. The spectacular grounds are home to outstanding facilities, excellent teaching and superb pastoral care.

Founded in 1862, Haileybury is proud of its history, tradition, community and values, taking the best from the past while looking to the future. Academic rigour and outstanding co-curricular provision are at the heart of the school, offering Haileyburians a truly all round education and ensuring they leave as confident, tolerant and ambitious individuals who are leaders, life-long learners and who can make a difference in the world beyond school.

Pupils may join at 11+, 13+ or 16+. Flexiboarding is available in Lower School (Years 7 and 8) allowing families to consider this option without committing to full boarding early in a child's senior school career. From Removes (Year 9) onwards, full boarding is offered with the additional flexibility of pupils being able (if they so wish) to return home on Saturday evenings. Haileybury's boarding to day ratio is around 2:1. Our boarding numbers continue to rise and The Master attributes this success to the fact that the College provides its boarders with a fulfilling, happy experience.

Haileybury's co-curricular opportunities offer rich and valuable experiences to every pupil. The list of activities, clubs, performances, workshops, events and tours they are involved in is long and varied, including music ensembles, recitals, drama productions, dance, world-class visiting performers and speakers, Combined Cadet Force, Duke of Edinburgh Awards scheme, Model United Nations, sailing, rowing, rugby, football, hockey, lacrosse, netball, swimming, charity and community action and so much more.

Both the IB Diploma (since 1998) and A levels are offered in the Sixth Form. Haileybury consistently features in The Times league table of top IB schools in the UK. The average IB score of Haileybury pupils was 36 in 2015 against a UK average of 33 with 25% of our pupils scoring over 39 points. In 2015, 55% of all A Levels were graded A* to A with 79% of pupils achieving A* to B grades. (I)GCSE results saw 63% of pupils attain A* and A grades with one third of the year group gaining nine or more A* and A grades.

We warmly invite you to visit Haileybury to discover why your child will flourish here. To arrange an appointment or for further information on Open Mornings and Scholarships, please contact The Registrar, Mrs Iona Hutchinson, registrar@haileybury.com, 01992 706 353

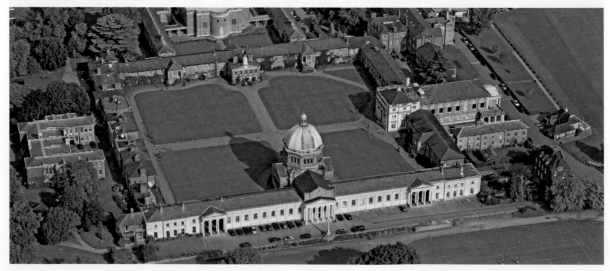

LVS Ascot (Licensed Victuallers' School)

PATRON
HM THE QUEEN

(Founded 1803)

London Road, Ascot, Berkshire SL5 8DR

Tel: 01344 882770

Fax: 01344 890648

Email: enquiries@lvs.ascot.sch.uk

Website: www.lvs.ascot.sch.uk

Headmistress: Mrs Christine Cunniffe BA (Hons), MMus, MBA

Appointed: September 2010

School type: Coeducational Day & Boarding

Religious Denomination:
Non-denominational

Age range of pupils: 4–18

No. of pupils enrolled as at 01/01/2016: 870

Fees per annum as at 01/01/2016:

Day: £9,528–£17,079

Full Boarding: £24,384–£30,006

Average class size: 18

LVS Ascot is a non-selective, co-educational day and boarding school of 870 pupils aged 4-18. It is a through-school so pupils can begin their school career at LVS Ascot at age 4 and remain there until they complete Sixth Form.

Exam results in 2015 saw rises in the proportion of students receiving A* and A grades, despite a fall in the averages nationally, at both GCSE and A Level.

The school is located on a bright and spacious site amongst 25 acres of landscaped gardens and playing fields. As one of the most modern boarding and day schools in the UK, the purpose built campus provides excellent facilities in a safe and stimulating environment, including a sports centre with indoor swimming pool, fitness centre, sports hall and all-weather sports pitch, dance studio, medical centre, a 300 seat theatre, drama studio and a music technology suite with recording studio, plus a Learning Resource Centre and over 500 networked computer workstations.

Both Junior and Senior school follow the National Curriculum, but with the added feature of a wide range of GCSE, A Level and Vocational options, catering for each individual pupil's strengths. An extensive range of activities and extra-curricular clubs and societies underpin academic studies by providing opportunities for pupils to extend their horizons in team sports, drama and music, visits, clubs, hobbies and interests.

Pastoral care is a great priority at LVS Ascot. In the Senior School each child is allocated to a house, and within that to a tutor group. House Masters and Mistresses, supported by teams of tutors, oversee the welfare and development of their pupils. In the Junior School, pastoral care is undertaken by the children's class teacher. Students are encouraged to give their best, whether the goal is university entrance, success at GCSE, honour on the sports field, artistic endeavour, or coping with the trials and tribulations of growing up. LVS Ascot aims to develop 'caring, confident citizens' for the future.

Academic Scholarships and Bursaries are available – please request further details. Our special arrangement with the HM Forces enables us to discount our fees by 10-20% to all HM Forces and UK Diplomatic personnel.

Mayfield School

Mayfield

(Founded 1863)
The Old Palace, Mayfield,
East Sussex TN20 6PH

Tel: +44 (0)1435 874600
Fax: +44 (0)1435 872627
Email: registrar@mayfieldgirls.org
Website: www.mayfieldgirls.org
Head: Ms Antonia Beary MA,
Mphil(Cantab), PGCE
Appointed: 2008
School type: Girls' Boarding & Day
Religious Denomination:
Catholic (we accept all faiths)

Age range of girls: 11–18
No. of pupils enrolled as at 01/09/2015: 356
Sixth Form: 100
No. of boarders: 170
Fees per annum as at 01/09/2015:
Day: £19,125
Weekly Boarding: £30,900
Full Boarding: £30,900
Average class size: Max 15

As competition for places at independent London secondary schools puts unbearable pressure on prep school children and their parents, Mayfield Head says: "Don't panic! There is another way, and it doesn't mean compromising your children's education".

Since its foundation over 150 years ago, Mayfield has become one of Britain's leading girls' schools. Set in beautiful Sussex countryside and yet within an hour of London, and is a home to nearly 360 boarding and day girls aged between 11 and 18.

Mayfield provides each pupil with an academic experience designed to challenge and enrich her, leading not only to excellent results followed by the top universities, but a sense of perspective. Girls learn to enjoy study for its own sake, the importance of cultural and spiritual values, not to mention a healthy attitude to life outside the classroom. Education is more than just exam certificates.

However, the results speak for themselves with outstanding academic success year on year.

Last year saw some very impressive results:

2015

- 100% A*/A achieved in Further Maths, Music, Spanish and History of Art, Ceramics
- 100% A*-B for nineteen subjects
- 83% A*-B across all subjects
- Highest Grade in the country for Ceramics
- 52% of girls achieved straight A*/A grades
- A* achieved for over 30% of all grades

Academic excellence is only part of the Mayfield story. Success is achieved by giving girls the confidence to be the best they can be, inside and outside the classroom. Girls play team sports, use the fitness suite and use the outstanding Equestrian Centre. Creative talents developed in art and ceramics, dance, music, textiles, film, photography and drama are equally as important as Maths and Science.

From fencing to top class equestrian facilities, ballet to debating, Mayfield challenges its girls to realise their full potential, endowing them with a lifelong love of learning in order that they leave mature, educated and independent young women, confident in their beliefs and prepared to make a positive difference in the world. Described by the ISI as 'outstanding' and by *Country Life* as 'one of the finest schools in the land', a Mayfield education combines academic rigour, breadth of opportunity and a strong sense of community embodying our motto 'Actions not Words'.

At Mayfield, each girl is accepted for who she is and we instil in her the confidence to find her strengths and build on them. We will give her the time, space and emotional support she needs to flourish. We will expect her to think independently and help her to become a woman of faith and reason. We will stimulate her imagination and nurture her creativity in every subject she studies. Our enthusiastic teachers will inspire in her a lifelong love of learning.

A Mayfield girl is challenged to set herself demanding targets and helped to find strategies to achieve them. She will learn to question her own and other people's ideas and we expect her to make informed decisions. Her actions will be inspired by a sense of justice and integrity, sustained by her own faith and her respect for others. In sum, she will have the chance to grow to be herself. Mayfield is a vibrant community. Traditionally, we have attracted pupils from all round the world, as well as locally.

Such a cosmopolitan ethos helps the girls to understand and appreciate different cultures and perspectives and to value diversity. Friendships are forged here which sustain and support not only through school, but on into the future and we are proud to welcome successive generations of girls back to Mayfield.

While Mayfield retains a strong sense of pride in its history, a school with vision must use its heritage to construct the best possible future for its pupils. The doors of Mayfield's new state-of-the-art Sixth Form Centre opened in September 2013. This award-winning building is a harmonious combination of cutting edge technology with dedicated seminar and lecture areas providing ideal preparation for university, situated in the most historic part of the school alongside the 14th Century Chapel. All Sixth Formers now have their own study space, with their learning enhanced by the use of touch-screen display boards, iPads, smart televisions and high-speed broadband for independent research. The internet-enabled lecture room allows students access to university outreach programmes, guest lecturers and an extensive careers programme.

Excellent ICT facilities throughout the centre benefit the girls in a number of ways, including their preparation for university interviews. Finding the right school for your children is a priority for every parent.

To see first-hand how we can help your daughter to flourish academically, to develop her talents – wherever they lie – and discover hidden ones, join us for an open day or personal visit. Please contact Mrs Jennifer Gandy 01435 874642 or via email registrar@mayfieldgirls.org

Pangbourne College

(Founded 1917)

Pangbourne, Reading, Berkshire RG8 8LA

Tel: 0118 984 2101
Fax: 0118 984 1239
Email: registrar@pangbourne.com
Website: www.pangbourne.com
Headmaster: Thomas J C Garnier
School type:
Coeducational Boarding & Day
Age range of pupils: 11–18

No. of pupils enrolled as at 01/01/2016: 423
Boys: 288 **Girls:** 135 **Sixth Form:** 148
Fees per annum as at 01/01/2016:
Day: £15,999–£22,548
Full Boarding: £22,533–£31,890
Average class size: 15-20
Teacher/pupil ratio: 1:15

Pangbourne is an independent, coeducational boarding and day school for 11-18 year olds that combines a rich nautical history with a modern approach to education.

Pangbourne is a place where the individual matters. We have a beautiful site and excellent facilities but, first and foremost, this is a 'people place'. We are committed to the personal development of our pupils in the fullest sense. They are encouraged to work hard towards academic success and we are proud of the results which they achieve, but just as important is the development of their characters: their confidence and values, their creative and physical skills and their appreciation of who they are and what they can contribute to the world.

The College has the advantage of being set in 230 acres of wonderful Berkshire countryside, designated an Area of Outstanding Natural Beauty yet within easy reach of excellent transport connections. In its generous rural setting, Pangbourne nonetheless provides a smaller school environment where there is room to focus on the individual. Pangbourne is known for its outstanding pastoral care – recognised as excellent in the recent ISI report – and we take an integrated approach to caring for each pupil. We are not complacent about the challenges which young people face and are always seeking to improve the support which we can provide.

Pangbournians are encouraged not only to challenge themselves and reach their potential but also to be happy and fulfilled. The College offers a comprehensive co-curricular programme which enables pupils to find their niche and thrive as their specific abilities are recognised and developed.

Our Flag Values of Kindness, Selflessness, Moral Courage, Initiative, Industry, Resilience and Integrity underpin all we do as a College. They are rooted in our Christian ethos and go a long way to prepare our pupils for life's challenges and the responsibilities of adulthood. Our aim is to equip Pangbournians with the strongest possible foundations for their future.

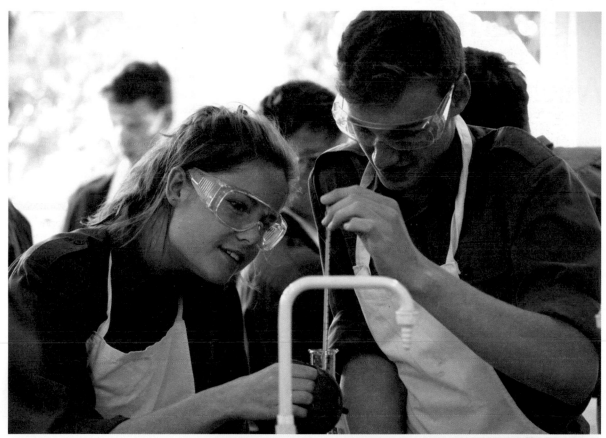

The only way to experience the authentic Pangbourne is to come and visit us, enjoy a tour of the College and speak to the pupils here who will give you a real insight into what Pangbourne is today.

"The personal development of Pangbourne's students is outstanding, meeting the College's aim to develop the character of all students. This is supported by an excellent, broad curriculum which enables students to progress academically and supports the development of the whole individual."

ISI Inspection Report

"A distinctive school that puts huge emphasis on self-discipline, teamwork and leadership. Caring and supportive, Pangbourne buzzes with activity and encourages every pupil to have a go and get involved."

Good Schools Guide

Michael Hall School

Michael Hall
a Steiner Waldorf School

(Founded 1925)
Kidbrooke Park, Priory Road, Forest Row,
East Sussex RH18 5BG
Tel: 01342 822275

Fax: 01342 826593
Email: info@michaelhall.co.uk
Website: www.michaelhall.co.uk
Chairs of the College of Teachers:
School type:
Coeducational Day & Boarding
Age range of pupils: 3–19

No. of pupils enrolled as at 01/01/2016:
Boys: 238 **Girls:** 259
No. of boarders: 18
Fees per annum as at 01/01/2016:
Day: £7,900–£11,250
Full Boarding: £5,400–£7,610
Average class size: 15-22

Michael Hall is an Independent School in the heart of the Ashdown Forest, Sussex. We cater for children from age 0 to 18 years old. Children travel from London, Brighton and Tunbridge Wells by bus and train as well as the surrounding villages and we offer a boarding with families' facility for those that do not wish to travel every day.

The Steiner curriculum teaches subjects in ways that correspond to the developmental stage of the child. The Steiner approach follows 95% of countries around the world in delaying formal learning until the age of 6, and by the age of 11, students are often academically ahead of their peers.

The number of Steiner students attending Oxford and Cambridge is well above the National average. Universities favour Steiner school pupils because they're great all-round thinkers and exceedingly good at their own research.

We educate the physical, emotional, intellectual, cultural and spiritual aspects of each child, the results speak for themselves. We are the longest running Steiner school in the English-speaking world. We celebrated our 90th birthday this year!

Come and find out for yourself, either at an Open Morning, spend a morning in the classroom as a child would (A Day in the Classroom), or take a Private Tour. Please see our website for more information www.michaelhall.co.uk/visit-us.

The school is highly successful in helping pupils to discover, nurture and develop their interests and unique talents, which are celebrated and lead to their growing self-knowledge and self-esteem. (SIS) Ofsted Inspection 2015

"This school is a beacon of professionalism among UK Steiner schools and the children who emerge are confident, articulate, international, open-minded and grounded, lucky them!" Good Schools Guide 2014

Roedean School

ROEDEAN

(Founded 1885)
Roedean Way, Brighton,
East Sussex BN2 5RQ

Tel: 01273 667500
Fax: 01273 680791
Email: info@roedean.co.uk
Website: www.roedean.co.uk
Headmaster: Mr. Oliver Bond BA(Essex), PGCE, NPQH
Appointed: 2013
School type: Girls' Boarding & Day
Age range of girls: 11–18

No. of pupils enrolled as at 01/01/2016: 440
Sixth Form: 177
No. of boarders: 293
Fees per annum as at 01/01/2016:
Day: £14,970–£19,470
Weekly Boarding: £26,730–£29,820
Full Boarding: £28,860–£34,950
Average class size: 18
Teacher/pupil ratio: 1:7

With A*-A grades in nearly 55% of A-levels at Roedean last academic year, and over 19% at A*, the girls demonstrated that they can perform exceptionally well under the intense pressure of public examinations. Their hard work resulted in an impressive leap up the league tables, and Roedean is delighted to be the most successful girls' school in Sussex at A-level in 2015. Nearly 60% of leavers go to Russell Group universities each year, and highly competitive Art Foundation courses are also popular.

A-level study is both exciting and liberating, allowing the students to pursue their passions in depth and focus on developing their strengths; the girls are encouraged to challenge themselves to go beyond what they are taught in order to develop the key skills they will need later in life. The fact that 39% of all grades at GCSE level last year were awarded A* and

a fifth of the cohort achieved only A*-A grades augurs well for our students' Sixth Form studies.

Roedean girls achieve very highly in a wide range of fields, from academia to sport, and music to painting. We believe strongly that challenge and breadth leads to excellence; girls push themselves to develop personally, as well as questioning what they learn and do. The girls' academic successes are matched in the Performing Arts, with distinctions at the highest level in music and dance, and one student has just won a place in the National Children's Orchestra of Great Britain, despite stiff competition from 1250 others. In Sport, we are very pleased that we currently have three National Champions at Roedean, in sprinting, table tennis, and street dance.

Roedean provides girls with an all-embracing education which goes far

beyond excellent academic results. "Girls all – unconsciously – smile when asked about life at school. Endorsement doesn't come much more authentic." (Good Schools' Guide 2014).

Roedean commands a stunning position to the east of Brighton, looking out over the English Channel. All the girls, whether day girls or boarders, are fully integrated into boarding houses which have recently undergone a multi-million pound refurbishment; in recent articles in the Sunday Times Style magazine and in Tatler, the boarding houses are likened to a boutique hotel, reflecting how well contemporary style has been married with heritage features.

Girls at Roedean are determined to do it all, and excellently. They understand that challenge leads to success, and they relish it.

The King's School, Canterbury

The King's School
Canterbury

(Founded 597AD)
The Precincts, Canterbury, Kent CT1 2ES
Tel: 01227 595501
Fax: 01227 766255

Email: info@kings-school.co.uk
Website: www.kings-school.co.uk
Head: Mr P Roberts
Appointed: 2011
School type:
Coeducational Boarding & Day
Age range of pupils: 13–18

No. of pupils enrolled as at 01/01/2016: 824
Sixth Form: 380
Fees per annum as at 01/01/2016:
Day: £26,055
Full Boarding: £34,440
Average class size: Max 19 in Yr 9
Teacher/pupil ratio: 1:8

Founded in 597AD, The King's School is reputedly the oldest school in the world. It is also one of the country's leading co-educational boarding schools located in the idyllic surroundings of the Precincts of Canterbury Cathedral, just one hour from Central London.

The School has a strongly academic curriculum that is continually adapting to encompass the ever-changing demands of modern education. We place emphasis on scholarly excellence and our pupils progress to further education at leading universities in the UK and abroad. Through regular monitoring of academic progress, the School's aim is to enable every individual to make the most of their abilities and to fulfil their potential.

We believe that much of what is most valuable in education takes place outside the classroom. The wide-ranging co-curricular programme has been developed to provide opportunities for all pupils to discover their passions and encourage them to develop these talents through a comprehensive range of co-curricular activities. Art, Drama, Music and Sport play a major part in School life, alongside the Combined Cadet Force and the Duke of Edinburgh Award scheme. Other activities enjoyed by the pupils range from chocolate making and chess to Social Services and The Linacre Society, our society for future medical students.

King's Week, the School's own festival of arts which takes place at the end of each summer term, involves hundreds of pupils in a showcase of creativity. Over 35 performances comprise the festival. We open with 'Jazz on a Summer Sunset', and continue with three major play productions and a number of musical concerts. We have the six King's choirs singing 'The Serenade' in the Cathedral Cloisters, Horse Riding, Rock and Jazz concerts and many classical concerts from our range of ensembles, ending each academic year on a fitting note of achievement and enjoyment.

Music is a central part of life at the School with a range of disciplines flourishing, from a large Symphony Orchestra, to a 40-voice SATB choir of Cathedral Standard. There are some 60 Music Scholars in the school at any one time.

Headmaster Peter Roberts comments 'At the heart of a King's education is the dual pursuit of academic and extra-curricular excellence. The self-discipline, intellect and wide-ranging interests that such a pursuit engenders are highly prized in our modern global society. The quality of the teaching and the breadth of the activities outside the classroom mean that the lessons learnt and the skills acquired stay with the pupils for life.'

The main school site is situated in the precincts of Canterbury Cathedral, a UNESCO World Heritage Site, providing a beautiful and inspiring backdrop to what has been described as 'a university for young people'. The School also comprises the historic St Augustine's Abbey, Birley's, a 22 acre multi-purpose sports field with pavilion, and a purpose-built sports recreation centre owned and managed by the School.

Rowan Preparatory School

ROWAN PREPARATORY SCHOOL
8 1936
CELEBRATING 80 YEARS

(Founded 1936)

Brae: 41 Gordon Road, Claygate, Surrey KT10 0PY
Hill: 6 Fitzalan Road, Claygate, Surrey KT10 0LX
Tel: 01372 462627
Fax: 01372 470782
Email:
school.registrar@rowanprepschool.co.uk
Website: www.rowanprepschool.co.uk

Headteacher: Mrs Susan Clarke
Appointed: September 2004
School type: Girls' Day
Age range of girls: 2–11
No. of pupils enrolled as at 01/01/2016: 330
Fees per term as at 01/01/2016:
Day: £3,366–£4,465
Average class size: 18-20

In 1936, Rowan opened its doors to seven young pupils. Its founder, Miss Millar, was determined to create an environment condusive to learning, she wanted Rowan to be a school where girls enjoyed their studies, developed a strong sense of self and established lasting friendships. Today Rowan is part of United Learning and under the guidance of only its sixth Headmistress and in its 80th year, its reputation continues to go from strength to strength.

Rowan is a school where girls achieve personal excellence, but above all it is a school where girls are fulfilled. The girls move from Nursery to Year 2 at Rowan Brae and transfer to Rowan Hill aged seven.

The Brae has a warm, friendly and happy atmosphere with a stimulating learning environment, both indoors and outdoors. It creates an inspiring and engaging place to learn with outstanding lessons and excellent resources allowing all pupils to thrive. Girls in Year 2 are fully prepared for the seamless transition and exciting challenges which lay ahead at the Hill.

Pupils at the Hill develop a thirst for knowledge, an appreciation of all subject areas and a deeper understanding of how to analyse and apply information across different areas of learning and in everyday life. The varied creative and outdoor curriculum continues to stimulate and inspire in all subject areas of day-to-day learning. Dynamic and challenging lessons, adapted to suit the girls' needs ensure that they can truly achieve personal excellence.

Rowan is a vibrant, friendly and highly motivated community. The girls achieve outstanding success in their senior school examinations at 11 and also excel in a wide range of musical, sporting and creative activities. Rowan values the achievements of all its pupils as they fulfil their aspirations developing personal strengths and talents. The pupils are proud to be Rowan girls and they invite you to come and see them at work.

Tonbridge School

TONBRIDGE
SCHOOL

(Founded 1553)
Tonbridge, Kent TN9 1JP

Tel: 01732 365555
Fax: 01732 363424
Email: admissions@tonbridge-school.org
Website: www.tonbridge-school.co.uk
Headmaster: T H P Haynes
Appointed: 2005
School type: Boys' Boarding & Day
Age range of boys: 13–18

No. of pupils enrolled as at 01/01/2016: 778
Sixth Form: 317
No. of boarders: 454
Fees per annum as at 01/01/2016:
Day: £27,216
Full Boarding: £36,288
Average class size: GCSE 16, A level 9
Teacher/pupil ratio: 1:7.6

Tonbridge School is one of the leading boys' schools in the country. Boarders and day boys of varying backgrounds are offered an education remarkable both for its breadth of opportunity and the exceptional standards routinely achieved in all areas of school life.

Tonbridge School aims to provide a caring and enlightened environment in which the talents of each individual flourish. We encourage boys to be creative, tolerant and to strive for academic, sporting and cultural excellence. Respect for tradition and an openness to innovation are equally valued. A well-established house system at the heart of the school fosters a strong sense of belonging. Tonbridge seeks to celebrate its distinctive mixture of boarders and day boys; this helps to create a unique broadening and deepening of opportunity. We want boys to enjoy their time here, but also to be made aware of their social and moral responsibilities. Tonbridgians should enter into the adult world with the knowledge and self-belief to fulfil their own potential and, in many cases, to become leaders in their chosen field. Equally, we hope to foster a life-long empathy for the needs and views of others.

The school is extremely successful in its university entrance, with many leavers going to Oxbridge, and strives for excellence in all fields, yet the ethos of the school is one of strong participation and acceptance of each others' strengths and weaknesses rather than blind concentration on results.

Tonbridge School is just off the M25, on the edge of the Kent/Surrey/Sussex borders and attracts families from all over southern England. It lies in about 150 acres of land on the edge of the town of Tonbridge, and thus provides a good balance between town and country living.

Families are warmly welcomed to come and see Tonbridge and to meet the Headmaster. We hope that a visit will leave you not only impressed by the facilities and the achievements of the boys, but also by the sense of fun and openness which the boys encounter here on a daily basis. Please contact our admissions department on 01732 304297 or admissions@tonbridge-school.org. For further information about Tonbridge please visit our website: www.tonbridge-school.co.uk.

Directory

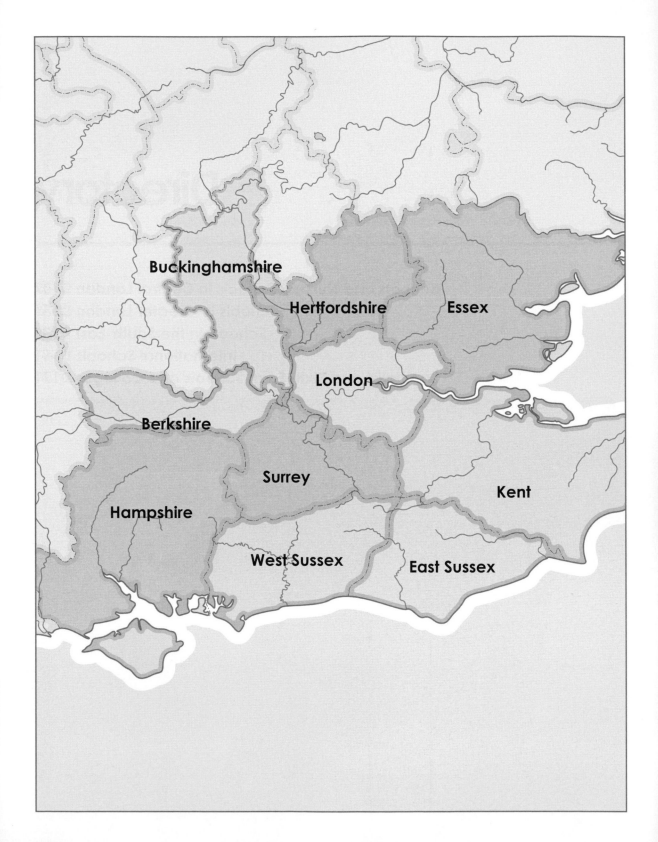

Buckinghamshire

Hertfordshire   Essex

London

Berkshire

Surrey

Kent

Hampshire

West Sussex

East Sussex

Schools and Nursery Schools in Central London

KEY TO SYMBOLS

- 🕇 *Boys' school*
- 🕇 *Girls' school*
- 🌍 *International school*
- 16 *Tutorial or sixth form college*
- Ⓐ *A levels*
- 🏠 *Boarding accommodation*
- £ *Bursaries*
- IB *International Baccalaureate*
- ✎ *Learning support*
- 16 *Entrance at 16+*
- 🎓 *Vocational qualifications*
- (IAPS) *Independent Association of Prep Schools*
- (HMC) *The Headmasters' & Headmistresses' Conference*
- (ISA) *Independent Schools Association*
- (GSA) *Girls' School Association*
- (BSA) *Boarding Schools' Association*
- Ⓢ *Society of Heads*

Unless otherwise indicated, all schools are coeducational day schools. Single-sex and boarding schools will be indicated by the relevant icon.

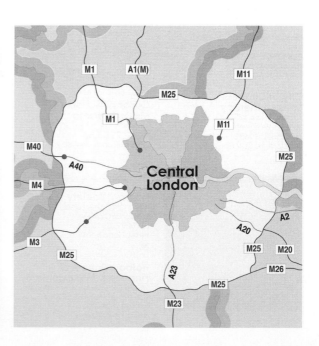

London

Central London

Accent International Consortium for Academic Programs Abroad
99-103 Great Russell Street, London WC1B 3LA
Tel: 020 7813 7723
Head: Natasa Blecic
16+

Broadgate Day Nursery
21 Curtain Road, Hackney, London EC2A 3LW
Tel: 020 7247 3491
Principal: Jacky Roberts NNEB
Age range: 0–5
No. of pupils: 50

CATS College London
43-45 Bloomsbury Square, London WC1A 2RA
Tel: 02078 411580
Principal: Mr Mark Love
Age range: 14–20
No. of pupils: VIth235
Fees: Day £16,460–£35,740 FB £33,560–£52,840
♿ Ⓐ Ⓔ 16+

Cavendish College
35-37 Alfred Place, London WC1E 7DP
Tel: 020 7580 6043
Principal: Dr J Sanders BSc, MBA, PhD
16+

Charterhouse Square School
40 Charterhouse Square, London EC1M 6EA
Tel: 020 7600 3805
Head of School: Mrs Caroline Lloyd BEd (Hons)
Age range: 3–11
No. of pupils: 196
Fees: Day £4,575

City Lit Centre & Speech Therapy
Keeley House, Keeley Street, London WC2B 4BA
Tel: 020 7492 2600
Principal: Mr G W Horgan
16+

CITY OF LONDON SCHOOL
For further details see p. 46
Queen Victoria Street, London EC4V 3AL
Tel: 020 7489 0291
Email: admissions@clsb.org.uk
Website: www.clsb.org.uk
Head: Mrs S Fletcher MA
Age range: B10–18
No. of pupils: 940 VIth250
Fees: Day £15,633
♿ Ⓐ Ⓔ 16+

City of London School for Girls
St Giles' Terrace, Barbican, London EC2Y 8BB
Tel: 020 7847 5500
Headmistress: Mrs E Harrop
Age range: G7–18
Fees: Day £14,409
♿ Ⓐ Ⓔ 16+

Dallington School
8 Dallington Street, Islington, London EC1V 0BW
Tel: 020 7251 2284
Headteacher: Mrs M C Hercules
Age range: 3–11
No. of pupils: 116
Fees: Day £9,216–£11,742

ÉCOLE JEANNINE MANUEL – LONDON
For further details see p. 50
43-45 Bedford Square, London WC1B 3DN
Tel: 020 3829 5970
Email: contact@jmanuel.uk.net
Website: www.ecole jeanninemanuel.org.uk
Principal: Pauline Prévot
Age range: 3–14 years
No. of pupils: 190

eCollege London
1-3 Rivington Street, London EC2A 3DT
Tel: 020 7729 9755
Head: Sheila Prendergast
16+

Financial Training Academy
4 Frederick's Place, Old Jewry, London EC2R 8AB
Tel: 0870 4232316/020 7397 1210
Head: Mr Rafi Ahmad
16+

Guildhall School of Music & Drama
Barbican, London EC2Y 8DT
Tel: 020 7382 7192
Principal: Barry Ife CBE, FKC, HonFRAM
Fees: Day £0

Hansard Society
40-43 Chancery Lane, London WC2A 1JA
Tel: 020 7438 1222
Head: Fiona Booth
16+

Holborn School of Finance & Management
25 Old Gloucester Street, Queen Square, London WC1N 3AN
Tel: 020 7404 2422
Head: Felix Orogun
16+

HULT-International Business School
46-47 Russell Square, Bloomsbury, London WC1B 4JP
Tel: 020 7584 9696
Provost: Mr Ray Hilditch BA, MBA, PGCE, FRSA
Age range: 17–60
No. of pupils: 300
Fees: Day £4,000 FB £10,260
16+ ✈

Italia Conti Academy of Theatre Arts
Italia Conti House, 23 Goswell Road, London EC1M 7AJ
Tel: 020 7608 0047
Principal: Anne Sheward
Age range: 10–21
16+ Ⓐ 16+

Kensington College
23 Bloomsbury Square, London WC1A 2PJ
Tel: 020 7580 1113
Fees: Day £0
16+

Kidsunlimited Nurseries – Mango Tree
62-66 Farringdon Road, London EC1R 3GA
Tel: 08458 500 222

Leapfrog Day Nurseries – London City
49 Clifton Street, London EC2A 4EX
Tel: 020 7422 0088
Manager: Jo Collins
Age range: 0–5

Leapfrog Day Nurseries – Smithfield
14 West Smithfield, London EC1A 9HY
Tel: 020 7778 0100
Manager: Estelle Cook-Sadeghi
Age range: 0–5

London College of English & Advanced Studies Ltd
178 Goswell Road, London EC1V 7DT
Tel: 020 7250 0610
Fees: Day £0
16+

London College of International Business Studies
14 Southampton Place, London WC1A 2AJ
Tel: 020 7242 1004
Heads: Mr Philip Moore & Ms Irene Chong
16+

London School of Accountancy & Management
3rd Floor, 12-20 Camomile Street, London EC3A 7PT
Tel: 020 7623 8777
Head: Mr Dak Patel
16+

London School of Business & Management
Central House, 14 Upper Woburn Place, London WC1H 0NN
Tel: 020 7388 8877
Head: Mr Alistair Andrews
16+

National Council for Drama Training
1-7 Woburn Walk, London WC1H 0JJ
Tel: 020 7387 3650
Director: Adele Bailey
16+

Pitman Training Centre
Warnford Court, 29 Throgmorton Street, London EC2N 2LT
Tel: 020 7256 6668
Principal: Mrs J Almond
Fees: Day £0
16+

Royal Academy of Dramatic Art
62-64 Gower Street, London WC1E 6ED
Tel: 020 7636 7076
Principal: Nicholas Barter MA, FRSA
16+

Sotheby's Institute of Art – London
30 Bedford Square, Bloomsbury, London WC1B 3EE
Tel: 020 7462 3232
Director: Ms Megan Aldrich
Fees: Day £0
16+

ST PAUL'S CATHEDRAL SCHOOL
For further details see p. 72
2 New Change, London EC4M 9AD
Tel: 020 7248 5156
Email: admissions@ spcs.london.sch.uk
Website: www.spcslondon.com
Headmaster: Mr Neil Chippington MA, MEd, FRCO
Age range: 4–13
No. of pupils: 252
Fees: Day £12,939–£13,932 FB £8,057
♿ Ⓔ ✈

**The College of
Central London**
Frazer House, 32-38 Leman
Street, London E1 8EW
Tel: +44 (0) 20 7173 6054
Principal: Nicolas Kailides
Fees: Day £3,300
16⁺ 16⁺

**The Courtauld
Institute of Art**
Somerset House, Strand,
London WC2R 0RN
Tel: 020 7848 2777
Director: Dr Deborah Swallow
18⁺

The London Film School
24 Shelton Street,
London WC2H 9UB
Tel: 020 7836 9642
Director: Ben Gibson
Fees: Day £0
16⁺

The Lyceum
6 Paul Street, London EC2A 4JH
Tel: 020 7247 1588
Joint Headteachers: Mr Jeremy
Rowe & Mrs Lynn Hannay
Age range: 4–11
No. of pupils: 100
Fees: Day £8,700–£13,800

The Method Studio London
Conway Hall, 25 Red Lion
Square, London WC1R 4RL
Tel: 020 7831 7335
16⁺

**The School of Computer
Technology**
73 Great Eastern Street,
London EC2A 3HR
Tel: 020 7739 9002
Fees: Day £0
16⁺

Urdang Academy
The Old Finsbury Town
Hall, Rosebery Avenue,
London EC1R 4RP
Tel: 020 7713 7710
Principal: Stephanie Pope
ARAD (dip PDTC)
Age range: 10–16

Williams College
Thavies Inn House, 5 Holborn
Circus, London EC1N 2HB
Tel: 020 7583 9222
Head: Mr Mujeeb Pathamanathan
16⁺

East London

Al-Falah Primary School
48 Kenninghall Road,
Clapton, London E5 8BY
Tel: 020 8985 1059
Headteacher: Mr M A Hussain
Age range: 5–11
No. of pupils: 83
Fees: Day £1,600

Al-Mizan School
46 Whitechapel Road,
London E1 1JX
Tel: 020 7650 3070
Head: Mr Ziaurr Ahman
Age range: B7–18
No. of pupils: 200 VIth13
Fees: Day £2,400
♂ Ⓐ 16⁺

**Alphabet House Day
(Montessori) Nursery**
Methodist Church, Windmill
Lane, Stratford, London E15 1PG
Tel: 020 8519 2023
Principal: Ms Kemi Balogun

**Alphabet House
Nursery School**
23 Harold Road, Upton
Park, London E13 0SQ
Tel: 020 8548 9466
Principal: Ms Kemi Balogun

Amhurst Nursery
13, The Avenue, Waltham
Forest, London E4 9LB
Tel: 020 8527 1614
Officer in Charge: Mrs Mills

**Ann Tayler Children's
Centre Nurser**
1-13 Triangle Road (off Westgate
Street), Hackney, London E8 3RP
Tel: 020 7275 6022
Fees: Day £10

Azhar Academy
235A Romford Road, Forest
Gate, London E7 9HL
Tel: 020 8534 5959
Headteacher: Mrs R Rehman
Age range: G11–16
No. of pupils: 189
♀

Beis Trana Girls' School
186 Upper Clapton Road,
London E5 9DH
Tel: 020 8815 8003
Age range: G3–16
No. of pupils: 270
♀

**Bethnal Green
Montessori School**
68 Warner Place, Bethnal
Green, London E2 7DA
Tel: 020 7739 4343
Head: Sidonie Winter
Age range: 2–6

Billet's Corner Day Nursery
11 Walthamstow Avenue,
London E4 8ST
Tel: 020 8523 3823
Principal: B Harmsworth

Building Crafts College
Kennard Road, Stratford,
London E15 1AH
Tel: 020 8522 1705
Principal: Mr John Taylor
16⁺ ♿

**Bushytails Day Nursery
and Nursery School**
591 Manchester Road,
Docklands, London E14 3NU
Tel: 020 7537 7776
Headmistress: Christine
G Bush NNEB
Age range: 0–5
No. of pupils: 15

Childsplay Day Nursery
283 Hall Lane, Chingford,
London E4 8NU
Tel: 020 8529 6058
Age range: 0–5

Chingford House School
22 Marlborough Road, Waltham
Forest, London E4 9AL
Tel: 020 8527 2902; 07749
899 498
Head teacher: Helen McNulty
Age range: 0–5
Fees: Day £5,460–£8,320
✎

City of London College
71 Whitechapel High
Street, London E1 7PL
Tel: 020 7247 2166
Head: Mr David Nixon
16⁺

City of London College
80 Backchurch Lane, London E1 1LX
Tel: 020 7247 2166
Head: Mr David Nixon
16⁺

**East End Computing
& Business College**
149 Commercial Road,
London E1 1PX
Tel: 020 7247 8447
Head: Anthony Wilkinson
16⁺

East London College
Panther House, 647-661 High
Road, London E11 4RD
Tel: 020 8539 2224
16⁺

FARADAY SCHOOL
For further details see p. 53
Old Gate House, 7 Trinity Buoy
Wharf, London E14 0FH
Tel: 020 8965 7374
Email: info@
newmodelschool.co.uk
Website:
www.faradayschool.co.uk
Head Teacher: Miss S Stark
Age range: 4–11
No. of pupils: 100
Fees: Day £2,930
£

Forest Glade Nursery
15 Dyson Road, London E11 1NA
Tel: 020 8989 9684
Age range: 0–5
✎

Forest School
College Place, Snaresbrook,
London E17 3PY
Tel: 020 8520 1744
Warden: Mr Anthony Faccinello
Age range: 4–18
No. of pupils: 1355 VIth260
Fees: Day £11,049–£16,335
♂ ♀ Ⓐ £ ✎ 16⁺

Gatehouse School
Sewardstone Road, Victoria
Park, London E2 9JG
Tel: 020 8980 2978
Headmistress: Mrs Belinda Canham
JP, BA(Hons), PGCE(Froebel)
Age range: 3–11
No. of pupils: 320
Fees: Day £6,920–£8,502
£ ✎

Get Along Gang Playgroup
St Mary of Eton Church Hall,
Eastway, Hackney, London E9 5JA
Tel: 020 8533 0926

**Grangewood
Independent School**
Chester Road, Forest
Gate, London E7 8QT
Tel: 020 8472 3552
Headteacher: Mrs B A Roberts
Age range: 3–11
No. of pupils: 61
✎

**Green Gables Montessori
Primary School**
The Institute, 302 The Highway,
Wapping, London E1W 3DH
Tel: 020 7488 2374
Head: Mrs V Hunt
Age range: 0–8
No. of pupils: 45
Fees: Day £740–£10,480

Guildhall College
60 Nelson Street, London E1 2DE
Tel: 020 7480 9000
Head: Mr Terence Moore
16⁺

Happy Child Day Nursery
The Old Town Hall, 14B
Orford Road, Walthamstow
Village, London E17 9NL
Tel: 020 8520 8880
Head: Mrs Margaret Murphy

**Happy Faces at
Wisdom Kids Nursery**
524 High Street, London E12 6QN
Tel: 020 8478 2805

Humpty Dumpty Nursery
24 Fairlop Road, Waltham
Forest, London E11 1BL
Tel: 020 8539 3810
Age range: 1–5

Hyland House School
Holcombe Road, Tottenham,
London N17 9AD
Tel: 020 8520 4186
Headmistress: Mrs T Thorpe
Age range: 3–11
Fees: Day £2,520

Independent Place Nursery
26/27 Independent Place,
Shacklewell Lane, Hackney,
London E8 2HD
Tel: 020 7275 7755
Head: Ms Dawn Pennington
Age range: 0–5
No. of pupils: 43

Interlink College of Technology & Business
Interlink House, Unit 11, Unity
Works, 22 Sutherland Road,
Walthamstow, London E17 6JW
Tel: 0208 531 1118
Head: Mr Kanmi Alo

Kaye Rowe Nursery School
Osborne Road, London E7 0PH
Tel: 020 8534 4403

Kids Inc Day Nursery – Chingford
3 Friday Hill West, Chingford
Hatch, London E4 6UP
Tel: 020 8524 6745

Kids Inc Day Nursery – South Woodford
71 Cleveland Road, South
Woodford, London E18 2AE
Tel: 020 8518 8855
Manager: Sarah-Jane Smith NNEB
Age range: 3months–5

Lanterns Nursery and Pre-school
F4-F6 Lanterns Court, 22
Millharbour, London E14 9TU
Tel: 020 7363 0951

Leapfrog Day Nurseries – Chingford
2 Larkswood Leisure Park, 175 New
Road, Chingford, London E4 9EY
Tel: 020 8524 7063
Manager: Catalina Harding
Age range: 0–5

Leapfrog Day Nurseries – London Excel
5 Western Gateway,
London E16 1AU
Tel: 020 7474 7487
Manager: Sarah Jordan
Age range: 0–5

Leaview Community Nursery Ltd
Leaview House, Springfield,
London E5 9EJ
Tel: 020 8806 9012
Co-ordinator: Leticia
Adu AdvMontDip
Age range: 6months–5
Fees: Day £3,000–£6,250

Little Green Man Nursery
15 Lemna Road, Waltham
Forest, London E11 1HX
Tel: 020 8539 7228
Age range: 0–5
No. of pupils: 46

London Crown College
80-90 Mile End Road,
London E1 4UN
Tel: 020 7790 3330
Head: Mr Firoz Hasan

London East Academy
46-80 Whitechapel Road,
London E1 1JX
Tel: 020 7650 3070
Headteacher: Musleh Faradhi
Age range: B11–18
No. of pupils: VIth18
Fees: Day £3,000

London Oriental Academy
Suite B, 1-3 Kempton Road,
East Ham, London E6 2LD
Tel: 020 8470 9876
Head: Saraswathi Namasivayam

London School of Commerce & IT
128 Commercial Road,
London E1 1NL
Tel: 020 7702 2509
Head: Dr Abul Kalam

London School of Computer Education
Second Floor, 1-3 Norton
Folgate, London E1 6DB
Tel: 020 7392 9696
Head: Mr David Kohn

London School of Management & Technology
Queensway House, 109 High
Street, Stretford, London E15 2QQ
Tel: 020 8534 9996

Low Hall Nursery
Low Hall Lane, London E17 8BE
Tel: 020 8520 1689

Lubavitch House School (Junior Boys)
135 Clapton Common,
London E5 9AE
Tel: 020 8800 1044
Head: Rabbi D Golomb
Age range: B5–11
No. of pupils: 101
Fees: Day £520–£3,100

Madani Girls School
Myrdle Street, London E1 1HL
Tel: 020 7377 1992
Headteacher: Mrs F Liyawdeen
Age range: G11–18
No. of pupils: 248 VIth11
Fees: Day £1,900

Magic Roundabout Nursery – Docklands
Jack Dash House, 2 Lawn House
Close, Marsh Wall, London E14 9YQ
Tel: 020 7364 6028

Magic Roundabout Nursery – Walthamstow
161 Wadham Road, Centre Way,
Walthamstow, London E17 4HU
Tel: 020 8523 5551

Market Nursery
Wilde Close, Off Pownall Road,
Hackney, London E8 4JS
Tel: 020 7241 0978
Head: Ms Hazel Babb
No. of pupils: 24

Merryfield Montessori Nursery
76 Station Road, Waltham
Forest, London E4 7BA
Tel: 020 8524 7697
No. of pupils: 45

Metropolitan College of London
22-27 The Oval, London E2 9DT
Tel: 020 7159 2601/7168 2024
Head: Mr Mazumdar Kumar

Noah's Ark Nursery
within Mildmay Hospital, Hackney
Road, London E2 7NA
Tel: 020 7613 6346

Normanhurst School
68-74 Station Road,
Chingford, London E4 7BA
Tel: 020 8529 4307
Headmistress: Mrs Claire Osborn
Age range: 2–16
No. of pupils: 250
Fees: Day £7,470–£11,235

Oliver Thomas Nursery School
Mathews Avenue, East
Ham, London E6 6BU
Tel: 020 8552 1177
Head Teacher: Dianne Walls
Age range: 3–5

Paragon Christian Academy
233-241 Glyn Road, London E5 0JP
Tel: 020 8985 1119
Headteacher: Mrs J A Lynch
Age range: 5–16
No. of pupils: 34

Pillar Box Montessori Nursery & Pre-Prep School
107 Bow Road, London E3 2AN
Tel: 020 8980 0700
Age range: 0–7
Fees: Day £250–£500

Promised Land Academy
St Cedds Hall, Webb Gardens,
Plaistow, London E13 8SR
Tel: 0207 473 3229
Head: Mr A Coote
Age range: 4–16

Quwwat-ul Islam Girls School
16 Chaucer Road, Forest
Gate, London E7 9NB
Tel: 020 8548 4736
Headteacher: Mrs B Khan
Age range: G4–11
No. of pupils: 150

Rascals Day Nursery
34 Verulam Avenue,
Walthamstow, London E17 8ER
Tel: 020 8520 2417
Head: Teresa Aguda
Age range: 2–5

Reed Learning
29th Floor, One Canary
Wharf, London E14 5BR
Tel: 020 7519 6030

River House Montessori School
3-4 Shadwell Pierhead, Glamis
Road, London E1W 3TD
Tel: 020 7538 9886
Headmistress: Miss S Greenwood
Age range: 3–12
Fees: Day £2,700–£9,000

Smarty Pants Day Nursery
1 Plashet Road, London E13 0PZ
Tel: 020 8471 2620
Principal: Jennifer Lewis
& Sylvia Lewis
No. of pupils: 46

Snaresbrook Preparatory School
75 Woodford Road, South
Woodford, London E18 2EA
Tel: 020 8989 2394
Head of School: Mr Christopher Curl
Age range: 3–11
No. of pupils: 164
Fees: Day £6,696–£8,952

Spitalfields Nursery
21 Lamb Street, London E1 6EA
Tel: 020 7375 0775
Principal: Angela Dorian

St Joseph's Convent School For Girls
59 Cambridge Park,
Wanstead, London E11 2PR
Tel: 020 8989 4700
Headteacher: Ms C Glover
Age range: G3–11
No. of pupils: 171
Fees: Day £5,355

Stepping Stones Day Nursery – Forest Gate
St Bonaventure's School, St Anthony's Road, London E7 9QB
Tel: 020 8470 6999

Stepping Stones Day Nursery – Stratford
Brickfield Congregational Church, Welfare Road, London E15 4HT
Tel: 020 8534 8777

Sunbeams Day Nursery
10 Bushwood, Leytonstone, London E11 3AY
Tel: 020 8530 2784
Principal: Kim Frisby

Sunshine Day Nursery
167 Wallward Road, Leytonstone, London E11 1AQ
Tel: 020 8556 6889
Officer in Charge: Ms Nikki Bailey

Talmud Torah Machikei Hadass School
96-98 Clapton Common, London E5 9AL
Tel: 020 8800 6599
Headteacher: Rabbi C Silbiger
Age range: B4–11
No. of pupils: 271
(symbol)

The Happy Nest Nursery Ltd
Fellows Court Family Centre, Weymouth Terrace, Hackney, London E2 8LR
Tel: 020 7739 3193

The Music School
59a High Street, Wanstead, London E11 2AE
Tel: 020 8502 0932
(16 symbol)

Tinkerbells Nursery
185 Coppermill Lane, Walthamstow, London E17 7HU
Tel: 020 8520 8338
Principal: Sue Walker

Tom Thumb Nursery
1-7 Beulah Road, London E17 9LG
Tel: 020 8520 1329
Age range: 2–5
No. of pupils: 32

Tree House Nursery & After School
35 Woodbine Place, London E11 2RH
Tel: 020 8532 2535

Western Governors Graduate School
27-33 Bethnal Green Road, London E1 6LA
Tel: 020 7033 9596
Principal: Mark Chatlani
(16 symbol)

Whitechapel College
1-13 Adler Street, London E1 1EG
Tel: 020 8555 3355
Principal: Luke Julius Maughan-Pawsey
(16 symbol)

Winston House Preparatory School
140 High Road, London E18 2QS
Tel: 020 8505 6565
Head Teacher: Mrs Marian Kemp
Age range: 3–11
Fees: Day £5,850–£7,050

North London

5 E College of London
Selby Centre, Selby Road, London N17 8JL
Tel: 020 8885 3456/5454
Head: Mr Raj Doshi
(16 symbol)

Academy of the Science of Acting & Directing
9-15 Elthorne Road, London N19 4AJ
Tel: 020 7272 0027
Principal: Helen Pierpoint BSc, PhD
(16 symbol)

Annemount School
18 Holne Chase, Hampstead Garden Suburb, London N2 0QN
Tel: 020 8455 2132
Principal: Mrs G Maidment BA(Hons), MontDip
Age range: 2–7
No. of pupils: 100
Fees: Day £2,500–£4,500

Appletree Nursery
59A Osbaldeston Road, Hackney, London N16 7DL
Tel: 020 8806 3525

Asquith Nursery – Crouch Hill
33 Crouch Hill, London N4 4AP
Tel: 020 7561 1533
Age range: 3 months–5

Asquith Nursery – Finsbury Park
Dulas Street, Finsbury Park, Islington, London N4 3AF
Tel: 020 7263 3090
Age range: 3 months–5

Asquith Nursery – Salcombe
33 The Green, Southgate, London N14 6EN
Tel: 020 8882 2136

Avenue Nursery & Pre-Preparatory School
2 Highgate Avenue, London N6 5RX
Tel: 020 8348 6815
Principal: Mrs. Mary Fysh
Age range: 3 1/2–7 1/2
No. of pupils: 79
(symbol)

Beatty Road Nursery
162 Albion Road, Hackney, London N16 9JS
Tel: 020 7249 7404
Principal: Geraldine Sinnott

Beis Aharon School
97-99 Bethune Road, London N16 5ED
Tel: 020 88007 368
Head: Y Pomerantz
Age range: B2–12
No. of pupils: 177
(symbol)

Beis Chinuch Lebonos Girls School
Woodberry Down Centre, Woodberry Down, London N4 2SH
Tel: 020 88097 737
Headmistress: Mrs Bertha Schneck
Age range: G2–16
No. of pupils: 421
(symbol)

Beis Malka Girls School
93 Alkham Road, London N16 6XD
Tel: 020 8806 2070
Headmaster: M Dresdner
Age range: G5–16
No. of pupils: 339
(symbols)

Beis Rochel D'Satmar Girls School
51-57 Amhurst Park, London N16 5DL
Tel: 020 8800 9060
Headmistress: Mrs A Scher
Age range: G2–17
No. of pupils: 788
(symbol)

Bnois Jerusalem School
79-81 Amhurst Park, London N16 5DL
Tel: 020 8802 7470
Head: Mrs Sonnenschein
Age range: G3–16
(symbol)

Busy Bees Nursery
c/o David Lloyd Leisure Club, Leisure Way, High Road, Finchley, London N12 0QZ
Tel: 020 8343 8500
Manager: Toni Difonzo
Age range: 3months–5
No. of pupils: 18

Channing School
The Bank, Highgate, London N6 5HF
Tel: 020 8340 2328
Head: Mrs B M Elliott
Age range: G4–18
No. of pupils: 746 VIth108
Fees: Day £14,085–£15,255
(symbols)

City of London Business College
Ebenezer House, 726-728 Seven Sisters Road, London N15 5NH
Tel: 020 8800 6621
Head: Mr Kwateng
(16 symbol)

City of London Business College
Gaunson House, Units 1 / 1A / 2, Markfield Road, London N15 4QQ
Tel: 020 8808 2810
Head: Mr Kwateng
(16 symbol)

Coconut Nursery
133 Stoke Newington Church Street, London N16 0UH
Tel: 020 7923 0720

Court Theatre Training Co
55 East Road, London N1 6AH
Tel: 020 7739 6868
Artistic Director: June Abbott
(16 symbol)

Finchley & Acton Yochien School
6 Hendon Avenue, Finchley, London N3 1UE
Tel: 020 8343 2191
Headteacher: Mr Katsumasa Kitagaki
Age range: 2–6
No. of pupils: 145

Floral Place Day Nursery
2 Floral Place, Northampton Grove, London N1 2PL
Tel: 020 7354 9945

Getters Talmud Torah
86 Amhurst Park, London N16 5AR
Tel: 020 8802 2512
Headteacher: Mr David Kahana
Age range: B4–11
No. of pupils: 171
(symbol)

Grange Park Preparatory School
13 The Chine, Grange Park, Winchmore Hill, London N21 2EA
Tel: 020 8360 1469
Headteacher: Mrs B McLaughlin
Age range: G4–11
No. of pupils: 90
Fees: Day £9,900
(symbols)

Greek Secondary School of London
Avenue Lodge, Bounds Green Road, London N22 7EU
Tel: 020 8881 9320
Headteacher: Antonia Valavani
Age range: 13–18
No. of pupils: 200
(symbols)

Hackney Care For Kids
61 Evering Road, Hackney,
London N16 7PR
Tel: 020 7923 3471

Highgate
North Road, Highgate,
London N6 4AY
Tel: 020 8340 1524
Head Master: Mr A S Pettitt MA
Age range: 3–18
No. of pupils: 1541 VIth312
Fees: Day £15,135–£17,475
(A) (£) (✐) (16)

Highgate Junior School
Cholmeley House, 3 Bishopswood
Road, London N6 4PL
Tel: 020 8340 9193
Principal: Mr S M James BA
Age range: 7–11
Fees: Day £10,695–£11,955

Highgate Pre-Preparatory School
7 Bishopswood Road,
London N6 4PH
Tel: 020 8340 9196
Principal: Mrs Diane Hecht
Age range: 3–7
No. of pupils: 140
Fees: Day £16,200

Impact Factory
Suite 121, Business Design Centre,
52 Upper Street, London N1 0QH
Tel: 020 7226 1877
Founding Partners: Robin
Chandler & Jo Ellen Grzyb
(16)

Keble Preparatory School
Wades Hill, London N21 1BG
Tel: 020 8360 3359
Headmaster: Mr G McCarthy
Age range: B4–13
Fees: Day £9,390–£11,670
(✿) (£) (✐)

Kerem House
18 Kingsley Way, London N2 0ER
Tel: 020 8455 7524
Headmistress: Mrs D Rose
Age range: 2–5
No. of pupils: 96
Fees: Day £2,025–£5,160
(✐)

Kerem School
Norrice Lea, London N2 0RE
Tel: 020 8455 0909
Acting Head Teacher:
Miss Alyson Burns
Age range: 3–11
Fees: Day £8,250–£6,675
(✐)

Kidsunlimited Nurseries – Camden
The Mary Seacole Nursery,
Tollington Way, London N7 8QX
Tel: 01625 585222

Laurel Way Playgroup
Nansen Village, 21 Woodside
Avenue, London N12 8AQ
Tel: 020 8445 7514
Head: Mrs Susan Farber
Age range: 3–5

Leapfrog Day Nurseries – Enfield
2 Florey Square, Highlands
Village, London N21 1UJ
Tel: 020 8360 6610
Manager: Emma Howell
Age range: 0–5

London School of Business & Computing
Business Design Centre, 52
Upper Street, London N1 0QH
Tel: 020 7288 6307/8
Head: Dr Viramouttou
(16)

London Studio Centre
42-50 York Way, Kings
Cross, London N1 9AB
Tel: 020 7837 7741
Director & CEO: Mr Nic Espinosa
Age range: 18+
(16)

Lubavitch House School (Senior Girls)
107-115 Stamford Hill,
Hackney, London N16 5RP
Tel: 020 8800 0022
Headmaster: Rabbi
Shmuel Lew FRSA
Age range: G11–17
No. of pupils: 102
Fees: Day £3,900
(✿) (A)

Lubavitch Orthodox Jewish Nursery – North London
107-115 Stamford Hill,
Hackney, London N16 5RP
Tel: 020 8800 0022
Head: Mrs F Sudak

MARS Montessori Islington Green Nursery
4 Collins Yard, Islington
Green, London N1 2XU
Tel: 020 7704 2805
Head: Angela Euesden
Age range: 2–5
No. of pupils: 24

Montessori House
5 Princes Avenue, Muswell
Hill, London N10 3LS
Tel: 020 8444 4399
Head: Ms Lisa Christoforou
Age range: 6 months–7 years
No. of pupils: 100
Fees: Day £5,355–£9,450
(✐)

Mustard School
Parish Hall, Nuttall Street,
London N1 5LR
Tel: 020 7739 3499
Headteacher: Mr A F Johnson
Age range: 3–18
No. of pupils: 47 VIth3
Fees: Day £3,060
(✐)

New Park Montessori School
67 Highbury New Park,
Islington, London N5 2EU
Tel: 020 7226 1109

Norfolk House School
10 Muswell Avenue, Muswell
Hill, London N10 2EG
Tel: 020 8883 4584
Head Teacher: Ms Sam Habgood
Age range: 4–11
No. of pupils: 130
Fees: Day £9,855

North London Grammar School
110 Colindeep Lane, Hendon,
London NW9 6HB
Tel: 0208 205 0052
Head Teacher: Hakan Gokce
Age range: 11–18
No. of pupils: VIth20
Fees: Day £7,500
(A) (£)

North London Muslim School
131-133 Fore Street, Edmonton,
London N18 2XF
Tel: 020 8345 7008
Headteacher: Mr W Abdulla
Age range: 4–10
No. of pupils: 21

North London Rudolf Steiner School
1-3 The Campsbourne,
London N8 7PN
Tel: 020 8341 3770
Age range: 2.5–7
No. of pupils: 40
(✐)

One-Tech (UK) Ltd
1st Floor, 12 Cheapside, High
Road, London N22 6HH
Tel: 020 8889 0707
Head: Mr Len Sutherland
(16)

Palmers Green High School
Hoppers Road, Winchmore
Hill, London N21 3LJ
Tel: 020 8886 1135
Headmistress: Mrs Christine
Edmundson BMus(Hons),
MBA, PGCE, LRAM, ARCM
Age range: G3–16
No. of pupils: 300
Fees: Day £5,985–£10,785
(✿) (£) (✐)

Pardes House Grammar School
Hendon Lane, Finchley,
London N3 1SA
Tel: 020 8349 4222
Headteacher: Mr S Mallett
Age range: B10–16
No. of pupils: 222
(✿)

Pentland Day Nursery
224 Squires Lane, Finchley,
London N3 2QL
Tel: 020 8970 2441
Principal: Rachele Parker

Phoenix Academy
85 Bounces Road, Edmonton,
London N9 8LD
Tel: 020 8887 6888
Headteacher: Mr A Hawkes
Age range: 11–16
No. of pupils: 19

Phoenix House Nursery School
27 Stamford Hill, London N16 5TU
Tel: 020 8880 2550
Principal: Noreen Payne

Pre-School Learning Alliance
The Fitzpatrick Building, 188
York Way, London N7 9AD
Tel: 020 7697 2500
Chief Executive: Steve Alexander

Primary Steps Day Nursery
37 Moss Hall Grove, Finchley,
London N12 8PE
Tel: 020 8446 9135
Manager: Ms Carol Kewley
NNEB, CPQS, NVQ
Age range: 1–5
No. of pupils: 36

Rainbow Nursery
Yorkshire Grove Estate, Nevill
Road, London N16 8SP
Tel: 020 7254 7930

Rosemary Works Independent School
1 Branch Place, London N1 5PH
Tel: 020 7739 3950
Head: Dorothy Davey
Age range: 3–11
No. of pupils: 104
Fees: Day £6,195
(✐)

Salcombe Pre-School
Green Road, Southgate,
London N14 4AD
Tel: 020 8441 5356
Headmistress: Mrs Sarah-Jane
Davies BA(Hons) QTS MEd

Salcombe Preparatory School
224-226 Chase Side,
Southgate, London N14 4PL
Tel: 020 8441 5356
Headmistress: Mrs Sarah-Jane
Davies BA(Hons) QTS MEd
Age range: 4–11
No. of pupils: 236
Fees: Day £7,890
(£)

St Andrew's Montessori
St Andrew's Church, Thornhill
Square, London N1 1BQ
Tel: 020 7700 2961
Head: Samantha Rawson MontDip
Age range: 2–5
No. of pupils: 40
Fees: Day £4,200–£6,525
(✐)

St Paul's Steiner School
1 St Paul's Road, Islington,
London N1 2QH
Tel: 020 7226 4454
College of Teachers:
College of Teachers
Age range: 2–14
No. of pupils: 136
(£) (✐)

Sunrise Day Nursery
1 Cazenove Road, Hackney,
London N16 6PA
Tel: 020 8806 6279/8885 3354
Principal: Didi Ananda Manika
Age range: 2–11
No. of pupils: 50
Fees: Day £3,900–£4,976

Sunrise Primary School
55 Coniston Road, Tottenham,
London N17 0EX
Tel: 020 8806 6279 (Office); 020
8885 3354 (School)
Head: Mrs Mary-Anne
Lovage MontDipEd, BA
Age range: 2–11
No. of pupils: 30
Fees: Day £5,343

Talmud Torah Bobov Primary School
87 Egerton Road, London N16 6UE
Tel: 020 8809 1025
Headteacher: Rabbi A Just
Age range: B3–13
No. of pupils: 320

Talmud Torah Chaim Meirim School
26 Lampard Grove, London N16 6XB
Tel: 020 8806 0017
Principal: Rabbi S Hoffman
Age range: B6–13

Talmud Torah Yetev Lev School
111-115 Cazenove Road,
London N16 6AX
Tel: 020 8806 3834
Headteacher: Mr J Stauber
Age range: B2–11
No. of pupils: 567

Tawhid Boys School
21 Cazenove Road,
London N16 6PA
Tel: 020 8806 2999
Headteacher: Mr Usman Mapara
Age range: B10–15
No. of pupils: 115
Fees: Day £2,000

Tayyibah Girls School
88 Filey Avenue, Stamford
Hill, London N16 6JJ
Tel: 020 8880 0085
Headmistress: Mrs N B Qureishi MSc
Age range: G5–15
No. of pupils: 270
Fees: Day £1,630

Teddies Nurseries New Southgate
60 Beaconsfield Road, New
Soutgate, London N11 3AE
Tel: 020 8368 7915
Age range: 3 months–5 years

The Children's House School
77 Elmore Street, London N1 3AQ
Tel: 020 7354 2113
Head: Jill Rothwell
Age range: 2–4
No. of pupils: 73
Fees: Day £1,550–£1,675

The Children's House Upper School
King Henry's Walk, London N1 4PB
Tel: 020 7249 6273
Headteacher: Mrs J Rothwell
Age range: 4–7
No. of pupils: 60
Fees: Day £3,250

The City College
University House, 55 East
Road, London N1 6AH
Tel: 020 7253 1133
Principal: A Andrews MCMI
Age range: 18–40
Fees: Day £0

The Dance Studio
843-845 Green Lanes,
London N21 2RX
Tel: 020 8360 5700

The Gower School Montessori Nursery
18 North Road, Islington,
London N7 9EY
Tel: 020 7700 2445
Principal: Miss Emma Gowers
Age range: 3 months–5 years
No. of pupils: 237

The Gower School Montessori Primary
10 Cynthia Street, Barnsbury,
London N1 9JF
Tel: 020 7278 2020
Principal: Miss Emma Gowers
Age range: 4–11
No. of pupils: 237
Fees: Day £4,680–£19,129

The Grove Nursery
83-93 Shepperton Road,
Islington, London N1 3DF
Tel: 020 7226 4037
Owners: Ms Rebecca Browne
& Ms Elaine Catchpole
Age range: 0–5

The Highgate Activity Nurseries
1 Church Road, Highgate,
London N6 4QH
Tel: 020 8348 9248
Head: Helena Prior
Age range: 2–5
Fees: Day £5,460–£9,620

The Institute – Hampstead Garden Suburb
The Institute Office, 11 High
Road, London N2 8LL
Tel: 020 8829 4141
Institute Principal: Fay Naylor

The London Academy of Health & Beauty
53 Alkham Road, Stoke
Newington, London N16 7AA
Tel: 020 8806 1135
Fees: Day £0

The Montessori House
5 Princes Avenue, Muswell
Hill, London N10 3LS
Tel: 020 8444 4399

The Poor School & Workhouse Theatre
242 Pentonville Road,
Islington, London N1 9JY
Tel: 020 7837 6030
Director: Paul Caister

The Sam Morris Centre
Parkside Crescent, London N7 7JG
Tel: 020 7609 1735

Tiny Tots Nursery School
Walker Hall, Christchurch Parish
Centre, The Green, Waterfall Road,
Southgate, London N14 7EG
Tel: 020 8447 9098
Age range: 2–5

TTTYY School
14 Heathland Road,
London N16 5NH
Tel: 020 8802 1348
Headmaster: Mr S B Gluck
Age range: B2–13
No. of pupils: 187

Twinkle Stars Day Nursery
416 Seven Sisters Road,
Hackney, London N4 2LX
Tel: 020 8802 0550
Admin Officer: Noori Mohamed
Age range: 1–5

Vista Training
107-115 Stamford Hill,
London N16 5RP
Tel: 020 8802 8772

Vita et Pax School
Priory Close, Southgate,
London N14 4AT
Tel: 020 8449 8336
Headmistress: Mrs M
O'Connor BEd(Hons)
Age range: 3–11
Fees: Day £6,150

Woodberry Day Nursery
63 Church Hill, Winchmore
Hill, London N21 1LE
Tel: 020 8882 6917
Manager: Michelle Miller
Age range: 6 weeks–5
No. of pupils: 62

Yesodey Hatorah School
2-4 Amhurst Park, London N16 5AE
Tel: 020 8826 5500
Headteacher: Rabbi Pinter
Age range: 3–16
No. of pupils: 920

North-West London

Abbey Nursery School
Cricklewood Baptist Church,
Sneyd Road, Cricklewood,
London NW2 6AN
Tel: 020 8208 2202
Head: Mrs Ruby Azam

Abercorn School
Infant Department, 28 Abercorn
Place, London NW8 9XP
Tel: 020 7286 4785
High Mistress: Mrs Andrea
Greystoke BA(Hons)
Age range: 2–13
No. of pupils: 360
Fees: Day £7,245–£13,425

Al-Sadiq & Al-Zahra Schools
134 Salusbury Road,
London NW6 6PF
Tel: 020 7372 7706
Headteacher: Dr M Movahedi
Age range: 4–16
No. of pupils: 389

Arnold House School
1 Loudoun Road, St John's
Wood, London NW8 0LH
Tel: 020 7266 4840
Headmaster: Mr Vivian Thomas
Age range: B5–13
No. of pupils: 270
Fees: Day £5,300

Asquith Nursery – Golders Green
212 Golders Green Road, Golders
Green, London NW11 9AT
Tel: 020 8458 7388
Age range: 1–5
No. of pupils: 68

Asquith Nursery – Hendon
46 Allington Road, Hendon,
London NW4 3DE
Tel: 020 8203 9020
Age range: 3 months–5

Asquith Nursery – Hill Park
5 Sunningfields Road,
Hendon, London NW4 4QR
Tel: 020 8201 5816
Age range: 3 months–5

Asquith Nursery – West Hampstead
11 Woodchurch Road, West
Hampstead, London NW6 3PL
Tel: 020 7328 4787
Age range: 3 months–5

Ayesha Community Education
133 West Hendon, Broadway,
London NW9 7DY
Tel: 0208 203 8445
Headteacher: Mrs Sadiya Hadadi
Age range: G4–18
No. of pupils: VIth16
Fees: Day £3,000

Beehive Montessori School
Christchurch Hall, Christchurch Avenue, Brondebury Park, London NW6 7BJ
Tel: 020 8451 5477
Headmistress: Ms Lucilla Baj
Age range: 2–5
Fees: Day £2,550

Beis Hamedrash Elyon
211 Golders Green Road, London NW11 9BY
Tel: 020 8201 8668
Headteacher: Mr C Steinhart
Age range: B11–14
No. of pupils: 45
①

Beis Soroh Schneirer
Arbiter House, Wilberforce Road, London NW9 6AT
Tel: 020 8343 1190
Head: Mrs R Weiss
Age range: G2–11
No. of pupils: 150
①

Belmont, Mill Hill Preparatory School
The Ridgeway, London NW7 4ED
Tel: 020 8906 7270
Headmaster: Mr Leon Roberts MA
Age range: 7–13
No. of pupils: 472
Fees: Day £15,500
£ ✎

Beth Jacob Grammar School for Girls
Stratford Road, Hendon, London NW4 2AT
Tel: 020 8203 4322
Headteacher: Mrs D Steinberg
Age range: G11–17
No. of pupils: 264
①

Bluebells Nursery
Our Lady Help of Christians Church Hall, Lady Margaret Road, London NW5 2NE
Tel: 020 7284 3952
Principal: Ms Anita Pearson
Age range: 2–5
No. of pupils: 20

Brampton College
Lodge House, Lodge Road, Hendon, London NW4 4DQ
Tel: 020 8203 5025
Principal: B Canetti BA(Hons), MSc
Age range: 15–20
Fees: Day £2,735–£12,470
⑯ Ⓐ

British American Drama Academy
14 Gloucester Gate, London NW1 4HG
Tel: 020 7487 0730
Head: Paul Costello
⑯

Broadhurst School
19 Greencroft Gardens, London NW6 3LP
Tel: 020 7328 4280
Headmistress: Miss D M Berkery CertEd
Age range: 2–5
No. of pupils: 145
Fees: Day £6,480–£10,950
✎

Brondesbury College for Boys
8 Brondesbury Park, London NW6 7BT
Tel: 020 8830 4522
Headteacher: Mr Dan Salahuddin Clifton
Age range: B11–16
No. of pupils: 93
① £

Camden Community Nurseries
99 Leighton Road, London NW5 2RB
Tel: 020 7485 2105

Chalcot Montessori School AMI
9 Chalcot Gardens, London NW3 4YB
Tel: 020 7722 1386
Principal: Ms Joanna Morfey AMI Dip
Age range: 2–6
No. of pupils: 28
Fees: Day £6,960–£7,260

Chaston Nursery & Pre-preparatory School
Chaston Place, Off Grafton Terrace, London NW5 4JH
Tel: 020 7482 0701
Head: Mrs Sandra Witten DipEd, DMS
Age range: 0–5
No. of pupils: 69
Fees: Day £7,020–£12,732

Chaston Nursery School
30 Palmerston Road, London NW6 2JL
Tel: 020 7372 2120
Head: Mr Roger Witten
Age range: 0–5
No. of pupils: 48
Fees: Day £6,504–£12,216

Cherryfields Nursery School
523 Finchley Road, Hampstead, London NW3 7BB
Tel: 020 8905 3350
Head: Mrs Pamela Stewart

Church Row Nursery
Crypt Room, Hampstead Parish Church, Church Row, Hampstead, London NW3 6UU
Tel: 020 7431 2603
Head: Mrs Marianne Wilson

City Mission Nursery
2 Scrub Lane, London NW10 6RB
Tel: 0208 960 0838
Age range: 6 months–5

City of Westminster College
The Cockpit Theatre (Perfoming Arts, Sound & Lighting), Gateforth Street, London NW8 8EH
Tel: 020 7258 2920
Principal: Mr Robin Shreeve
🌐 Ⓐ

City of Westminster College
Cosway Street Centre (Applied Sciences), Cosway Street, London NW1 6TH
Tel: 020 7258 2705
Principal: Mr Robin Shreeve

College Francais Bilingue De Londres
87 Holmes Road, Kentish Town, London NW5 3AX
Tel: +44 (0) 20 7993 7400
Principal: Mr François-Xavier Gabet
Age range: 5–15
No. of pupils: 210
🌐

DEVONSHIRE HOUSE PREPARATORY SCHOOL
For further details see p. 47
2 Arkwright Road, Hampstead, London NW3 6AE
Tel: 020 7435 1916
Email: enquiries@ devonshirehouseprepschool. co.uk
Website: www.devonshire houseschool.co.uk
Headmistress: Mrs S. Piper BA(Hons)
Age range: B2–13 G2–11
No. of pupils: 620
Fees: Day £9,060–£16,635
£

Eton Nursery Montessori School
45 Buckland Crescent, London NW3 5DJ
Tel: 020 7722 1532
Head: Mrs H Smith

Fine Arts College, Hampstead
24 Lambolle Place, Belsize Park, London NW3 4PG
Tel: 020 7586 0312
Co Principals: Candida Cave & Nicholas Cochrane
Age range: 13–19
No. of pupils: 115
Fees: Day £6,000–£15,600
⑯ Ⓐ £ ⑯

Francis Holland School, Regent's Park, NW1
Clarence Gate, Ivor Place, Regent's Park, London NW1 6XR
Tel: 020 7723 0176
Head: Mrs Vivienne Durham MA(Oxon)
Age range: G11–18
No. of pupils: 464 VIth120
Fees: Day £17,700
① Ⓐ £ ⑯

Golders Hill School
666 Finchley Road, London NW11 7NT
Tel: 020 8455 2589
Headmistress: Mrs A T Eglash BA(Hons)
Age range: 2–7
No. of pupils: 180
Fees: Day £831–£6,870

Goodwyn School
Hammers Lane, Mill Hill, London NW7 4DB
Tel: 020 8959 3756
Principal: Struan Robertson
Age range: 3–11
No. of pupils: 223
Fees: Day £3,645–£7,673.40

Gower House School & Nursery
Blackbird Hill, London NW9 8RR
Tel: 020 8205 2509
Headmaster: Mr M Keane
Age range: 2–11
No. of pupils: 200
Fees: Day £5,010–£5,835

Grimsdell, Mill Hill Pre-Preparatory School
Winterstoke House, Wills Grove, Mill Hill, London NW7 1QR
Tel: 020 8959 6884
Head: Mrs Kate Simon BA, PGCE
Age range: 3–7
No. of pupils: 182
Fees: Day £1,971–£4,285
✎

Hampstead Hill Pre-Prep & Nursery School
St Stephen's Hall, Pond Street, Hampstead, London NW3 2PP
Tel: 020 7435 6262
Principal: Mrs Andrea Taylor
Age range: B2–7+ G2–7+
Fees: Day £11,000–£14,000
✎

Happy Child Day Nursery
59 Longstone Avenue, Harlesden, London NW10 3TY
Tel: 020 8961 3485
Age range: 3 months–5

Happy Child Day Nursery
2 Victoria Road, Kilburn, London NW6 6QG
Tel: 020 7328 8791
Age range: 3 months–5

Happy Child Day Nursery
St Anne's & St Andrew's Church Hall, 125 Salisbury Road, Queens Park, London NW6 6RG
Tel: 020 7625 1966
Age range: 2–5

Heathside Preparatory School
16 New End, Hampstead, London NW3 1JA
Tel: +44 (0)20 7794 5857
Headteacher: Ms Melissa Remus Elliot MSc
Age range: 2–13
No. of pupils: 370
Fees: Day £9,300–£14,250
✎

Hendon Montessori School
7 Denehurst Gardens,
London NW4 3QS
Tel: 020 8202 8516

Hendon Preparatory School
20 Tenterden Grove, Hendon,
London NW4 1TD
Tel: 020 8203 7727
Headmaster: Mr David Baldwin
Age range: 2–13
Fees: Day £7,650 £9,945
£ ✏

Hendon Secretarial College
15 Watford Way, Hendon,
London NW4 3JL
Tel: 020 8202 3677
16⁺

Hereward House School
14 Strathray Gardens,
London NW3 4NY
Tel: 020 7794 4820
Headmaster: Mr T W Burden
Age range: B4–13
No. of pupils: 170
Fees: Day £13,065–£14,205
🏃

Highgate Children's Centre
Highgate Studios, 53 79 Highgate
Road, London NW5 1TL
Tel: 020 7485 5252
Principal: Lorraine Thompson

Hill Park Pre-School
5 Sunningfields Road,
Hendon, London NW4 4QR
Tel: 020 8201 5816
Age range: 1–5
No. of pupils: 92

INTERNATIONAL COMMUNITY SCHOOL
For further details see p. 57
4 York Terrace East, Regents
Park, London NW1 4PT
Tel: +44 20 7935 1206
Email: admissions@ics.uk.net
Website: www.icschool.co.uk
Head of School: Ms Rose Threlfall
Age range: 3–18
No. of pupils: 260
Fees: Day £16,650–£22,100
🌐 (IB) ✏ 16⁺

Islamia Girls' High School
129 Salusbury Road,
London NW6 6PE
Tel: 020 7372 3472
Headteacher: Ms S Jabeen
Age range: G11–16 years
Fees: Day £6,500
🏃

Joel Nursery
214 Colindeep Lane, Colindale,
London NW9 6DF
Tel: 020 8200 0189
Age range: 2–5
✏

Kentish Town Day Nursery
37 Ryland Road, London NW5 3EH
Tel: 020 7284 3600
Manager: Carol Kewley
Age range: 3 months–5 years
No. of pupils: 55

Kentish Town Montessori School
34 Oakford Road, Kentish
Town, London NW5 1AH
Tel: 020 7485 1056

Kidsunlimited Nurseries – Regents Place
1 Triton Mall, Regents Place,
Longford Street, London NW1 3FN
Tel: 01625 585222

Kidsunlimited Nurseries – St Pancras
The Fig Tree Nursery, St
Pancras Hospital, 4 St Pancras
Way, London NW1 0PE
Tel: 01625 585222

Kindercare Montessori Nursery
Bridge Park Business Centre,
Harrow Road, London NW10 0RG
Tel: 020 8838 1688
Age range: 2–5
Fees: Day £4,420

L'Ile Aux Enfants
22 Vicar's Road, London NW5 4NL
Tel: 020 7267 7119
Headmistress: Mrs Chailleux
Age range: 3–11
No. of pupils: 192
Fees: Day £3,270

Lakefield Catering & Educational Centre
Maresfield Gardens,
Hampstead, London NW3 5RY
Tel: 020 7794 5669
Course Director: Mrs Maria Brown
Age range: G16–24
No. of pupils: 16
Fees: FB £1,160
🏃 16⁺ 🏛 £ ✏ 16⁺ 🎿

Leapfrog Day Nurseries – Mill Hill
30 Millway, Mill Hill, London NW7 3RB
Tel: 020 8906 9123
Manager: Ellen Pollard
Age range: 0–5

Little Cherubs Kindergarten
2 Belgrave Close, Mill Hill,
London NW7 3QG
Tel: 020 8959 2420
Head: Mrs Pauline D Mitson
No. of pupils: 19

London Academy of Dressmaking and Design
18 Dobree Avenue, Willesden,
London NW10 2AE
Tel: 020 8451 7174
Principal: Mrs P A Parkinson MA
Age range: 13+
Fees: Day £2,650
16⁺ ✏ 16⁺ 🎿

London Jewish Girls' High School
18 Raleigh Close, Hendon,
London NW4 2TA
Tel: 020 8203 8618
Headteacher: Mr Joel Rabinowitz
Age range: G11–16
🏃

London Thames College
Crown House, North Circular Road,
Park Royal, London NW10 7PN
Tel: 020 8961 9003
Head: Dr Archana Raheja
16⁺

LYNDHURST HOUSE PREP SCHOOL
For further details see p. 60
24 Lyndhurst Gardens,
Hampstead, London NW3 5NW
Tel: 020 7435 4936
Email: pmg@
lyndhursthouse.co.uk
Website:
www.lyndhursthouse.co.uk
Headmaster: Andrew
Reid MA(Oxon)
Age range: B4–13
No. of pupils: 165
Fees: Day £5,515–£6,160
🏃 ✏

MAPLE WALK SCHOOL
For further details see p. 62
62A Crownhill Road,
London NW10 4EB
Tel: 020 8963 3890
Email: admin@
maplewalkschool.co.uk
Website:
www.maplewalkschool.co.uk
Head Teacher: Mrs S Gillam
Age range: 4–11
No. of pupils: 200
Fees: Day £2,846
£ ✏

Maria Montessori Children's House – West Hampstead
St Mary's Community Hall, 134a
Abbey Road, London NW6 4SN
Tel: 020 7624 5917

Maria Montessori Institute
26 Lyndhurst Gardens,
Hampstead, London NW3 5NW
Tel: 020 7435 3646
Director of Training & School:
Mrs Lynne Lawrence BA,
Mont Int Dip(AMI)
Age range: 18+
No. of pupils: 50
Fees: Day £7,100
16⁺

Maria Montessori School – Hampstead
26 Lyndhurst Gardens,
Hampstead, London NW3 5NW
Tel: +44 (0)20 7435 3646
Director of School: Mrs L Lawrence
Age range: 2–11
No. of pupils: 60
Fees: Day £5,400

Mill Hill School
The Ridgeway, Mill Hill
Village, London NW7 1QS
Tel: 020 8959 1176
Head: Dr Dominic Luckett
Age range: 13–18
No. of pupils: 689 VIth259
Fees: Day £13,860 FB £21,900
🌐 (A) 🏛 £ ✏ 16⁺

Naima Jewish Preparatory School
21 Andover Place, London NW6 5ED
Tel: 020 7328 2802
Headteacher: Mr Michael
Cohen MA, NPQH
Age range: 3–11
Fees: Day £5,997–£7,470
£ ✏

Nancy Reuben Primary School
Finchley Lane, Hendon,
London NW4 1DJ
Tel: 020 82025646
Head: D A David
Age range: 3–11
No. of pupils: 207

Neasden Montessori School
St Catherine's Church Hall, Dudden
Hill Lane, London NW2 7RX
Tel: 020 8208 1631
Head: Mrs J Sen Gupta
BA, MontDip(AMI)
Age range: 2–5

North Bridge House Junior School
8 Netherhall Gardens,
London NW3 5RR
Tel: 0207 267 6266
Head Teacher: Mrs J Hockley
Age range: 5–6
No. of pupils: 208
Fees: Day £14,700
✏

North Bridge House Nursery
33 Fitzjohns Avenue,
London NW3 5JY
Tel: 020 7435 9641
Head: Mrs A Allsopp
Age range: 2 years 9
months–5 years
No. of pupils: 229
Fees: Day £3,225–£11,865

North Bridge House Preparatory School
1 Gloucester Avenue,
London NW1 7AB
Tel: 020 7267 6266
Head: Brodie Bibby
Age range: 7–13
No. of pupils: 486
Fees: Day £15,585
£ ✏

NORTH BRIDGE HOUSE SCHOOL
For further details see p. 68
65 Rosslyn Hill, London NW3 5UD
Tel: 020 7267 6266
Email: admissions@
northbridgehouse.com
Website:
www.northbridgehouse.com
Age range: 2 years 9
months–18 years

North Bridge House Senior School
65 Rosslyn Hill, Hampstead,
London NW3 5UD
Tel: 020 7267 6266
Head Teacher: Mrs G Masefield
Age range: 11–16
No. of pupils: 310
Fees: Day £14,985

NW5 Theatre School
14 Fortess Road, London NW5 2EU
Tel: 020 7482 3236
Founder: George O'Gorman
Age range: 16–30
Fees: Day £3,600

Octagon Nursery School
St Saviour's Church Hall, Eton
Road, London NW3 4SU
Tel: 020 7586 3206

OYH Primary School
Finchley Lane, Hendon,
London NW4 1DJ
Tel: 020 8202 5646
Headteacher: D A David
Age range: 3–11
No. of pupils: 180

Pre-School Playgroups Association
Barrow Hill Junior School, Barrow
Hill Road, London NW8 7AL
Tel: 020 7586 8879

Rainbow Montessori School
13 Woodchurch Road,
Hampstead, London NW6 3PL
Tel: 020 7328 8986
Head Mistress: Maggy
Miller MontDip
Age range: 5–12
Fees: Day £3,250–£3,297

Ready Steady Go – Camden
123 St Pancras Way,
London NW1 0SY
Tel: 020 7586 5862
Principal: Jennifer Silverton
Age range: 2–5

Ready Steady Go – Fitzroy Road
Primrose Hill Community Centre,
29 Hopkinson's Place, Fitzroy
Road, London NW1 8TN
Tel: 020 7586 5862
Headmistress: Jennifer
Silverton BA(Hons), PGTC
Age range: 2–3
Fees: Day £1,800–£3,960

Ready Steady Go – Primrose Hill
12a King Henry's Road,
London NW3 3RP
Tel: 020 7586 5862
Principal: Jennifer Silverton
Age range: 2–5

Ready Steady Go – St John's Wood
21 Alexandra Road,
London NW8 0DP
Tel: 020 7586 5862
Head of School: Jennifer Silverton
Age range: 2–5

Rooftops Nursery
Preistly House, Athlone
Street, London NW5 4LN
Tel: 020 7267 7949

Royal Academy of Music
Marylebone Road,
London NW1 5HT
Tel: 020 7873 7300
Principal: Professor Curtis Price

Royal Central School of Speech and Drama
Embassy Theatre, Eton
Avenue, London NW3 3HY
Tel: 020 7722 8183
Principal & CEO: Professor
Gary Crossley
Fees: Day £0

Saint Christina's R C Preparatory School
25 St Edmunds Terrace, Regent's
Park, London NW8 7PY
Tel: 020 7722 8784
Headteacher: Mrs P Mortimer
Age range: B3–7 G3–11
No. of pupils: 224
Fees: Day £11,076

Sarum Hall
15 Eton Avenue, London NW3 3EL
Tel: 020 7794 2261
Headmistress: Mrs Christine Smith
Age range: G3–11
No. of pupils: 170
Fees: Day £6,048–£10,065

South Hampstead High School GDST
3 Maresfield Gardens,
London NW3 5SS
Tel: 020 7435 2899
Headmistress: Mrs J E Stephen BSc
Age range: G4–18
No. of pupils: 852 VIth162
Fees: Day £9,342–£12,006

Southbank International School – Hampstead
16 Netherhall Gardens,
London NW3 5TH
Tel: 020 7243 3803
Principal: Shirley Harwood
Age range: 3–11

St Anthony's School for Boys
90 Fitzjohn's Avenue, Hampstead,
London NW3 6NP
Tel: 020 7431 1066
Headmaster: Mr Paul Keyte
Age range: B4–13
No. of pupils: 310
Fees: Day £16,800–£17,160

St Christopher's School
32 Belsize Lane, Hampstead,
London NW3 5AE
Tel: 020 7435 1521
Head: Mrs S A West
BA(Hons), PGCE, MA
Age range: G4–11
No. of pupils: 235
Fees: Day £12,450

St Johns Wood Pre-Preparatory School
St Johns Hall, Lords
Roundabout, Prince Albert
Road, London NW8 7NE
Tel: 020 7722 7149
Headmistress: Ms D Louskas
Age range: 3–7
No. of pupils: 70
Fees: Day £7,620–£12,090

St Margaret's School
18 Kidderpore Gardens,
Hampstead, London NW3 7SR
Tel: 020 7435 2439
Principal: Mr M Webster BSc, PGCE
Age range: G4–16
No. of pupils: 156
Fees: Day £10,410–£12,060

St Marks Square Nursery School
St Marks Church, Regents
Park Road, Primrose Hill,
London NW1 7TN
Tel: 020 7586 8383
Head: Dr Sheema Parsons BEd
Age range: 2–6
No. of pupils: 28
Fees: Day £2,400

St Martin's School
22 Goodwyn Avenue, Mill
Hill, London NW7 3RG
Tel: 020 8959 1965
Head: Mrs Angela Wilson DipEd
Age range: 3–11
No. of pupils: 125
Fees: Day £6,500

ST MARY'S SCHOOL HAMPSTEAD
For further details see p. 71
47 Fitzjohn's Avenue,
Hampstead, London NW3 6PG
Tel: 020 7435 1868
Email: enquiries@stmh.co.uk
Website: www.stmh.co.uk
Head Teacher: Miss Angela
Rawlinson BA, MA(1st Class
Honours), DipTchng, NPQH
Age range: B2 years 9
months–7 years G2 years
9 months–11 years
No. of pupils: 300
Fees: Day £6,975–£12,915

St Nicholas School
22 Salmon Street, London NW9 8PN
Tel: 020 8205 7153
Headmistress: Mrs Alyce
Gregory CertEd
Age range: 5–11
No. of pupils: 80
Fees: Day £5,760

Sue Nieto Theatre School
19 Parkside, London NW7 2LJ
Tel: 020 8201 1500
Principal: Sue Nieto
Age range: 3–18

Sunflower Days Nursery
41 Selvage Lane, London NW7 3SS
Tel: 020 8906 1609
Age range: 6months–8

Swaminarayan School
260 Brentfield Road, Neasden,
London NW10 8HE
Tel: 020 8965 8381
Headteacher: Nilesh Manani
Age range: 2–18
No. of pupils: 452 VIth36
Fees: Day £7,818–£10,707

Talmud Torah Torat Emet
27 Green Lane, London NW4 2NL
Tel: 020 8201 7770
Headteacher: Rabbi M Nissim
Age range: B5–9

Teddies Nurseries West Hampstead
2 West End Lane, London NW6 4NT
Tel: 020 7372 3290
Age range: 3 months–5 years

The Academy School
3 Pilgrims Place, Rosslyn Hill,
Hampstead, London NW3 1NG
Tel: 020 7435 6621
Headteacher: Mr Garth Evans
Age range: 6–14

The American School in London
One Waverley Place,
London NW8 0NP
Tel: 020 7449 1221
Head: Mrs Coreen Hester
Age range: 4–18
No. of pupils: 1350
Fees: Day £21,950–£25,650

The Beehive on Queen's Park Montessori School
147 Chevening Road,
London NW6 6DZ
Tel: 020 8969 2235
Age range: 2–5
Fees: Day £3,900–£4,300

The Cavendish School
31 Inverness Street, Camden
Town, London NW1 7HB
Tel: 020 7485 1958
Headmistress: Mrs T Dunbar
BSc(Hons), PGCE, NPQH
Age range: G3–11
No. of pupils: 218
Fees: Day £11,550

The Childrens Centre
40 Nicoll Road, London NW10 9AB
Tel: 020 8961 6648
Age range: 2–5
No. of pupils: 50

The Childrens Centre
Christ Church, St Albans
Road, London NW10 8UG
Tel: 020 8961 9250
Head: Denise Lepore
Age range: 18 months–5
No. of pupils: 25

The Hall School
23 Crossfield Road, Hampstead,
London NW3 4NU
Tel: 020 7722 1700
Headmaster: P Lough MA
Age range: B4–13
No. of pupils: 440
Fees: Day £9,300–£11,400

The Interior Design School
22 Lonsdale Road, Queens
Park, London NW6 6RD
Tel: 020 7372 2811
Principal: Ms Iris Dunbar

The Islamia Schools' Trust
129 Salusbury Road,
London NW6 6PE
Tel: 020 7372 3472

The King Alfred School
Manor Wood, North End
Road, London NW11 7HY
Tel: 020 8457 5200
Head: Mrs Dawn Moore
MA(London)
Age range: 4–18
No. of pupils: 615 VIth70
Fees: Day £12,624–£15,219

The Little Ark Montessori
80 Westbere Road,
London NW2 3RU
Tel: 020 7794 6359
Principal: Angela Coyne MontDip
Age range: 2–5

The Mount, Mill Hill International School
Milespit Hill, Mill Hill Village,
London NW7 2RX
Tel: +44 (0)20 8906 6368
Head of School: Ms Sarah Bellotti
Age range: 13–17 years
Fees: Day £7,264 FB £11,900

The Mulberry House School
7 Minster Road, West
Hampstead, London NW2 3SD
Tel: 020 8452 7340
Headteacher: Ms Julie Kirwan
Age range: 2–8
No. of pupils: 184
Fees: Day £8,460–£15,698

The Oak Tree Nursery
2 Arkwright Road, Hampstead,
London NW3 6AD
Tel: 020 7435 1916
Head: Mrs S Alexander
Age range: 2–3
Fees: Day £4,650

The Phoenix School
36 College Crescent,
London NW3 5LF
Tel: 020 7722 4433
Headmistress: Mrs Lisa
Mason-Jones
Age range: 3–7
No. of pupils: 130
Fees: Day £2,585–£3,795

The School of the Islamic Republic of Iran
100 Carlton Vale, London NW6 5HE
Tel: 020 7372 8051
Headteacher: Mr Farzad Farzan
Age range: 6–16
No. of pupils: 53

The Village School
2 Parkhill Road, Belsize
Park, London NW3 2YN
Tel: 020 7485 4673
Headmistress: Miss C E F
Gay BSc(Hons), PGCE
Age range: G3–11
No. of pupils: 100
Fees: Day £14,490

Theatretrain
69 Great North Way,
London NW4 1HS
Tel: 020 8202 2006
Director: Kevin Dowsett CertEd,
AdvDip(Drama in Education)
Age range: 6–18

Toddlers Inn Nursery School
Cicoly Davies Hall, Cochrano
Street, London NW8 7NX
Tel: 020 7586 0520
Principal: Ms Laura McCole

Torah Vodaas
Julian Headon House,
West Hendon Broadway,
London NW9 7AL
Tel: 02036704670
Head of School: Mr Mark Shelton
Age range: B2–11

Trevor-Roberts School
55-57 Eton Avenue,
London NW3 3ET
Tel: 020 7586 1444
Headmaster: Simon
Trevor-Roberts BA
Age range: 5–13
Fees: Day £12,270–£14,070

University College School
Frognal, Hampstead,
London NW3 6XH
Tel: 020 7435 2215
Headmaster: Mr M J Beard MA
Age range: B11–18
No. of pupils: 850 VIth300
Fees: Day £16,005

University College School (Junior)
11 Holly Hill, London NW3 6QN
Tel: 020 7435 3068
Headmaster: Mr Lewis Hayward
MA (Oxon Lit. Hum), MA (OU,
ED. Management), PGCE
Age range: B7–11
No. of pupils: 250
Fees: Day £5,105

Wentworth Tutorial College
6-10 Brentmead Place,
London NW11 9LH
Tel: 020 8458 8524/5
Principal: Alan Davies BSc, MSc
Age range: 14–19
No. of pupils: 115

York Rise Nursery
St Mary Brookfield Hall, York
Rise, London NW5 1SB
Tel: 020 7485 7962
Headmistress: Miss Becca Coles
Age range: 2–5

South-East London

ABC Childrens Centre
48 Chapel Rd, West Norwood,
London SE27 0UR
Tel: 020 8766 0246
Principal: Ms E Carr

Alleyn's School
Townley Road, Dulwich,
London SE22 8SU
Tel: 020 8557 1500
Headmaster: Dr G Savage
MA, PhD, FRSA
Age range: 4–18
No. of pupils: 1223 VIth291
Fees: Day £14,139–£16,587

Alpha Meridian Colleges
Meridian House, Greenwich High
Road, Greenwich, London SE10 8TL
Tel: 020 8853 4111
Head: Mr Kudsi Tuluoglu

Anerley Montessori Nursery
45 Anerley Park, London SE20 8NQ
Tel: 020 8778 2810
Headmistress: Mrs P Bhatia
Age range: 3 months–5
Fees: Day £2,750–£4,600

Asquith Nursery – Elizabeth Terrace
18-22 Elizabeth Terrace,
Eltham, London SE9 5DR
Tel: 020 8294 0377
Age range: 3 months–5

Asquith Nursery – New Eltham
699 Sidcup Road, New
Eltham, London SE9 3AQ
Tel: 020 8851 5057
Age range: 3 months–5

Asquith Nursery – Peckham Rye
24 Waveney Avenue, Peckham
Rye, London SE15 3UE
Tel: 020 7635 5501
Age range: 4 months–5

Asquith Nursery – West Dulwich
Chancellor Grove, West
Dulwich, London SE21 8EG
Tel: 020 8761 6750
Age range: 3 months–5

Bellenden Day Nursery
Faith Chapel, 198 Bellenden
Road, London SE15 4BW
Tel: 020 7639 4896
Manager: Jason Cranston

Bellerbys College
Bounty House, Greenwich,
London SE8 3DE
Tel: 020 8694 7000
Head: Mr Andy Quin
Age range: 15–19
Fees: Day £9,600–£13,800
FB £16,730–£20,930

Blackheath & Bluecoats Day Nursery
Old Dover Road, Blackheath,
London SE3 8SJ
Tel: 020 8858 8221 Ext:147
Principal: Tracy Malyon

Blackheath Day Nursery
The Rectory Field, Charlton,
London SE3 8SR
Tel: 020 8305 2526
Headmistress: Mrs Shipley
Age range: 0–5
No. of pupils: 61

BLACKHEATH HIGH SCHOOL GDST
For further details see p. 44
Vanbrugh Park, Blackheath,
London SE3 7AG
Tel: 020 8853 2929
Email: info@bla.gdst.net
Website: www.blackheath
highschool.gdst.net
Head: Mrs Carol Chandler-
Thompson BA (Hons)
Exeter, PGCE Exeter
Age range: G3–18
No. of pupils: 780

Blackheath Montessori Centre
Independents Road,
Blackheath, London SE3 9LF
Tel: 020 8852 6765
Headmistress: Mrs Jane
Skillen MontDip
Age range: 3–5
No. of pupils: 36

Blackheath Nursery & Preparatory School
4 St Germans Place,
Blackheath, London SE3 0NJ
Tel: 020 8858 0692
Headmistress: Mrs P J Thompson
Age range: 3–11
Fees: Day £8,130–£11,190

Blake Hall College
10-11 Dock Offices, Surrey Quays
Road, London SE16 2XU
Tel: 020 7252 2033
Head: Mr Brink Gardner

Bright Horizons at Tabard Square
10-12 Empire Square, Tabard
Street, London SE1 4NA
Tel: 020 7407 2068

Broadfields Day Nursery
96 Broadfields Road, Catford,
London SE6 1NG
Tel: 020 8697 1488
Head: Elainne Dalton
Age range: 4 months–5

Clive Hall Day Nursery
rear of 54 Clive Road,
London SE21 8BY
Tel: 020 8761 9000

Colfe's Preparatory School
Horn Park Lane, Lee,
London SE12 8AW
Tel: 020 8463 8240
Head: Mrs Sarah Marsh
Age range: 3–11
No. of pupils: 355
Fees: Day £8,730–£10,134

Colfe's School
Horn Park Lane, Lee,
London SE12 8AW
Tel: 020 8852 2283
Head: Mr R F Russell MA(Cantab)
Age range: 3–18
No. of pupils: 1020

Dulwich College
London SE21 7LD
Tel: 020 8693 3601
Master: Dr J A F Spence
Age range: B7–18
No. of pupils: 1589 VIth470
Fees: Day £18,231 WB
£35,679 FB £38,052

Dulwich College Kindergarten & Infants School
Eller Bank, 87 College
Road, London SE21 7HH
Tel: 020 8693 1538
Head: Mrs H M Friell
Age range: 3 months–7 years
No. of pupils: 251

Dulwich College Preparatory School
42 Alleyn Park, Dulwich,
London SE21 7AA
Tel: 020 8766 5500
Headmaster: Mr M W
Roulston MBE, MEd
Age range: B3–13 G3–5
No. of pupils: 817
Fees: Day £4,350–£13,542
WB £18,213–£19,662

Dulwich Nursery
adj Sainsbury's Dulwich Store, 80
Dog Kennel Hill, London SE22 8DB
Tel: 020 7738 4007
Principal: Amanda Shead

Eltham College
Grove Park Road, Mottingham,
London SE9 4QF
Tel: 020 8857 1455
Headmaster: Mr P J
Henderson BA, FRSA
Age range: B7–18 G16–18
No. of pupils: 830 VIth220
Fees: Day £10,800–£12,525

Eltham Green Day Nursery
Eltham Green School, Queenscroft
Road, London SE9 5EQ
Tel: 020 8850 4720
Head: Mrs Walker
Age range: 3months–5
No. of pupils: 30

First Steps Montessori Day Nursery & Pre School
254 Upland Road, East
Dulwich, London SE22 0DN
Tel: 020 8299 6897
Principal: Karime Dinkha
Age range: 2–5
No. of pupils: 43

Five Steps Community Nursery
31-32 Alpine Road, London SE16 2RE
Tel: 020 7237 2376

Goldsmith International Business School
N107 (North Building), Westminster
Business Square, 45 Durham
Street, London SE11 5JH
Tel: 020 7820 8212
Head: Mr Emman Aluko

Greenwich School of Management
Meridian House, Royal Hill,
Greenwich, London SE10 8RD
Tel: 020 8516 7800
Head: Dr W G Hunt

Greenwich Steiner School
Woodlands, 90 Mycenae Road,
Blackheath, London SE3 7SE
Tel: 020 8858 4404
Age range: 3–14
No. of pupils: 180
Fees: Day £5,310–£8,004

Half Moon Montessori Nursery
Methodist Church Hall, 155 Half
Moon Lane, London SE24 9HU
Tel: 020 7326 5300
Age range: 2–5
No. of pupils: 65

Hamilton College
9 Albert Embankment,
London SE1 7SP
Tel: 020 7820 1133/020
7793 9801
Head: Mr Zubair Ahmad

Happy Faces Montessori
35 West Park, London SE9 4RZ
Tel: 020 8857 9990
Age range: 18 months–5

Happy Faces Nursery
161 Sumner Road, Peckham,
London SE15 6JL
Tel: 020 7701 3320

Heath House Preparatory School
37 Wemyss Road, Blackheath,
London SE3 0TG
Tel: 020 8297 1900
Head Teacher: Mrs Sophia
Laslett CertEd PGDE
Age range: 3–11
No. of pupils: 120
Fees: Day £9,585–£13,185

HERNE HILL SCHOOL
For further details see p. 54
The Old Vicarage, 127 Herne
Hill, London SE24 9LY
Tel: 020 7274 6336
Email: enquiries@
hernehillschool.co.uk
Website:
www.hernehillschool.co.uk
Headteacher: Mrs Ngaire Telford
Age range: 2+ to–7
No. of pupils: 275
Fees: Day £1,790–£4,435

Hillyfields Day Nursery
41 Harcourt Road, Brockley,
London SE4 2AJ
Tel: 020 8694 1069
Head: Ms Lisa Reeves

Holborn College
Woolwich Road, London SE7 8LN
Tel: 020 8317 6000
Principal: Mr Mohamed Maladwala

James Allen's Girls' School
East Dulwich Grove, Dulwich,
London SE22 8TE
Tel: 020 8693 1181
Headmistress: Mrs Marion Gibbs
BA(Hons), PGCE, MLitt, FRSA
Age range: G4–18
No. of pupils: VIth200
Fees: Day £12,540–£14,103

Kaplan Financial (London)
179-191 Borough High
Street, London SE1 1HR
Tel: 020 7407 5000
Head: Mr Vinod Siyani

Kings Kids Christian School
New Testament Church of
God, Bawtree Road, New
Cross, London SE14 6ET
Tel: 020 8691 5813
Headteacher: Mrs M Okenwa
Age range: 5–11
No. of pupils: 36

Lingfield Day Nursery (Blackheath)
37 Kidbrooke Grove,
Kidbrooke, London SE3 0LJ
Tel: 020 8858 1388
Manager: Sophie Campbell
Age range: 18 months–5
No. of pupils: 30
Fees: Day £9,350

Lingfield Day Nursery (Grove Park)
155 Baring Road, London SE12 0LA
Tel: 020 8851 7800
Manager: Samantha Goodwright
Age range: 18 months–5
No. of pupils: 30
Fees: Day £8,700

Little Cherubs Day Nursery
2a Bell Green Lane,
London SE26 5TB
Tel: 020 8778 3232

Lollipops Child Care Ltd
27 Southwood Road,
London SE9 3QE
Tel: 020 8859 5832
Principal: Miss L Thompson

London Bridge Business Academy
7-13 Melior Street, London SE1 3QP
Tel: 020 7378 1000
Head: Shmina Mandal
16+

London Christian School
40 Tabard Street, London SE1 4JU
Tel: 020 3130 6430
Headmistress: Miss Georgina Hale
Age range: 3–11
No. of pupils: 105
Fees: Day £7,725
£

London College of Accountancy
200 Great Dover Street,
London SE1 4YB
Tel: 020 7407 1119
Head: Mr Ravi Gill
16+

London College of Computing & Management
Atrium Suite, The Hop Exchange, 24
Southwark Street, London SE1 1TY
Tel: 020 7378 6333
Head: Dr Waheed Iqbal
16+

London College of Engineering & Management
18-36 Wellington Street,
London SE18 6PF
Tel: 020 8854 6158
Head: Mr Shakhar Sharman
16+

London Institute of Shipping and Transport
51-55 Waterloo Road,
London SE1 8TX
Tel: 020 7928 0029
Head: Dr N Kyritsis
16+

Magic Roundabout Nursery – Kennington
35 Sutherland House, Sutherland
Square, London SE17 3EE
Tel: 020 7277 3643

Marathon Science School
1-9 Evelyn Street, Surrey
Quays, London SE8 5RQ
Tel: 020 7231 3232
Headteacher: Mr Uzeyir Onur
Age range: B11–16
No. of pupils: 67
👦 👦

Maritime Greenwich College
4th Floor, Royal Sovereign House, 40
Beresford Street, London SE18 6BF
Tel: 0208 305 8508
Head: Mr N Kandel
16+

McAlpine Dance Studio
Longfield Hall, 50 Knatchbull
Road, London SE5 9QY
Tel: 020 8673 4992
16+

Mother Goose Nursery
The Pavilion, 65 Greendale Fields,
off Wanley Road, London SE5 8JZ
Tel: 020 7738 7700
Age range: 0–5

Mother Goose Nursery
248 Upland Road, East
Dulwich, London SE22 0NU
Tel: 020 8693 9429
Age range: 1–5

Mother Goose Nursery
34 Waveney Avenue,
Nunhead, London SE15 3UE
Tel: 020 7277 5951
Age range: 1–5

Mother Goose Nursery (Head Office)
133 Brookbank Road,
Lewisham, London SE13 7DA
Tel: 020 8694 8700
Age range: 1–5

Nell Gwynn Nursery
Meeting House Lane,
London SE15 2TT
Tel: 020 7252 8265

Oakfield Preparatory School
125-128 Thurlow Park Road, West
Dulwich, London SE21 8HP
Tel: 020 8670 4206
Head of School: Ms. Jane Stevens
Age range: 2–11 years
No. of pupils: 420
Fees: Day £9,750

Octavia House School, Vauxhall
Vauxhall Primary School, Vauxhall
Street, London SE11 5LG
Tel: 02036 514396
Executive Head: Mr James Waite
Age range: 5–14
No. of pupils: 65

Octavia House School, Walworth
Larcom House, Larcom
Street, London SE17 1RT
Tel: 02036 514396
Head of School: Mr James Waite

One World Day Nursery
11 Thurlby Road, London SE27 0RN
Tel: 020 8761 3308

Peter Pan Nursery
353 Bromley Road, London SE6 2RP
Tel: 020 8695 0082

Riverston School
63-69 Eltham Road, Lee
Green, London SE12 8UF
Tel: 020 8318 4327
Headmistress: Mrs S E Salathiel
Age range: 9 months–19 years
No. of pupils: 215
£ ✐ 16+ 🕸

ROSEMEAD PREPARATORY SCHOOL, DULWICH
For further details see p. 69
70 Thurlow Park Road,
London SE21 8HZ
Tel: 020 8670 5865
Email: admin@
rosemeadprepschool.org.uk
Website: www.rosemead
prepschool.org.uk
Headmaster: Arthur Bray CertEd
Age range: 3–11
No. of pupils: 349
Fees: Day £10,272–£11,286
£ ✐

School of Technology & Management
Kingshead House, Kingshead
Yard, London SE1 1NA
Tel: 020 7378 0052
16+

Skallywags Day Nursery
St Crispin Hall, Southwark Park
Road, London SE16 2HU
Tel: 020 7252 3225
Headmistress: Miss Allison
Armstrong NVQ
Age range: 3 months–5 years
No. of pupils: 65

Springfield Christian School
145 Perry Hill, Catford,
London SE6 4LP
Tel: 020 8291 4433
Principal: Mr B Oludimu BSc
Age range: 2–11
No. of pupils: 85
Fees: Day £2,550–£4,710
✐

St Dunstan's College
Stanstead Road, London SE6 4TY
Tel: 020 8516 7200
Headmistress: Mrs J D Davies BSc
Age range: 3–18
No. of pupils: 870
🕸 A £ IB 16+

St Olave's Preparatory School
106 Southwood Road, New
Eltham, London SE9 3QS
Tel: 020 8294 8930
Head: Mr J Tilly
Age range: 3–11
No. of pupils: 220
Fees: Day £5,414–£8,700
✐

St Patricks Montessori Nursery School
91 Cornwall Road, London SE1 8TH
Tel: 020 7928 5557

Step by Step Day Nursery
Benden House, Monument
Gardens, Campshill Road, Hither
Green, London SE13 6PY
Tel: 020 8297 5070
Co-ordinator: Mrs Irene Langford

Sydenham High School GDST
19 Westwood Hill, London SE26 6BL
Tel: 020 8557 7000
Headteacher: Kathryn Pullen MA
Age range: G4–18
No. of pupils: 630 VIth70
Fees: Day £11,466–£14,592
👦 A £ ✐ 16+

Teddies Nurseries Greenwich
Chevening Road, Greenwich,
London SE10 0LB
Tel: 020 8858 8266
Age range: 3 months–5 years

Teddies Nurseries West Dulwich
Baptist Church, Gipsy Road, West
Norwood, London SE27 9RB
Tel: 020 8761 8827
Age range: 3 months–5 years

The British School of Osteopathy
275 Borough High Street,
London SE1 1JE
Tel: 020 7407 0222
Principal & Chief Executive: Martin
Collins BSc(Hons), PhD, MSc,
Cbiol, MIBiol, FRSH, DO, ILTM
Fees: Day £0
16+

The Oak Tree Nursery
Tell Grove, Southwark,
London SE22 8RH
Tel: 020 8693 0306
✐

The Pavilion Nursery
Catford Cricket Club Pavilion,
Penerley Road, London SE6 2LQ
Tel: 020 8698 0878
Head: Mrs Karen Weller
Age range: 2–5
✐

The Pointer School
19 Stratheden Road,
Blackheath, London SE3 7TH
Tel: 020 8293 1331
Headmaster: Mr R J S Higgins
MA, BEd, CertEd, FCollP
Age range: 3–11
No. of pupils: 370
Fees: Day £6,912–£13,782
£ ✏

**The Villa Pre-Preparatory
School & Nursery**
54 Lyndhurst Grove, Peckham,
London SE15 5AH
Tel: 020 7703 6216
Head Teacher: Suzy Prebble
Age range: 2–7
No. of pupils: 210

**The Village
Montessori School**
Kingswood Hall, Kingswood
Place, London SE13 5BU
Tel: 020 8318 6720
Director: Catherine
Westlake MontDip
Age range: 3–5
Fees: Day £1,491

The Village Nursery
St Mary's Centre, 180 Ladywell
Road, Lewisham, London SE13 7HU
Tel: 020 8690 6766
Principal: Frances Rogers

Thornsbeach Day Nursery
10 Thornsbeach Road,
London SE6 1DX
Tel: 020 8697 7699
Manager: Mrs M James
Age range: 2–5

**Toad Hall Montessori
Nursery School**
37 St Mary's Gardens,
Kennington, London SE11 4UF
Tel: 020 7735 5087
Principal: Mrs V K Rees
NNEB, MontDip
Age range: 2–5
No. of pupils: 40
Fees: Day £6,300

Trinity Child Care
Holy Trinity Church Hall, Bryan
Road, London SE16 5HF
Tel: 020 7231 5842
Manager: Sharron Williams
Age range: 2–5
No. of pupils: 60
Fees: Day £6,240

**Virgo Fidelis
Preparatory School**
Central Hill, Upper Norwood,
London SE19 1RS
Tel: 020 8653 2169
Head Teacher: Mrs Meg Baines
Age range: 3–11
Fees: Day £2,520–£6,930
£ ✏

Waterloo Day Nursery
The Chandlery, 50 Westminster
Bridge Road, London SE1 7QY
Tel: 020 7721 7432
Principal: Julie Ellis

Willow Park
19 Glenlyon Road, Eltham,
London SE9 1AL
Tel: 020 8850 8753
Principal: Mrs McMahon

South-West
London

345 Nursery School
Fitzhugh Community Clubroom,
Fitzhugh Grove, Trinity Road,
London SW18 3SA
Tel: 020 8870 8441
Principal: Mrs Annabel Dixon
Age range: 3–5
No. of pupils: 42
Fees: Day £3,555
✏

Abacus Day Care Nursery
United Reform Church, Grafton
Square, London SW4 0DE
Tel: 020 7720 7290
Headmistress: Mrs Cynthia Clarke

**ABACUS Early Learning
Nursery School –
Balham Day Nursery**
135 Laitwood Road, Balham,
London SW12 9QH
Tel: 020 8675 8093

**ABACUS Early Learning
Nursery School –
Stretham Day Nursery**
7 Drewstead Road, Streatham
Hill, London SW16 1LY
Tel: 020 8677 9117
Principals: Mrs M Taylor
BEd & Ms S Petgrave
Age range: 12 mths–5 years
No. of pupils: 40

Abbey College – London
22 Grosvenor Gardens,
Belgravia, London SW1W 0DH
Tel: 020 7824 7300
Principal: Mr Mark Love BEd
Age range: 14–19
No. of pupils: 150 VIth150
Fees: Day £5,950–£16,400
FB £30,200
16¹ Ⓐ 🏫 £ ✏ 16¹

**Academy of Live &
Recorded Arts**
Studio1, Royal Victoria
Patriotic Building, John Archer
Way, London SW18 3SX
Tel: 020 8870 6475
Principal: Anthony Castro
Age range: 18+
No. of pupils: 108
Fees: Day £3,000–£9,888
16¹ £ ✏

Al-Muntada Islamic School
7 Bridges Place, Parsons
Green, London SW6 4HW
Tel: 020 7471 8283
Headteacher: Salma Ullah
Age range: 4–11
No. of pupils: 165
Fees: Day £2,500

Al-Risalah Nursery
10A Gatton Road, Tooting,
London SW17 0EE
Tel: 020 8767 0716
Head of School: Nasir Qurashi

**Al-Risalah Secondary
School**
145 Upper Tooting Road,
London SW17 7TJ
Tel: 020 8767 6057
Headmaster: Nasir Qurashi
Age range: 3–16
No. of pupils: 250

Alphabet Nursery School
Chatham Hall, Northcote Road,
Battersea, London SW11 6DY
Tel: 020 8871 7473
Principal: Mrs A McKenzie-Lewis
No. of pupils: 40
Fees: Day £1,500–£1,800

Asquith Nursery – Balham
36 Radbourne Road, Balham,
London SW12 0EF
Tel: 020 8673 1405

**Asquith Nursery
– Battersea**
18/30 Latchmere Road,
Battersea, London SW11 2DX
Tel: 020 7228 7008
Age range: 3 months–5

Asquith Nursery – Lambeth
50 Groveway, Stockwell,
London SW9 0AR
Tel: 020 7793 9922
Age range: 0–5
No. of pupils: 25

Asquith Nursery – Putney
107-109 Norroy Road, Putney,
London SW15 1PH
Tel: 020 8246 5611
Age range: 3 months–5

**Asquith Nursery –
Raynes Park**
c/o David Lloyd Leisure
Club, Bushey Road, Raynes
Park, London SW20 8TE
Tel: 020 8543 9005
Age range: 3 months–5

**Battersea Pre-
School & Nursery**
18/30 Latchmere Road,
Battersea, London SW11 2DX
Tel: 020 7228 4722
Head: Miss Sharon Nelson
Age range: 0–5
No. of pupils: 86

Beechwood School
55 Leigham Court Road,
Streatham, London SW16 2NJ
Tel: 020 8677 8778
Headmistress: Mrs M Marshall
Age range: 0–11
No. of pupils: 100
Fees: Day £6,726–£7,875

Beehive Nursery School
St Margarets Church Hall, Putney
Park Lane, London SW15 5HU
Tel: 020 8780 5333
Headmistress: Lindsay Deans
Age range: 2–5
No. of pupils: 16
Fees: Day £1,140

Bees Knees Nursery School
within Brookside Community Hall,
12 Priory Lane, London SW15 5JL
Tel: 020 8876 8252
Headmistress: Jo Wood
Age range: 2–5

Bertrum House School
290 Balham High Road,
London SW17 7AL
Tel: 020 8767 4051
Principal: Miss. Kirsty Pirrie
Age range: 2–7
No. of pupils: 94
Fees: Day £1,630–£4,090
✏

Blundells Day Nursery
The Old Court, 194-196 Sheepcote
Lane, Battersea, London SW11 5BW
Tel: 020 7924 4204
Headmistress: Susan Stevens
Age range: 18 months–5
No. of pupils: 66
Fees: Day £4,655–£8,575
✏

Bobby's Playhouse
16 Lettice Street, London SW6 4EH
Tel: 020 7384 1190
Principal: Mrs Emma Hannay
Age range: 3 months–5 years
Fees: Day £11,000

Broomwood Hall School
68-74 Nightingale Lane,
London SW12 8NR
Tel: 020 8682 8830
Head of School: Mrs
Carole Jenkinson
Age range: B4–8 G4–13
No. of pupils: 670
Fees: Day £13,680–£16,815
✏

Busy Bee Nursery School
106 Felsham Road, Putney,
London SW15 1DQ
Tel: 020 8780 1615
Headmistress: Mrs Lucy Lindsay
Age range: 2–5

Busy Bee Nursery School
19 Lytton Grove, Putney,
London SW15 2EZ
Tel: 020 8789 0132
Headmistress: Dr Sally Corbett
Age range: 2–5

CAMERON HOUSE
For further details see p. 45
4 The Vale, Chelsea,
London SW3 6AH
Tel: 020 7352 4040
Email: into@
cameronhouseschool.org
Website:
www.cameronhouseschool.org
Headmistress: Mrs Lucie
Moore BEd(Hons)
Age range: 4–11
No. of pupils: 120
Fees: Day £16,875

Carmena Christian Day Nurseries
47 Thrale Road, Streatham,
London SW16 1NT
Tel: 020 8677 8231
Head. Mrs S Allen

Centre Academy London
92 St John's Hill, Battersea,
London SW11 1SH
Tel: 020 7738 2344
Principal: Dr. Duncan
Rollo BA, MA, PhD
Age range: 9–19
Fees: Day £27,600–£40,100

Chelsea Independent College
517-523 Fulham Road,
London SW6 1HD
Tel: 020 7610 1114
Principal: Dr Kevin Savage
Age range: 14–19
No. of pupils: 202
Fees: Day £3,160–£18,100
FB £16,760–£36,400

Chelsea Kindergarten
St Andrews Church, Park Walk,
Chelsea, London SW10 0AU
Tel: 020 7352 4856
Headmistress: Miss Lulu
Tindall MontDip
Age range: 2–5
Fees: Day £3,900–£6,120

Clapham Day Nursery
3 Peardon Street, London SW8 3BW
Tel: 020 7498 3165
Manager: Nicolette
Warnes NNEB, NVQ4
Age range: 3 months–5
No. of pupils: 72

Clapham Montessori
St Paul's Community Centre,
St Paul's Church, Rectory
Grove, London SW4 0DX
Tel: 020 7498 8324
Head: Mrs R Bowles BSc, IntMontDip
Age range: 2–5

Clapham Park Montessori
St James' Church House, 10 West
Road, Clapham, London SW4 7DN
Tel: 020 7627 0352
Head: Mrs R Bowles BSc, IntMontDip
Age range: 2–5

Colet Court (St Paul's Preparatory School)
Colet Court, Lonsdale
Road, London SW13 9JT
Tel: 020 8748 3461
Headmaster: Mr T A
Meunier MA(Cantab)
Age range: B7–13
No. of pupils: 436
Fees: Day £15,729

Collingham
23 Collingham Gardens,
London SW5 0HL
Tel: 020 7244 7414
Principal: Mr G Hattee
MA(Oxon), DipEd
Age range: 14–19
No. of pupils: VIth200
Fees: Day £4,140–£11,850

Cresset Kindergarten
The Waldorf School of South
West London, 12 Ballam Park
Road, London SW12 8DR
Tel: 020 8673 4881
Principal: Pat Hague

Crown Kindergartens
Coronation House, Ashcombe
Road, Wimbledon,
London SW19 8JP
Tel: 020 8540 8820
Principal: Mrs Acres
Age range: 1–5
No. of pupils: 28

Dawmouse Montessori Nursery School
34 Haldane Road, Fulham,
London SW6 7EU
Tel: 020 7381 9385
Principal: Mrs Emma V
Woodcock NNEB, MontDip
Age range: 2–5
No. of pupils: 72

DOLPHIN SCHOOL
For further details see p. 49
106 Northcote Road,
London SW11 6QW
Tel: 020 7924 3472
Email: admissions@
dolphinschool.org.uk
Website:
www.dolphinschool.org.uk
Principal: Mr J Schmidt
BA(Hons), BEd, BPE
Age range: 2–11
No. of pupils: 317
Fees: Day £10,785–£11,895

Donhead
33 Edge Hill, London SW19 4NP
Tel: 020 8946 7000
Headmaster: Mr G C McGrath
BA(Hons), PGCE, MBA(Ed)
Age range: B4–11
No. of pupils: 280
Fees: Day £7,800–£8,325

Duff Miller College
59 Queen's Gate, South
Kensington, London SW7 5JP
Tel: 020 7225 0577
Principal: C Kraft BSc, BPS
Age range: 14–19
No. of pupils: 370
Fees: Day £3,800–£19,300
FB £17,400–£37,600

Eaton House Belgravia
3-5 Eaton Gate, London SW1W 9BA
Tel: 020 7730 9343
Headmistress: Mrs Annabel Abbott
Age range: B4–8
Fees: Day £14,670

Eaton House The Manor Girls School
58 Clapham Common
Northside, London SW4 9RU
Tel: 020 7924 6000
Head: Mrs Sarah Segrave
Age range: G4–11
Fees: Day £14,244

Eaton House The Manor Pre Prep School
58 Clapham Common
Northside, London SW4 9RU
Tel: 020 7924 6000
Head of School: Mr Huw May
Age range: B4–8
No. of pupils: 220
Fees: Day £14,244

Eaton House The Manor Prep School
58 Clapham Common
Northside, London SW4 9RU
Tel: 020 7924 6000
Head: Mr Jeremy Edwards
Age range: B8–13
No. of pupils: 165
Fees: Day £17,424

Eaton House The Vale
2 Elvaston Place, London SW7 5QH
Tel: 020 7924 6000
Head: Mr Robin Greenwood
Age range: 3–11
Fees: Day £7,416–£14,670

Eaton Square School
79 Eccleston Square,
London SW1V 1PP
Tel: 020 7931 9469
Headmaster: Mr Sebastian
Hepher BEd(Hons)
Age range: 2–13
No. of pupils: 529
Fees: Day £4,080–£19,785

Ecole Charles De Gaulle – Wix
Clapham Common North
Side, London SW4 0AJ
Tel: +44 20 7738 0287
Headteacher: Mr Blanchard
Age range: 5–11
No. of pupils: 100

Ecole Marie D'Orliac
60 Clancarty Road,
London SW6 3AA
Tel: +44 7736 020 58 63
Principal: Mr Olivier Rauch
Age range: 4–11
No. of pupils: 50

Elm Park Nursery School
90 Clarence Avenue,
Clapham, London SW4 8JR
Tel: 020 8678 1990
Head: Ms Jacqueline Brooks
No. of pupils: 113

Emanuel School
Battersea Rise, London SW11 1HS
Tel: 020 8870 4171
Headmaster: Mr Mark
Hanley-Browne
Age range: 10–18
No. of pupils: 840 VIth208
Fees: Day £17,019

Eveline Day & Nursery Schools
14 Trinity Crescent, Upper
Tooting, London SW17 7AE
Tel: 020 8672 4673
Headmistress: Ms Eveline Drut
Age range: 3 months–11 years
No. of pupils: 80
Fees: Day £11,059

Falkner House
19 Brechin Place, South
Kensington, London SW7 4QB
Tel: 020 7373 4501
Headteacher: Mrs Anita
Griggs BA(Hons), PGCE
Age range: B3–4 G3–11
Fees: Day £8,025–£16,050

Finton House School
171 Trinity Road, London SW17 7HL
Tel: 020 8682 0921
Headmaster: Adrian
Floyd BSc, PGCE
Age range: 4–11
No. of pupils: 305
Fees: Day £11,880–£12,885

First Steps School of Dance & Drama
234 Lillie Road, London SW6 7QA
Tel: 020 7381 5224
Age range: 3–17
Fees: Day £2,700

Francis Holland School, Sloane Square, SW1
39 Graham Terrace,
London SW1W 8JF
Tel: 020 7730 2971
Head: Mrs Lucy Elphinstone MA(Cantab)
Age range: G4–18
No. of pupils: 500 VIth70
Fees: Day £16,350–£18,450

Fulham & Chelsea College
Eden House, 59 Fulham High Street, London SW6 3JJ
Tel: 020 7384 4500
Heads: Mr Xavier Amaladoss Arokiam & Ms Kristy Partridge

Garden House School
Boys' School & Girls' School, Turk's Row, London SW3 4TW
Tel: 020 7730 1652
Boys Head: C Warland BA(Hons)
Age range: B3–8 G3–11
No. of pupils: 449
Fees: Day £9,300–£15,885

Gateway House Nursery School
St Judes Church Hall, Heslop Road, London SW12 8EG
Tel: 020 8675 8258
Principal: Miss Elizabeth Marshall
Age range: 2–4
No. of pupils: 30
Fees: Day £1,010–£1,060

Glendower School
86/87 Queen's Gate,
London SW7 5JX
Tel: 020 7370 1927
Headmistress: Mrs Sarah Knollys BA, PGCE
Age range: G4–11+
No. of pupils: 206
Fees: Day £14,280

Hall School Wimbledon
Beavers Holt, Stroud Crescent, Putney Vale, London SW15 3EQ
Tel: 020 8788 2370
Headmaster: Timothy J Hobbs MA
Age range: 4–16
No. of pupils: 520
Fees: Day £9,999–£13,224

Hall School Wimbledon Senior School
17 The Downs, Wimbledon, London SW20 8HF
Tel: 020 8879 9200
Headmaster: Timothy J Hobbs MA
Age range: 11–16
No. of pupils: 520
Fees: Day £10,698–£14,151

Happy Nursery Days
Valens House, 132a Uppertulse Hill, London SW2 2RX
Tel: 020 8674 7804
Age range: 3 months–5

Happy Times Nursery
40 Parkgate Road,
London SW11 4NP
Tel: 020 7350 5959

Happy Times Nursery
The Limes, 123 Mortlake High Street, London SW14 8SN
Tel: 0800 652 2424

Hill House International Junior School
17 Hans Place, Chelsea,
London SW1X 0EP
Tel: 020 7584 1331
Headmaster: Richard Townend FLSM(Chm)
Age range: 4–13
No. of pupils: 980
Fees: Day £10,350–£14,100

Hornsby House School
Hearnville Road, Balham,
London SW12 8RS
Tel: 020 8673 7573
Headmaster: Mr Edward Rees
Age range: 4–11
Fees: Day £12,375–£13,305

Hurlingham School
122 Putney Bridge Road,
Putney, London SW15 2NQ
Tel: 020 8874 7186
Headteacher: Mr Jonathan Brough
Age range: 4–11
No. of pupils: 320
Fees: Day £14,400–£15,030

Ibstock Place School
Clarence Lane, London SW15 5PY
Tel: 020 8876 9991
Head: Mrs Anna Sylvester-Johnson BA(Hons), PGCE
Age range: 4–18
No. of pupils: 970
Fees: Day £4,755–£6,130

Inchbald School of Design
Interior Design Faculty, 7 Eaton Gate, London SW1W 9BA
Tel: 020 7730 5508
Principal: Mrs Jacqueline Duncan FIIDA, FIDDA
Age range: 18–50
No. of pupils: 120

JJAADA Interior Design Academy
28 Abbeville Mews, 88 Clapham Park Road, London SW4 7BX
Tel: 020 7494 3363

Judith Blacklock Flower School
4/5 Kinnerton Place South,
London SW1X 8EH
Tel: 020 7235 6235
Head: Judith Blacklock

Kensington Prep School GDST
596 Fulham Road, London SW6 5PA
Tel: 0207 731 9300
Head: Mrs P Lynch MA (St Andrews) PGCE
Age range: G4–11
No. of pupils: 289
Fees: Day £11,103

Kids Inc Day Nursery – East Sheen
459b Upper Richmond Road West, East Sheen, London SW14 7PR
Tel: 020 8876 8144

King's College Junior School
Southside, Wimbledon Common, London SW19 4TT
Tel: 020 8255 5335
Headmaster: Dr. G A Silverlock
Age range: B7–13
No. of pupils: 460

King's College School
Southside, Wimbledon Common, London SW19 4TT
Tel: 020 8255 5300
Head Master: A D Halls MA
Age range: B11–18 G16–18
No. of pupils: 855 VIth396
Fees: Day £19,830

Knightsbridge School
67 Pont Street, Knightsbridge,
London SW1X 0BD
Tel: 020 7590 5900
Head: Ms Shona Colaco MA, PGCE, MSB, CBiol
Age range: 3–13
No. of pupils: 400
Fees: Day £16,224–£17,265

L'ECOLE DE BATTERSEA
For further details see p. 58
Trott Street, Battersea,
London SW11 3DS
Tel: 020 7371 8350
Email: admin@lecoledespetits.co.uk
Website: www.lecoledespetits.co.uk
Director: Mrs F Brisset
Age range: 3–11
No. of pupils: 252
Fees: Day £10,515–£10,710

L'ECOLE DES PETITS
For further details see p. 59
2 Hazlebury Road, Fulham,
London SW6 2NB
Tel: 020 7371 8350
Email: admin@lecoledespetits.co.uk
Website: www.lecoledespetits.co.uk
Director: Mrs F Brisset
Age range: 3–6
No. of pupils: 136
Fees: Day £10,320–£10,620

L'Ecole du Parc
12 Rodenhurst Road,
London SW4 8AR
Tel: 020 8671 5287
Headteacher: Mrs E Sicking-Bressler
Age range: 1–5
No. of pupils: 55
Fees: Day £4,000–£7,500

Ladybird Nursery School
9 Knowle Close, London SW9 0TQ
Tel: 020 7924 9505

Leapfrog Day Nurseries – Fulham
The Hume Centre, Cortayne Road, Fulham, London SW6 3QA
Tel: 020 7384 0406
Manager: Elaine Stevenson
Age range: 0–5

Leapfrog Day Nurseries – Wandsworth
Dolphin House, Riverside West, Smugglers Way, Wandsworth, London SW18 1DE
Tel: 020 8877 1135
Manager: Clare Myers-Shaw
Age range: 0–5

Lion House School
The Old Methodist Hall, Gwendolen Avenue, London SW15 6EH
Tel: 020 8780 9446
Head: Miss H J Luard MontDip
Age range: 2–7
No. of pupils: 115

Little Acorns Nursery School
Church of St James The Less, Moreton Street, London SW1V 2PT
Tel: 020 7931 0898

Little People of Fulham
250a Lillie Road, Fulham,
London SW6 7PX
Tel: 020 7386 0006
Owner: Miss Jane Gleasure
Age range: 4 months–5

Little Red Hen Nursery School
Church of the Nazarene, 2 Grant Road, Battersea, London SW11 2NU
Tel: 020 7738 0321
Age range: 2–5
Fees: Day £1,470–£1,740

London College of Business & Computer Studies
219 Clapham Road,
London SW9 9BE
Tel: 020 7733 4868
Principal: Mr T Olarewaju

London College Wimbledon
LCW House, 2A Mansel Road, London SW19 4AA
Tel: 020 8944 1134

London Electronics College
20 Penywern Road, Earls Court, London SW5 9SU
Tel: 020 7373 8721
Principal: M D Spalding BSc (Hons),MSc,CEng,MIEE,PGCE,MCybSoc,FRSA,MIOD
Age range: 21–65
Fees: Day £5,100
16 A £ ✐ ☺

London Film Academy
The Old Church, 52a Walham Grove, London SW6 1QR
Tel: 020 7386 7711
Founders & Joint Principals: Daisy Gili & Anna Macdonald
16

London Study Centre
Munster House, 676 Fulham Road, London SW6 5SA
Tel: 020 7731 3549/736 4990
Principal: Margaret McLeod
Age range: 16

Lowther Nursery Unit
Stillingfleet Road, Barnes, London SW13 9AE
Tel: 020 8563 7769
Age range: 3–5

Lycee Francais Charles de Gaulle
35 Cromwell Road, London SW7 2DG
Tel: 020 7584 6322
Headteacher: Mr Olivier Rauch
Age range: 3–18
No. of pupils: 4007
Fees: Day £4,521–£10,791
☺ A £ 16

Magic Roundabout Nursery – Stockwell
Surrey Hall, Binfield Road, Stockwell, London SW4 6TB
Tel: 020 7498 1194

MANDER PORTMAN WOODWARD – LONDON
For further details see p. 61
90-92 Queen's Gate, London SW7 5AB
Tel: 020 7835 1355
Email: london@mpw.ac.uk
Website: www.mpw.ac.uk
Principal: Mr Steven Boyes BA MSc PGCE
Age range: 14–19
No. of pupils: 620
Fees: Day £8,247–£8,928
16 A ✐

Melrose House Nursery School
39 Melrose Road, London SW18 1LX
Tel: 020 8874 7769
Age range: 2–5

Melrose House Nursery School
55 Finlay Street, London SW6 6HF
Tel: 020 7736 9296

Mini Stars Day Nursery
St Margarets Church, Barcombe Avenue, London SW2 3HH
Tel: 020 8678 8600
Age range: 6 months–5
No. of pupils: 26

Miss Daisy's Nursery School
Fountain Court Club Room, Ebury Square, London SW1W 9SU
Tel: 020 7730 5797
Head: Daisy Harrison
Age range: 2–5
No. of pupils: 30
Fees: Day £1,050–£5,550

Modern Montessori International Ltd (London)
MMI House, 142 Micham Lane London, London SW16 6SN
Tel: 020 8769 5555
Head: Mrs Marianne Burke
16

Montessori School
St Paul's Community Centre, Rectory Grove, Clapham, London SW4 0DX
Tel: 020 7498 8324
Age range: 6 months–6

MORE HOUSE SCHOOL
For further details see p. 63
22-24 Pont Street, Knightsbridge, London SW1X 0AA
Tel: 020 7235 2855
Email: office@morehouse.org.uk
Website: www.morehouse.org.uk
Headmistress: Mrs. Amanda Leach
Age range: G11–18
No. of pupils: 211
Fees: Day £17,160
☺ A £ ✐ 16

Newton Prep
149 Battersea Park Road, London SW8 4BX
Tel: 020 7720 4091
Headmistress: Mrs Alison Fleming BA, MA Ed, PGCE
Age range: 3–13
No. of pupils: 640
Fees: Day £8,310–£17,625
£ ✐

Nightingale Montessori Nursery
St Lukes Community Hall, 194 Ramsden Road, London SW12 8RQ
Tel: 020 8675 8070
Principal: Mrs Tejas Earp
Age range: 2–5

Noah's Ark Nursery Schools (Dolphin School Trust)
St Michael's Church Hall, Cobham Close, London SW11 6SP
Tel: 020 7924 3472 opt 2
Head: Miss Annette Miller
Age range: 2–5
No. of pupils: 40
Fees: Day £4,725

Noah's Ark Nursery Schools (Dolphin School Trust)
Endlesham Church Hall, 48 Endlesham Road, London SW12 8JL
Tel: 020 924 3472 opt 2
Head: Miss Annette Miller
Age range: 2–5
No. of pupils: 32
Fees: Day £4,725

Noddy's Nursery School
Trinity Church Hall, Beaumont Road, Wimbledon, London SW19 6SP
Tel: 020 8785 9191
Principal: Mrs Sarah Edwards NNEB, Mont Dip
Age range: 2–5

Northcote Lodge School
26 Bolingbroke Grove, London SW11 6EL
Tel: 020 8682 8888
Headmaster: Mr Mark Smith
Age range: B8–13
No. of pupils: 220
Fees: Day £17,430
☺ ✐

Oliver House Preparatory School
7 Nightingale Lane, London SW4 9AH
Tel: 020 8772 1911
Headteacher: Ms Maureen Fields
Age range: 2–13
No. of pupils: 144
Fees: Day £4,200–£9,300

Paint Pots Montessori School – Chelsea
Chelsea Christian Centre, Edith Grove, London SW10 0LB
Tel: 020 7376 5780
Principal: Miss G Hood MontDip
Age range: 2.5–5
No. of pupils: 42
Fees: Day £2,130–£6,360
✐

Parkgate House School
80 Clapham Common North Side, London SW4 9SD
Tel: +44 (0)20 7350 2461
Principal: Miss Catherine Shanley
Age range: 2.5–11 years
No. of pupils: 245
Fees: Day £5,355–£14,010

Parsons Green Prep School
1 Fulham Park Road, Fulham, London SW6 4LJ
Tel: 020 7371 9009
Headteacher: Ms. Helen Stavert
Age range: 4–11
No. of pupils: 200
Fees: Day £4,995–£5,395
✐

Peques Anglo-Spanish School
St John's Church, North End Road, Fulham, London SW6 1PB
Tel: 020 7385 0055
Age range: 3 months–5

Playdays Day Nursery & Nursery School Ltd
58 Queens Road, Wimbledon, London SW19 8LR
Tel: 020 8946 8139

Pooh Corner Kindergarten
St Stephen's Church Hall, 48 Emperor Gate, London SW7 4HJ
Tel: 020 7373 6111

Primary Steps Day Nursery
459b Upper Richmond Road West, East Sheen, London SW14 7PR
Tel: 020 8876 8144
Manager: Ms Joyce Kledo NNEB
Age range: 1–5
No. of pupils: 75

PROSPECT HOUSE SCHOOL
For further details see p. 66
75 Putney Hill, London SW15 3NT
Tel: 020 8780 0456 Registrar: 020 8246 4897
Email: registrar@prospecths.org.uk
Website: www.prospecths.org.uk
Headmistress: Mrs Dianne Barratt MEd (Newcastle-upon-Tyne)
Age range: 3–11
No. of pupils: 300
Fees: Day £7,890–£16,440
£ ✐

Putney High School GDST
35 Putney Hill, London SW15 6BH
Tel: 020 8788 4886
Headmistress: Dr Denise Lodge BSc, MSc, PhD
Age range: G4–18
No. of pupils: VIth150
☺ A £ ✐ 16

Queen's Gate School
133 Queen's Gate, London SW7 5LE
Tel: 020 7589 3587
Principal: Mrs R M Kamaryc BA, MSc, PGCE
Age range: G4–18
No. of pupils: 523 VIth90
☺ A £ ✐ 16

Quest Business Training
5 Grosvenor Gardens, Belgravia, London SW1W 0BD
Tel: 020 7233 5957
Age range: 16–45
16 16

Ravenstone Preparatory School
24 Elvaston Place, South Kensington, London SW7 5NL
Tel: 020 7225 3131
Head of School: Dr Ronald Pritchard
Age range: 2–11
No. of pupils: 110
Fees: Day £11,280–£16,875
✐

Red Balloon Nursery School
St Mary Magdalene Church Hall, Trinity Road, Tooting, London SW17 7SD
Tel: 020 8672 4711
Headmistress: Ms T Millington-Drake MontDip
Age range: 2–5
Fees: Day £3,270–£3,450

Redcliffe School Trust Ltd
47 Redcliffe Gardens, Chelsea, London SW10 9JH
Tel: 020 7352 9247
Head: Mrs Susan Bourne BSc, PGCE
Age range: B3–8 G3–11
Fees: Day £14,610–£14,610

Ringrose Kindergarten – Chelsea
St Lukes Church Hall, St Lukes Street, London SW3 3RP
Tel: 020 7352 8784

Ringrose Kindergarten – Pimlico
32a Lupus Street, London SW1V 3DZ
Tel: 020 7976 6511
Headmistress: Mrs C Stark SRN, DipMont, RNI
Age range: 2–5
Fees: Day £2,250

Rising Star Montessori School
St Clement Church Hall, 286 Fulham Palace Road, London SW6 6HP
Tel: 020 7381 3511
Headmistress: Mrs Hortense Casson MontDip
Age range: 2–5
No. of pupils: 24
Fees: Day £2,700

Royal Academy of Dance
36 Battersea Square, London SW11 3RA
Tel: 020 7326 8000
Chief Executive: Luke Rittner
Fees: Day £0

Royal College of Art
Kensington Gore, London SW7 2EU
Tel: 020 7590 4444
Rector & Vice-Provost: Professor Christopher Frayling

Sinclair House Preparatory School
59 Fulham High Street, Fulham, London SW6 3JJ
Tel: 0207 736 9182
Principal: Mrs Carlotta T M O'Sullivan
Age range: 2–13
No. of pupils: 120
Fees: Day £10,950

Small Steps Community Childcare Centre
Bessborough Street, London SW1V 2JD
Tel: 020 7641 5998

Square One Nursery School
12 Ravenna Road, Putney, London SW15 6AW
Tel: 020 8788 1546

St Mary Magdalen Montessori Nursery School
61 North Worple Way, London SW14 8PR
Tel: 020 8878 0756
Head: Liz Maitland NNEB, RSH, MontDip
Age range: 2–5
No. of pupils: 43
Fees: Day £1,600

St Mary's Summerstown Montessori
46 Wimbledon Road, Tooting, London SW17 0UQ
Tel: 020 8947 7359
Head: Liz Maitland NNEB, RSH, MontDip
Age range: 18 months–5 years
No. of pupils: 30
Fees: Day £1,300

St Michael's Montessori Nursery School
St Michael's Church, Elm Bank Gardens, Barnes, London SW13 0NX
Tel: 020 8878 0116
Head Teacher: Debbie Goldberg
Age range: 2 1/2–5
No. of pupils: 50

St Michaels Nursery School
St Michaels Church Hall, Elm Bank Gardens, London SW13 0NX
Tel: 020 8878 0116
Principal: Mrs J L Gould
Age range: 2–5
No. of pupils: 36

St Nicholas Preparatory School
23 Princes Gate, Kensington, London SW7 1PT
Tel: 020 7225 1277
Headmaster: Mr Tony Lewis
Age range: 3–11
No. of pupils: 280
Fees: Day £11,475–£13,110

St Paul's School
Lonsdale Road, Barnes, London SW13 9JT
Tel: 020 8748 9162
High Master: Prof Mark Bailey
Age range: B13–18
No. of pupils: 897
Fees: Day £19,674 FB £29,466

St Philip's School
6 Wetherby Place, London SW7 4NE
Tel: 020 7373 3944
Headmaster: H J Biggs-Davison MA(Cantab)
Age range: B7–13
No. of pupils: 110
Fees: Day £12,750

Streatham & Clapham High School GDST
42 Abbotswood Road, London SW16 1AW
Tel: 020 8677 8400
Headmaster: Dr Millan Sachania
Age range: B3–5 G3–18
No. of pupils: 603 VIth70
Fees: Day £5,886–£9,810

Streatham Montessori Nursery School
66 Blairderry Road, Streatham Hill, London SW2 4SB
Tel: 020 8674 2208

Studio Day Nursery
91-93 Moore Park Road, Fulham, London SW6 2DA
Tel: 020 7736 9256
Head: Miss Jenny M R Williams NNEB, RSH(Norlander)
Age range: 2–5

Sussex House School
68 Cadogan Square, Knightsbridge, London SW1X 0EA
Tel: 020 7584 1741
Headmaster: Mr N P Kaye MA(Cantab), ACP, FRSA
Age range: B8–13
No. of pupils: 182
Fees: Day £16,200

Swedish School
82 Lonsdale Road, London SW13 9JS
Tel: 020 8741 1751
Head of School: Ms. Annika Simonsson Bergqvist
Age range: 3–18
No. of pupils: 242
Fees: Day £6,600

Teddies Nurseries Balham
272 Balham High Road, London SW17 7AJ
Tel: 020 8672 4809
Age range: 3 months–5 years

Teddies Nurseries Raynes Park
3 Spencer Road, Wimbledon, London SW20 0QN
Tel: 020 8947 2398
Age range: 3 months–5 years

Teddies Nurseries Southfields
Duntshill Mill, 21 Riverdale Drive, London SW18 4UR
Tel: 020 8870 2009
Age range: 3 months–5 years

Teddies Nurseries Streatham
113 Blegborough Road, London SW16 6DL
Tel: 020 8835 9898
Age range: 3 months–5 years

Telten Montessori Nursery School
Norbury Park Lawn Tennis Club, Ederline Avenue, London SW16 4RZ
Tel: 020 8764 2531/07974 249726
Proprietress: Mrs A Oke
Age range: 2–5
Fees: Day £562–£3,693

Thames Christian College
Wye Street, Battersea, London SW11 2HB
Tel: 020 7228 3933
Executive Head: Stephen Holsgrove PhD
Age range: 11–16
No. of pupils: 120
Fees: Day £9,660

The Boltons Nursery School
262b Fulham Road, Chelsea, London SW10 9EL
Tel: 020 7351 6993
Age range: 2–5
No. of pupils: 60
Fees: Day £2,370–£4,200

The Bumble Bee Nursery School
Church Hall, Church of the Ascension, Pountney Road, London SW11 5TU
Tel: 020 7350 2970
Principal: Bella Lyle

The Castle Kindergarten
20 Henfield Road, London SW19 3HU
Tel: 020 8544 0089
Headmistress: Mrs Beverley Davis DipEd
Age range: 2–5

The Crescent I Kindergarten
Flat 1, No 10 Trinity Crescent, London SW17 7AE
Tel: 020 8767 5882
Principal: Philip Evelegh

The Crescent II Kindergarten
Holy Trinity Church Hall, Trinity Road, London SW17 7SQ
Tel: 020 8682 3020

The Crescent III Kindergarten
Grafton Tennis Club, 70A Thornton Road, London SW12 0LF
Tel: 020 8675 9659

The Eveline Day Nursery Schools – Tooting
30 Ritherdon Road, Upper Tooting, London SW17 8QD
Tel: 020 8672 7549
Principal: Mrs T Larche

The Eveline Day Nursery Schools Ltd – SW17
Seeley Hall, Chillerton Road, London SW17 9BE
Tel: 020 8672 0501

The Eveline Day Nursery Schools Ltd – SW18
United Reform Church, Geraldine Road, London SW18 2NU
Tel: 020 8870 0966

The Eveline Day Nursery Schools Ltd – SW19
87a Quicks Road, London SW19 1EX
Tel: 020 8545 0699

The Hampshire School, Chelsea
15 Manresa Road, Chelsea, London SW3 6NB
Tel: 020 7352 7077
Principal: Mr Dónal Brennan
Age range: 3–13
No. of pupils: 307
Fees: Day £14,925–£16,440
£

The Harrodian School
Lonsdale Road, London SW13 9QN
Tel: 020 8748 6117
Headmaster: James R Hooke
Age range: 5–18
No. of pupils: 890 VIth95
Fees: Day £10,407–£15,219
A 16

The Heatherley School of Fine Art
80 Upcerne Road, Chelsea, London SW10 0SH
Tel: 020 7351 4190
Head of School: Mr John Walton RP, DFA(Lond)
Age range: 17–80
16

The Knightsbridge Kindergarten
St Peter's Church, 119 Eaton Square, London SW1W 0HQ
Tel: 020 7235 5305
Headmistress: Mrs P Powell-Harper
Age range: 2–5
Fees: Day £4,000

The Laurels School
126 Atkins Road, Clapham, London SW12 0AN
Tel: 020 8674 7229
Headmistress: Linda Sanders BA Hons (Bristol), MA (Madrid)

The Maria Montessori Children's House
St John's Ambulance Hall, 122-124 Kingston Road, London SW19 1LY
Tel: 020 8543 6353
Age range: 2–5

The Merlin School
4 Carlton Drive, Putney Hill, London SW15 2BZ
Tel: 020 8788 2769
Principal: Mrs Kate Prest
Age range: 4–8
No. of pupils: 170

THE MOAT SCHOOL
For further details see p. 74
Bishops Avenue, Fulham, London SW6 6EG
Tel: 020 7610 9018
Email: office@moatschool.org.uk
Website: www.moatschool.org.uk
Head: Ms Clare King
Age range: 9–16
Fees: Day £28,800

The Montessori Childrens House Ltd
St John's Church, 1 Spencer Hill, London SW19 4NZ
Tel: 020 8971 9135
Age range: 2–5

The Montessori Pavilion – The Kindergarten School
Vine Road, Barnes, London SW13 0NE
Tel: 020 8878 9695
Age range: 3–8
No. of pupils: 50
Fees: Day £1,950–£3,600

The Mouse House Nursery School
27 Mallinson Road, London SW11 1BW
Tel: 020 7924 1893
Headmistress: Amanda White-Spunner
Age range: 2–5
Fees: Day £1,650–£4,125

The Norwegian School
28 Arterberry Road, Wimbledon, London SW20 8AH
Tel: 020 8947 6617
Head: Mr Geir Johansen
Age range: 3–16

The Oval Montessori Nursery School
within Vauxhall Park, Fentiman Road, London SW8 1LA
Tel: 020 7735 4816
Head: Ms Louise Norwood
Age range: 2–5
Fees: Day £3,000

The Park Kindergarten
St Saviours Church Hall, 351 Battersea Park Road, London SW11 4LH
Tel: 020 7627 5125
Principal: Miss Lisa Neilsen MontDip
Age range: 2–5
Fees: Day £2,370

The Rainbow Playgroup
St Luke's Church Hall, St Luke's Street, London SW3 3RR
Tel: 020 7352 8156
Age range: 2–5

THE ROCHE SCHOOL
For further details see p. 75
11 Frogmore, London SW18 1HW
Tel: 020 8877 0823
Email: office@therocheschool.co.uk
Website: www.therocheschool.co.uk
Headmistress: Mrs V Adams BA(Hons), PGCE, MA
Age range: 2–11 years
No. of pupils: 239
Fees: Day £12,090–£13,050
£

The Rowans School
19 Drax Avenue, Wimbledon, London SW20 0EG
Tel: 020 8946 8220
Head Teacher: Mrs S Wingrove
Age range: 3–8
Fees: Day £5,460–£10,725

The Study Preparatory School
Wilberforce House, Camp Road, Wimbledon Common, London SW19 4UN
Tel: 020 8947 6969
Headmistress: Mrs Susan Pepper MA Oxon, PGCE
Age range: G4–11
No. of pupils: 315
£

The Waldorf School of South West London
PO Box 8541, London SW16 1ZB
Tel: 0208 772 3504
Age range: 3–14
No. of pupils: 80
Fees: Day £4,515–£6,217
£

The White House Preparatory School & Woodentops Kindergarten
24 Thornton Road, London SW12 0LF
Tel: 020 8674 9514
Principal: Ms Mary McCahery
Age range: 2–11
Fees: Day £9,800–£12,300
£

The Willow Nursery School
c/o Clapham Baptist Church, 823-825 Wandsworth Road, London SW8 3JX
Tel: 020 7498 0319
Head: Mrs Harriet Baring MontDip
Age range: 2–5
Fees: Day £3,000–£3,100

The Wimbledon Village Montessori School
26 Lingfield Road, London SW19 4QD
Tel: 020 8944 0772

The Zebedee Nursery School
4 Parsons Green, London SW6 4TN
Tel: 020 7371 9224
Headmistress: Miss Su Gahan NNEB, RSH
Age range: 2–5
No. of pupils: 32
Fees: Day £3,900

Thomas's Kindergarten – Battersea
St Mary's Church, Battersea Church Road, London SW11 3NA
Tel: 020 7738 0400
Headmistress: Miss Iona Jennings
Age range: 2–5
Fees: Day £1,365–£2,100

Thomas's Kindergarten – Pimlico
14 Ranelagh Grove, London SW1W 8PD
Tel: 020 7730 3596
Headmistress: Miss Tamara Spierenburg HBO

Thomas's Preparatory School – Battersea
28-40 Battersea High Street, London SW11 3JB
Tel: 020 7978 0900
Head: Ben V R Thomas MA
Age range: 4–13
No. of pupils: 547
Fees: Day £12,510–£18,330

Thomas's Preparatory School – Clapham
Broomwood Road, London SW11 6JZ
Tel: 020 7326 9300
Headmaster: Mr Philip Ward BEd(Hons)
Age range: 4–13
Fees: Day £10,365–£11,730
£

Thomas's Preparatory School – Fulham
Hugon Road, London SW6 3ES
Tel: 020 7751 8200
Head: Miss Annette Dobson BEd(Hons), PGCertDys
Age range: 4–11

Tiggers Nursery School
87 Putney Bridge Road, London SW15 2PA
Tel: 020 8874 4668
Headmistress: Natasha Green MontDip
Age range: 2–5
Fees: Day £1,425–£1,725

Toots Day Nursery
214 Totterdown Street, Tooting, London SW17 8TD
Tel: 020 8767 7017
Principal: Angela Duffell
Age range: 1–5

Tower House School
188 Sheen Lane, London SW14 8LF
Tel: 020 8876 3323
Head: Mr Gregory Evans
Age range: B4–13
No. of pupils: 180
Fees: Day £11,073–£12,558

Twice Times Nursery School
The Cricket Pavilion in South Park, Clancarty Road, London SW6 3AF
Tel: 020 7731 4929
Heads: Mrs A Welch MontDip & Mrs S Henderson MontDip
Age range: 2–5
No. of pupils: 50

Ursuline Preparatory School
18 The Downs, London SW20 8HR
Tel: 020 8947 0859
Headmistress: Mrs Anne Farnish BA (Hons) MA, NPQH, PGCE
Age range: B3–4 G3–11
Fees: Day £5,886–£9,600

Wandsworth Preparatory School
The Old Library, 2 Allfarthing Lane, London SW18 2PQ
Tel: 0208 870 4133

Westminster Abbey Choir School
Dean's Yard, London SW1P 3NY
Tel: 0207 654 4918
Headmaster: Jonathan Milton BEd
Age range: B8–13
No. of pupils: 35
Fees: FB £7,404

Westminster Cathedral Choir School
Ambrosden Avenue, London SW1P 1QH
Tel: 020 7798 9081
Headmaster: Mr Neil McLaughlan
Age range: B8–13
No. of pupils: 150
Fees: Day £13,656 FB £6,945

Westminster School
17 Dean's Yard, Westminster, London SW1P 3PF
Tel: 020 7963 1003
Headmaster: Mr Patrick Derham
Age range: B13–18 G16–18
No. of pupils: 744
Fees: Day £24,276–£26,322 FB £35,058

Westminster Tutors
86 Old Brompton Road, South Kensington, London SW7 3LQ
Tel: 020 7584 1288
Principal: Virginia Maguire BA, MLitt
Age range: 14–mature
No. of pupils: VIth40
Fees: Day £6,300–£20,400

Westminster Under School
Adrian House, 27 Vincent Square, London SW1P 2NN
Tel: 020 7821 5788
Headteacher: Mrs E A Hill MA
Age range: B7–13
No. of pupils: 265
Fees: Day £14,676

Willington School
Worcester Road, Wimbledon, London SW19 7QQ
Tel: 020 8944 7020
Head: Mr Michael Chanter
Age range: B4–13
No. of pupils: 250
Fees: Day £9,345–£11,385

Wiltshire Nursery
85 Wiltshire Road, Brixton, London SW9 7NZ
Tel: 020 7274 4446

Wimbledon Common Preparatory
113 Ridgway, Wimbledon, London SW19 4TA
Tel: 020 8946 1001
Head Teacher: Mrs Tracey Buck
Age range: B4–8
No. of pupils: 160
Fees: Day £10,725

Wimbledon High School GDST
Mansel Road, Wimbledon, London SW19 4AB
Tel: 020 8971 0900
Headmistress: Mrs H Hanbury
Age range: G4–18
No. of pupils: 900 VIth155
Fees: Day £11,445–£15,024

Wimbledon Park Montessori School
206 Heythorp Street, Southfields, London SW18 5BU
Tel: 020 8944 8584
Head: Ms Clare Collins
Age range: 2–5
Fees: Day £830–£950

Wimbledon School of Art
Merton Hall Road, London SW19 3QA
Tel: 020 8408 5000
Principal: Professor Roderick Bugg

Young England Kindergarten
St Saviour's Hall, St George's Square, London SW1V 3QW
Tel: 020 7834 3171
Principal: Mrs Kay C King MontDip
Age range: 2.5–5
Fees: Day £3,300–£4,950

West London

Acorn Nursery School
2 Lansdowne Crescent, London W11 2NH
Tel: 020 7727 2122
Principal: Mrs Jane Cameron BEd(Hons)
Age range: 2–5
Fees: Day £2,400

Acton Training Centre
296 High Street, Acton, London W3 9BJ
Tel: 020 8992 4144
Head: Mr Sukhev Virdi

Acton Yochien Nursery School
The Pavilion, Queens Drive Playing Fields, Acton, London W3 0HT
Tel: 020 8343 2192

Alan D Education
61-62 East Castle Street, London W1W 8NQ
Tel: 020 7580 1030
Director of Education: Alan Hemmings
Fees: Day £200 FB £12,400

Albemarle Independent College
18 Dunraven Street, London W1K 7FE
Tel: 020 7409 7273
Co-Principals: Beverley Mellon & James Eytle
Age range: 16–19
No. of pupils: 160
Fees: Day £15,000–£18,000

American InterContinental University (AIU) – London
110 Marylebone High Street, London W1U 4RY
Tel: 020 7467 5600
Dean: Dr Allan Plath
Age range: 16+

Arts Educational Schools London Sixth Form
Cone Ripman House, 14 Bath Road, Chiswick, London W4 1LY
Tel: 020 8987 6666
Head Teacher: Mr Adrian Blake
Age range: 16–18
No. of pupils: 85
Fees: Day £14,190

Arts Educational Schools London Years 7-11
Cone Ripman House, 14 Bath Road, Chiswick, London W4 1LY
Tel: 020 8987 6666
Head Teacher: Mr Adrian Blake
Age range: 11–16
No. of pupils: 141
Fees: Day £13,350

Ashbourne Independent Sixth Form College
17 Old Court Place, Kensington, London W8 4PL
Tel: 020 7937 3858
Principal: M J Kirby MSc, BApSc
Age range: 16–19
No. of pupils: 170
Fees: Day £19,725 FB £21,500

Ashbourne Middle School
17 Old Court Place, Kensington, London W8 4PL
Tel: 020 7937 3858
Principal: M J Kirby MSc, BApSc
Age range: 13–16
No. of pupils: VIth150
Fees: Day £14,725 FB £21,500

Avenue House School
70 The Avenue, Ealing, London W13 8LS
Tel: 020 8998 9981
Headteacher: Mr Sheppard
Age range: 3–11
No. of pupils: 135
Fees: Day £5,070–£8,670

Bales College
742 Harrow Road, Kensal Town, London W10 4AA
Tel: 020 8960 5899
Principal: William Moore
Age range: 11–19
No. of pupils: 90
Fees: Day £7,950–£8,550 FB £16,050

Barbara Speake Stage School
East Acton Lane, East Acton, London W3 7EG
Tel: 020 8743 1306
Principal: Miss B M Speake MBE, ARAD, MISTD, MIDTA
Age range: 3–16
Fees: Day £6,000–£6,300

BASSETT HOUSE SCHOOL
For further details see p. 42
60 Bassett Road, London W10 6JP
Tel: 020 8969 0313
Email: info@bassetths.org.uk
Website: www.bassetths.org.uk
Headmistress: Mrs Philippa Cawthorne MA (Soton) PGCE
Age range: 3–11
No. of pupils: 190
Fees: Day £7,890–£16,440

Blake College
162 New Cavendish Street, London W1W 6YS
Tel: 020 7636 0658
Course Director: D A J Cluckie BA, BSc
Fees: Day £4,720–£5,310

BPP Professional Education
142-144 Uxbridge Road,
London W12 8AA
Tel: +44 (0)2087 402222
Head: Martin Taylor
Fees: Day £0

Bright Futures
63-65 Portland Place,
Westminster, London W1B 1QR
Tel: 020 7580 8096
Principal: Dawn Savage

**Bright Sparks
Montessori School**
25 Minford Gardens,
London W14 0AP
Tel: 020 7371 4697
Headmistress: Matilda D'Angelo
Age range: 2–5
No. of pupils: 16

Busy Bee Nursery School
Addison Boys Club, Redan
Street, London W14 0AB
Tel: 020 7602 8905

**Bute House Preparatory
School for Girls**
Bute House, Luxemburg
Gardens, London W6 7EA
Tel: 020 7603 7381
Head: Mrs Helen Lowe
Age range: G4–11
No. of pupils: 306
Fees: Day £13,317

Buttercups Day Nursery
38 Grange Road, Chiswick,
London W4 4DD
Tel: 020 8995 6750

Buttercups Day Nursery
9 Florence Road, Ealing,
London W5 3TU
Tel: 020 8840 4838

Buttercups Day Nursery
St Lukes, Drayton Grove,
Ealing, London W13 0LA
Tel: 020 8997 8965

Buttercups Nursery School
Ealing Dance Centre, 96 Pitshanger
Lane, Ealing, London W5 1QX
Tel: 020 8998 2774
Principal: Mrs C Whitehouse

**Buttons Day
Nursery School**
99 Oaklands Road, London W7 2DT
Tel: 020 8840 3355
Head: Julie Parhar BSc, NVQ3
Age range: 3 months–5
No. of pupils: 62

Campbell Harris Tutors
185 Kensington High Street,
London W8 6SH
Tel: 020 7937 0032
Principals: Mr Mark Harris
& Ms Claire Campbell
Age range: 13+
Fees: Day £4,000–£9,000

**Caterpillar Montessori
Nursery School**
St Albans Church Hall, South
Parade, Chiswick, London W4 3HY
Tel: 020 8747 8531
Head: Mrs Alison Scott
Age range: 2–5
Fees: Day £2,700

Chepstow House School
19 Pembridge Villas,
London W11 3EP
Tel: 0207 243 0243
Headteacher: Angela Barr
Age range: 4–7

**Chiswick & Bedford
Park Prep School**
Priory House, Priory Avenue,
London W4 1TX
Tel: 020 8994 1804
Headmistress: Mrs C A Sunderland
Age range: B4–7+ G4–11
No. of pupils: 180
Fees: Day £8,850

Christie's Education
153 Great Titchfield Street,
London W1W 5BD
Tel: 020 7665 4350
Academic Director: Jon Waldon

**City of Westminster
College**
25 Paddington Green,
London W2 1NB
Tel: 020 7723 8826
Principal: Mr Robin Shreeve

**City of Westminster
College**
Queens Park Centre (Technical
Institute), Saltram Crescent,
London W10 3HW
Tel: 020 7258 2812
Principal: Mr Robin Shreeve

Clifton Lodge
8 Mattock Lane, Ealing,
London W5 5BG
Tel: 020 8579 3662
Head: Mr. Floyd Steadman
Age range: 3–13
No. of pupils: 146
Fees: Day £11,340–£12,405

**College of Naturopathic
& Complementary
Medicine Ltd**
41 Riding House Street,
London W1W 7BE
Tel: 01342 410 505
Head: Hermann Keppler

Connaught House School
47 Connaught Square,
London W2 2HL
Tel: 020 7262 8830
Principals: Mrs J A Hampton
& Mr F Hampton MA, RCA
Age range: B4–8 G4–11
No. of pupils: 75
Fees: Day £13,200–£14,700

David Game College
David Game House, 69 Notting
Hill Gate, London W11 3JS
Tel: 020 7221 6665
Principal: D T P Game MA, MPhil
Age range: 14–19
No. of pupils: 200 VIth150
Fees: Day £12,000–£13,000

Devonshire Day Nursery
The Vicarage, Dennet Street,
Chiswick, London W4 2AH
Tel: 020 8995 9538
Manager: Dawn Freeman
Age range: 6 weeks–5
No. of pupils: 70

DLD COLLEGE
For further details see p. 48
199 Westminster Bridge
Road, London SE1 7FX
Tel: 020 7935 8411
Email: dld@dld.org
Website: www.dldcollege.co.uk
Principal: Ms. Rachel
Borland MA
No. of pupils: 485
Fees: Day £17,800–£19,900
FB £15,000–£21,000

Durston House
12-14 Castlebar Road,
Ealing, London W5 2DR
Tel: 020 8991 6530
Headmaster: Mr Ian
Kendrick MA, BEd(Hons)
Age range: B4–13
No. of pupils: 415
Fees: Day £9,810–£12,570

**Ealing Independent
College**
83 New Broadway, Ealing,
London W5 5AL
Tel: 020 8579 6668
Principal: Dr Ian Moores
Age range: 13–22
No. of pupils: 100 VIth70
Fees: Day £3,865–£12,600

Ealing Montessori School
St Martin's Church Hall, Hale
Gardens, London W3 9SQ
Tel: 020 8992 4513
Head: Mrs Soin
No. of pupils: 36

**Ecole Francaise
Jacques Prevert**
59 Brook Green, London W6 7BE
Tel: 020 7602 6871
Principal: P Possenti
Age range: 4–11

**Elmwood Montessori
School**
St Michaels Centre, Elmwood
Road, London W4 3DY
Tel: 020 8994 8177/995 2621
Headmistress: Mrs S Herbert BA
Age range: 2–5
Fees: Day £3,480–£4,440

Fulham Prep School
200 Greyhound Road,
London W14 9SD
Tel: 020 7386 2448
Principal: Mrs J Emmett
Age range: 4–13
No. of pupils: 596
Fees: Day £14,400–£15,975

**Great Beginnings
Montessori School**
The Welsh Church Hall, 82a
Chiltern Street, Marylebone,
London W1H 5JE
Tel: 020 7486 2276
Age range: 2–6
Fees: Day £1,095–£1,650

**Greek Primary
School of London**
3 Pierrepoint Road, Acton,
London W3 9JR
Tel: 020 8992 6156
Age range: 1–11

**Halcyon London
International School**
33 Seymour Place, London W1H 5AU
Tel: 020 7258 1169
Principal: Duncan Partridge

**Hammersmith
Management College**
80-90 King Street, Hammersmith,
London W6 0QW
Tel: 020 8748 7481
Head: Mr J Nizami

Happy Child Day Nursery
St Gabriel's Church, Noel Road,
Acton, London W3 0JE
Tel: 020 8992 0855
Age range: 6 months–5

Happy Child Day Nursery
2A The Grove, Ealing,
London W5 5LH
Tel: 020 8566 1546
Age range: 1–5

Happy Child Day Nursery
Woodgrange Avenue, Ealing
Common, London W5 3NY
Tel: 020 8992 0209
Age range: 3 months–5

Happy Child Day Nursery
283-287 Windmill Road,
Ealing, London W5 4DP
Tel: 020 8567 2244
Age range: 3 months–5

Happy Child Day Nursery
Green Man Passage,
Ealing, London W13 0TG
Tel: 020 8566 5515
Age range: 3 months–5

**Happy Child
Training Centre**
109 Uxbridge Road, Ealing,
London W5 5TL
Tel: 020 8579 3955
16

Harvington School
20 Castlebar Road, Ealing,
London W5 2DS
Tel: 020 8997 1583
Headmistress: Mrs Anna Evans
Age range: B3–4 G3–16
No. of pupils: 210
Fees: Day £7,560–£9,840

**HAWKESDOWN HOUSE
SCHOOL KENSINGTON**
For further details see p. 56
27 Edge Street, Kensington,
London W8 7PN
Tel: 020 7727 9090
Email: admin@
hawkesdown.co.uk
Website:
www.hawkesdown.co.uk
Head: Mrs C Bourne
MA(Cantab)
Age range: B3–8
No. of pupils: 141
Fees: Day £14,550–£16,725

Heathfield House School
Turnham Green Church
Hall, Heathfield Gardens,
Chiswick, London W4 4JU
Tel: 020 8994 3385
Headteacher: Mrs Goodsman
Age range: 4–11
Fees: Day £6,300–£6,900

**Holland Park
Nursery School**
St Johns Church, Lansdowne
Crescent, London W11 2NN
Tel: 020 7221 2194
Age range: 3–5
Fees: Day £3,900

**Holland Park Pre Prep
School and Day Nursery**
5 & 9 Holland Road, Kensington,
London W14 8HJ
Tel: 020 7602 9066/020
7602 9266
Principal: Mrs Kitty Mason
Age range: 3 months–8 years
No. of pupils: 128
Fees: Day £4,650–£10,935

**Hotel and Catering
Training Company**
2nd Floor, South Wing, 26-
28 Hammersmith Grove,
London W6 7HT
Tel: 020 8735 9700
16

House Schools Group
42 Hartington Road, London W4 3TX
Tel: 020 8580 9626

**Instituto Espanol
Canada Blanch**
317a Portobello Road,
Kensington, London W10 5SZ
Tel: +44 (0) 20 8969 2664
Principal: Mr A Vitria
Age range: 4–19
No. of pupils: 405

**International School of
London (ISL) London**
139 Gunnersbury Avenue,
Ealing, London W3 8LG
Tel: +44 (0)20 8992 5823
**Middle & Lower School
Principal:** Andrew Mitchell
Age range: 3–18 years
No. of pupils: 480
Fees: Day £18,000–£24,600

James Lee Nursery School
Gliddon Road, London W14 9BH
Tel: 020 8741 8877

**Jigsaw Nursery &
Montessori School**
1 Courtfield Gardens,
London W13 0EY
Tel: 020 8997 8330

**Jumbo Montessori
Nursery School**
22 George Street, London W1H 3QY
Tel: 020 7935 2441
Age range: 2–5
No. of pupils: 35
Fees: Day £1,785

**Kidsunlimited Nurseries
– Ladbroke Grove**
34 Ladbroke Grove,
London W11 3BQ
Tel: 0845 850 0222

King Fahad Academy
Bromyard Avenue, Acton,
London W3 7HD
Tel: 020 8743 0131
**Acting Head of Primary
School:** Ms Julie Benafif
Age range: 3–18
No. of pupils: 446
Fees: Day £3,000

L'Ecole Bilingue
St David's Welsh Church, St
Mary's Terrace, London W2 1SJ
Tel: 020 7224 8427
Headteacher: Ms
Veronique Ferreira
Age range: 3–11
No. of pupils: 68
Fees: Day £6,000–£6,600

La Petite Ecole Francais
73 Saint Charles Square,
London W10 6EJ
Tel: +44 208 960 1278
Principal: Ms A Stones
Age range: 2–6

**Ladbroke Square
Montessori School**
43 Ladbroke Square,
London W11 3ND
Tel: 020 7229 0125
Principal: Mrs Sophia
Russell-Cobb MontDip
Age range: 3–5
Fees: Day £850–£1,350

Lansdowne College
40-44 Bark Place, London W2 4AT
Tel: 020 7616 4400
Principal: Mr Mark Love
Age range: 14–19
No. of pupils: 200
Fees: Day £3,530–£18,690
FB £17,130–£36,990
16 A £ £

Latymer Prep School
36 Upper Mall, Hammersmith,
London W6 9TA
Tel: 0845 638 5700
Principal: Mr Stuart Dorrian
BA(Hons), PGCE
Age range: 7–11
No. of pupils: 159
Fees: Day £14,490

Latymer Upper School
King Street, Hammersmith,
London W6 9LR
Tel: 0845 638 5800
Head: Mr D Goodhew MA(Oxon)
Age range: 11–18
No. of pupils: 1123 VIth354
Fees: Day £16,485
A £ 16

Le Herisson
River Court Methodist
Church, Rover Court Road,
Hammersmith, London W6 9JT
Tel: 020 8563 7664
Head Teacher: C Behroozi
Age range: 2–6
Fees: Day £8,730–£8,970

**Leapfrog Day
Nurseries – Chiswick**
4 Marlborough Road,
Chiswick, London W4 4ET
Tel: 020 8742 0011
Manager: Zahira Ghaswala
Age range: 0–5

**Leapfrog Day Nurseries
– Hammersmith,
Bute Gardens**
Bute Hall, 3a Bute Gardens,
Hammersmith, London W6 7DR
Tel: 020 8741 9445
Manager: Nadine Primus
Age range: 0–5

**Leapfrog Day Nurseries
– Hammersmith,
Centre West**
Broadway Shopping Centre,
Hammersmith Broadway,
London W6 9YD
Tel: 020 8563 7982
Deputy Manager:
Suzanne Jn-Pierre
Age range: 0–5

**Leiths School of
Food & Wine**
16-20 Wendell Road, Shepherd's
Bush, London W12 9RT
Tel: 020 8749 6400
Managing Director:
Camilla Schneideman
Age range: 17–99
No. of pupils: 96
16

**Little Cherubs
Nursery School**
Our Lady of Victories Church
Hall, 16 Abingdon Road,
Kensington, London W8 6AF
Tel: 020 7376 4460/07810
712241
Principal: Mrs M Colvin MontDip
Age range: 2–5
No. of pupils: 42
Fees: Day £5,970–£10,170

**Little People of
Shepherds Bush**
61 Hadyn Park Road, Shepherds
Bush, London W12 9AQ
Tel: 020 8749 5080
Owner: Miss Jane Gleasure
Age range: 4 months–5

Little People of Willow Vale
9 Willow Vale, London W12 0PA
Tel: 020 8749 2877
Head: Miss Jane Gleasure
Age range: 4 months–5

**Little Sweethearts
Montessori**
St Saviours Church Hall, Warwick
Avenue, London W9 2PT
Tel: 020 7266 1616

**London Academy of
Music & Dramatic Art**
155 Talgarth Road,
London W14 9DA
Tel: 020 8834 0500
Head of Examinations:
Dawn Postans
Age range: 17+
16 £

London College
1st Floor, 23-25 Eastcastle
Street, London W1W 8DF
Tel: 020 7580 7552
Head: Mr David Kohn
16

**London College of
Professional Training Ltd**
The Opportunities Centre, 370-376
Uxbridge Road, London W12 7LL
Tel: 020 8746 2120
Head: Mrs Margaret Arokiasamy
16

London Hotel School
Springvale Terrace, West
Kensington, London W14 0AE
Tel: 020 7665 0000
Head: Mr Rod Hardingham
16+

**London International
College**
147 Oxford Street, London W1D 2JE
Tel: 020 7734 6420
Principal: Mr T Ktorides
16+

**London School of
Management Ltd**
43-47 New Broadway,
Ealing, London W5 5AH
Tel: 020 8567 4355
Head: Mr R S Rupal
16+

London Skills Academy
123 Godolphin Road,
London W12 8JN
Tel: 020 8749 6711
Head: Dr Tunde Idowu
16+

**Maria Montessori
Children's House
– Notting Hill**
28 Powis Gardens, London W11 1JG
Tel: 020 7221 4141
Head: Mrs L Lawrence
Age range: 2–6
No. of pupils: 20
Fees: Day £4,500

**Maria Montessori
Nursery School**
Church of the Ascension
Hall, Beaufort Road,
Ealing, London W5 3EB
Tel: 07717 050761

**Maria Montessori
School – Bayswater**
St Matthew's Church, St
Petersburgh Place, London W2 4LA
Tel: +44 (0)20 7435 3646

**Montessori Centre
International**
18 Balderton Street,
London W1K 6TG
Tel: 020 7493 0165
Director: Ms Barbara Isaacs
Age range: 17–60
16+

**Montessori
Neighbourhood
Nursery School**
St Andrew's Church, Star
Road, London W14 9QE
Tel: 020 7386 5818
Head: Anita Grebot
Age range: 18 mths–5 yrs

Norland Place School
162-166 Holland Park Avenue,
London W11 4UH
Tel: 020 7603 9103
Headmaster: Mr Patrick Mattar MA
Age range: B4–8 years G4–11 years
Fees: Day £13,590–£16,389

**Notting Hill & Ealing
High School GDST**
2 Cleveland Road, West
Ealing, London W13 8AX
Tel: 020 8991 2165
Headmistress: Ms Lucinda Hunt
Age range: G4–18
No. of pupils: 903 VIth150
Fees: Day £12,849–£16,521

**Notting Hill
Preparatory School**
95 Lancaster Road,
London W11 1QQ
Tel: 020 7221 0727
Headmistress: Mrs Jane Cameron
Age range: 4–13
No. of pupils: 285
Fees: Day £4,890

**One World Montessori
Nursery & Pre-Prep**
69-71 Brock Green, Hammersmith,
London W6 7BE
Tel: 020 7603 6065
Headteacher: Ms N Greer
Age range: 2–8
No. of pupils: 21

**One World Preparatory
School**
10 Stanley Gardens,
Acton, London W3 7SZ
Tel: 020 87433300
Head: Ms Lisa Manser
Age range: 3–11
No. of pupils: 52
Fees: Day £3,000

**ORCHARD HOUSE
SCHOOL**
For further details see p. 64
16 Newton Grove, Bedford
Park, London W4 1LB
Tel: 020 8742 8544 Registrar:
020 8987 9886
Email: registrar@
orchardhs.org.uk
Website: www.orchardhs.org.uk
Headmistress: Mrs M V Edwards
BEd (Bedford), CertEd (Man)
Age range: 3–11
No. of pupils: 290
Fees: Day £7,890–£16,440

**Oxford House
College – London**
30 Oxford Street, London W1W 8AW
Tel: 020 7580 9785
Principal: Ms Muberra Orme
16+

**Paint Pots Montessori
School – Bayswater**
Bayswater United Reformed
Church, Newton Road,
London W2 5LS
Tel: 020 7792 0433
Principal: Miss G Hood MontDip
Age range: 2–5
Fees: Day £1,284–£3,981

Pembridge Hall
18 Pembridge Square,
London W2 4EH
Tel: 020 7229 0121
Headteacher: Mr Henry
Keighley-Elstub
Age range: G4–11
No. of pupils: 413

Playhouse Day Nursery
Leighton Hall, Elthorne Park
Road, London W7 2JD
Tel: 020 8840 2851
Age range: 2–5

Portland Place School
56-58 Portland Place,
London W1N 1NJ
Tel: 0207 307 8700
Head: Mr Tim Cook
Age range: 11–18
No. of pupils: 300 VIth50
Fees: Day £12,522–£16,425

Primary Steps Creche
Harbour Club, 1 Alfred
Road, London W2 5EU
Tel: 020 7266 9310
Manager: Nelufa
Akanjee CACHE Dip

Primary Steps Day Nursery
Homefield Recreation Ground,
Chiswick Lane, London W4 2QA
Tel: 020 8995 4648
Manager: Ms Maggie Wozniak

Queen's College
43-49 Harley Street,
London W1G 8BT
Tel: 020 7291 7000
Head: Dr F M R Ramsey
MA, DPhil(Oxon)
Age range: G11–18
No. of pupils: 360 VIth90

**Ravenscourt Park
Preparatory School**
16 Ravenscourt Avenue,
London W6 0SL
Tel: 020 8846 9153
Headmaster: Mr Carl Howes
Age range: 4–11
No. of pupils: 312
Fees: Day £15,606

**Ravenstone Pre-
Preparatory School**
The Long Garden, St
George's Fields, Albion
Street, London W2 2AX
Tel: 020 7262 1190
Head of School: Mrs Karen Dapson
Age range: 2–7
No. of pupils: 74
Fees: Day £11,280–£16,875

**Ray Cochrane
Beauty School**
118 Baker Street, London W1U 6TT
Tel: 020 7486 6291
Principal: Miss Baljeet Suri
CIDESCO, CIBTAC, FETC
Age range: 16–50
No. of pupils: 30
Fees: Day £2,195–£8,995

Richford Street Day Nursery
50 Richford Gate, 61-69 Richford
Street, London W6 7HZ
Tel: 020 8746 1015
Manager: Marlon Bones NVQ
Age range: 3 months–5 years
No. of pupils: 70

Rolfe's Nursery School
206-208 Kensington Park
Road, London W11 1NR
Tel: 020 7727 8300
Head: Mr Greg McDonald
Age range: 2–5
Fees: Day £4,950–£8,595

Sassoon Academy
56 Davies Mews, London W1K 5AA
Tel: 020 7399 6902
Education Manager:
Peter Crossfield
Age range: 16–45
Fees: Day £13,500

**Southbank International
School – Kensington**
36-38 Kensington Park
Road, London W11 3BU
Tel: 020 7243 3803
Principal: Siobhan McGrath
Age range: 3–11

**Southbank International
School – Westminster**
63-65 Portland Place,
London W1B 1QR
Tel: 020 7243 3803
Principal: Justine Oliver
Age range: 11–18/19

**Southbank International
School – Fitzrovia**
17 Conway Street, London W1T 6BN
Tel: +44 2076 312600

St Augustine's Priory
Hillcrest Road, Ealing,
London W5 2JL
Tel: 020 8997 2022
Headteacher: Mrs.
Sarah Raffray MA
Age range: G3–18
No. of pupils: 470
Fees: Day £3,180–£13,572

ST BENEDICT'S SCHOOL
For further details see p. 70
54 Eaton Rise, Ealing,
London W5 2ES
Tel: 020 8862 2254
Email: enquiries@
stbenedicts.org.uk
Website:
www.stbenedicts.org.uk
Headmaster: Mr C J
Cleugh BSc, MSc
Age range: 3–18
No. of pupils: 1106 VIth212
Fees: Day £11,520–£14,550
(A) (£) ⬡ (16)

St James Junior School
Earsby Street, London W14 8SH
Tel: 020 7348 1777
Headmistress: Mrs Catherine
Thomlinson BA(Hons)
Age range: B4–11 G4–10
Fees: Day £10,650
⬡ ⬡ (£)

St James Senior Girls' School
Earsby Street, London W14 8SH
Tel: 020 7348 1777
Headmistress: Mrs Sarah Labram BA
Age range: G10–18
No. of pupils: 325 VIth61
Fees: Day £17,310
⬡ (A) (£) ⬡ (16)

St Matthews Montessori School
North Common Road,
Ealing, London W5 2QA
Tel: 020 8579 2304
Principal: Mrs Y Abdulrahman

St Patrick's International College
24 Great Chapel Street,
London W1F 8FS
Tel: 020 7287 6664
Principal: Mr Girish Chandra
(16)

St Paul's Girls' School
Brook Green, London W6 7BS
Tel: 020 7603 2288
High Mistress: Ms Clarissa
Farr MA, PGCE
Age range: G11–18 years
No. of pupils: 740 VIth200
Fees: Day £20,874–£22,437
⬡ (A) (£) ⬡ (16)

St Peters Nursery School
59a Portobello Road,
London W11 3DB
Tel: 020 7243 2617
Headmistress: Beverley Gibbs

Sylvia Young Theatre School
1 Nutford Place, London W1M 5YZ
Tel: 020 7258 2330
Headteacher: Ms Frances
Chave BSc, PGCE, NPQH
Age range: 10–16
Fees: Day £7,135–£12,225 WB
£12,540 FB £16,125–£16,440
(16) ⬡

Tabernacle School
32 St Anns Villas, Holland
Park, London W11 4RS
Tel: 020 7602 6232
Headteacher: Mrs P Wilson
Age range: 3–16
Fees: Day £4,500

Teddies Nurseries Chiswick Park
Evershed Walk, London W4 5BW
Tel: 020 8995 4766
Age range: 3 months–5 years

The Ark Montessori Nursery
All Saints Church, Bollo Bridge
Road, Acton, London W3 8AX
Tel: 020 8993 3540

The Ark Montessori School
The Scout Hall, Rugby Road,
Chiswick, London W4 1AL
Tel: 020 8932 4766

The Falcons School for Boys
2 Burnaby Gardens,
Chiswick, London W4 3DT
Tel: 020 8747 8393
Headmaster: Mr Gordon Milne
Age range: B3–7
No. of pupils: 225
Fees: Day £3,875–£11,625
⬡ ⬡

The Falcons School for Girls
15 Gunnersbury Avenue,
Ealing, London W5 3XD
Tel: 020 8992 5189
Headteacher: Miss
Joan McGillewie
Age range: G4–11
No. of pupils: 102
Fees: Day £3,625
⬡ (£) ⬡

The Godolphin and Latymer School
Iffley Road, Hammersmith,
London W6 0PG
Tel: +44 (0)20 8741 1936
Head Mistress: Mrs R Mercer BA
Age range: G11–18
No. of pupils: 812
Fees: Day £19,224
⬡ ⬡ (A) (£) (IB) ⬡ (16)

The Japanese School
87 Creffield Road, Acton,
London W3 9PU
Tel: 020 8993 7145
Headteacher: Mrs Kiyoe Tsuruoka
Age range: 6–16
No. of pupils: 500

The Jordans Montessori Nursery School
Holy Innocents Church,
Paddenswick Road,
London W6 0UB
Tel: 0208 741 3230
Principal: Ms Sara Green
Age range: 2–5
Fees: Day £1,356–£3,270
⬡

THE LLOYD WILLIAMSON SCHOOL
For further details see p. 73
12 Telford Road, London W10 5SH
Tel: 020 8962 0345
Email: admin@lws.org.uk
Website: lloydwilliamson.co.uk
Co-Principals: Ms Lucy
Meyer & Mr Aaron Williams
Age range: 4 months–14 years
Fees: Day £13,050
⬡

The Meadows Montessori School
Dukes Meadows Community
Centre, Alexandra Gardens,
London W4 2TD
Tel: 020 8742 1327/8995 2621
Headmistress: Mrs S Herbert BA
Age range: 2–5
Fees: Day £3,030–£3,870
⬡

The Minors Nursery School
10 Pembridge Square,
London W2 4ED
Tel: 020 7727 7253
Headteacher: Ms Jane Ritchie
Age range: 2–5

The Sinclair Montessori Nursery School
The Garden Flat, 142 Sinclair
Road, London W14 0NL
Tel: 020 7602 3745
Headmistress: Miss C Burnaby-
Atkins MontDipEd, SENDip, NVQ
Age range: 2–5
No. of pupils: 24

The Square Montessori School
18 Holland Park Avenue,
London W11 3QU
Tel: 020 7221 6004
Principal: Mrs V Lawson-Tancred
No. of pupils: 20
Fees: Day £2,220

Thomas's Preparatory School – Kensington
17-19 Cottesmore Gardens,
London W8 5PR
Tel: 020 7361 6500
Headmistress: Miss Joanna Ebner
MA, BEd(Hons)(Cantab), NPQH
Age range: 4–11
Fees: Day £14,505–£15,795
(£) ⬡

West London College
Parliament House, 35 North Row,
Mayfair, London W1K 6DB
Tel: 020 7491 1841
Principal: Paul S Smith
BA(Hons), FRSA
Fees: Day £0
(16)

West London School of Management & Technology
99-103 St James Annexe,
The Broadway, West Ealing,
London W13 9BP
Tel: 020 8840 1177
Principal: Mr Syed Raza Gilani
(16)

Wetherby Pre-Preparatory School
11 Pembridge Square,
London W2 4ED
Tel: 020 7727 9581
Headmaster: Mr Mark Snell
Age range: B2 1/2–8
No. of pupils: 340
Fees: Day £19,620
⬡ ⬡

Wetherby Preparatory School
48 Bryanston Square,
London W1H 2EA
Tel: 020 7535 3520
Headteacher: Mr Nick Baker
Age range: B8–13
No. of pupils: 192
Fees: Day £4,665
⬡ ⬡

Windmill Montessori Nursery School
62 Shirland Road, London W9 2EH
Tel: 020 7289 3410
Principal: Miss M H Leoni
& Miss J Davidson
No. of pupils: 48
Fees: Day £3,600
⬡

World of Children
Log Cabin Childrens Centre, 259
Northfield Avenue, London W5 4UA
Tel: 020 8840 3400

Young Dancers Academy
25 Bulwer Street, London W12 8AR
Tel: 020 8743 3856
Head: Mrs K Williams
Age range: 11–16
Fees: Day £10,500–£11,100

Ysgol Gymraeg Llundain London Welsh School
Hanwell Community Centre,
Westcott Crescent, London W7 1PD
Tel: 020 8575 0237
Head Teacher: Mrs Julie Griffiths
Age range: 3–11
No. of pupils: 30
Fees: Day £1,950

Schools in Greater London

Essex D132
Hertfordshire D132
Kent D133
Middlesex D134
Surrey D135

KEY TO SYMBOLS

- 🚹 *Boys' school*
- 🚺 *Girls' school*
- 🌐 *International school*
- 16 *Tutorial or sixth form college*
- Ⓐ *A levels*
- 🛏 *Boarding accommodation*
- £ *Bursaries*
- IB *International Baccalaureate*
- ✎ *Learning support*
- 16+ *Entrance at 16+*
- 🎓 *Vocational qualifications*
- (IAPS) *Independent Association of Prep Schools*
- (HMC) *The Headmasters' & Headmistresses' Conference*
- (ISA) *Independent Schools Association*
- (GSA) *Girls' School Association*
- (BSA) *Boarding Schools' Association*
- Ⓢ *Society of Heads*

Unless otherwise indicated, all schools are coeducational day schools. Single-sex and boarding schools will be indicated by the relevant icon.

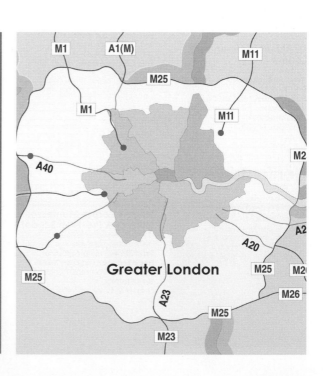

Essex

Avon House School
490-492 High Road, Woodford Green, Essex IG8 0PN
Tel: 020 8504 1749
Headteacher: Mrs A Campbell
Age range: 3–11
Fees: Day £8,355–£8,925

BANCROFT'S SCHOOL
For further details see p. 78
High Road, Woodford Green, Essex IG8 0RF
Tel: 020 8505 4821
Email: office@bancrofts.org
Website: www.bancrofts.org
Head: Mrs Mary Ireland BSc, DipEd, CBiol, MBS
Age range: 7–18
No. of pupils: 1123 VIth240
(A) (£) (✓) (16)

Beehive Preparatory School
233 Beehive Lane, Redbridge, Ilford, Essex IG4 5ED
Tel: 020 8550 3224
Headmaster: Mr C J Beasant BEd
Age range: 4–11
Fees: Day £4,900

Cranbrook College
Mansfield Road, Ilford, Essex IG1 3BD
Tel: 020 8554 1757
Executive Principal: Mr. David Morrison
Age range: B4–16
No. of pupils: 200
Fees: Day £6,405–£8,235
(👤) (£)

Eastcourt Independent School
1 Eastwood Road, Goodmayes, Ilford, Essex IG3 8UW
Tel: 020 8590 5472
Headmistress: Mrs Christine Redgrave BSc(Hons), DipEd, MEd
Age range: 3–11
Fees: Day £6,300

Gidea Park College
2 Balgores Lane, Gidea Park, Romford, Essex RM2 5JR
Tel: 01708 740381
Headmistress: Mrs Susan-Jayne Gooding BA
Age range: 3–11
No. of pupils: 177
Fees: Day £1,275–£2,500

Goodrington School
17 Walden Road, Hornchurch, Essex RM11 2JT
Tel: 01708 448349
Head Teacher: Mrs J R Ellenby
Age range: 3–11
Fees: Day £6,150

Ilford Grammar School
785 High Road, Seven Kings, Ilford, Essex IG3 8RW
Tel: 020 8599 8822
Headmistress: B P M Wiggs BSc(Hons), PGCE
Age range: 3–16
Fees: Day £5,250–£7,200

Ilford Ursuline R C Preparatory School
2 Coventry Road, Ilford, Essex IG1 4QR
Tel: 020 8518 4050
Headmistress: Mrs C Spinner
Age range: G3–11
No. of pupils: 159
(👤)

Immanuel School
Havering Grange Centre, Havering Road North, Romford, Essex RM1 4HR
Tel: 01708 764449
Principal: Miss Norcross
Age range: 3–16

Maytime Montessori Nursery – Cranbrook Road
341 Cranbrook Road, Ilford, Essex IG1 4UF
Tel: 020 8554 3079

Maytime Montessori Nursery – Eastwood Road
2 Eastwood Road, Goodmayes, Essex IG3 8XB
Tel: 020 8599 3744

Maytime Montessori Nursery – York Road
87 York Road, Ilford, Essex IG1 3AF
Tel: 020 8553 1524
Headteacher: Mrs M O'Mahoney
Age range: 0–6

Oakfields Montessori School
Harwood Hall, Harwood Hall Lane, Corbets Tey, Essex RM14 2YG
Tel: 01708 220117
Headmistress: Mrs K Malandreniotis
Age range: 2–11
Fees: Day £2,508–£4,260

Park School for Girls
20 Park Avenue, Ilford, Essex IG1 4RS
Tel: 020 8554 2466
Headmistress: Mrs N O'Brien BA
Age range: G7–18
No. of pupils: 230 VIth19
Fees: Day £4,755–£6,285
(👤) (A) (16)

Raphael Independent School
Park Lane, Hornchurch, Essex RM11 1XY
Tel: 01708 744735
Head of School: Mr Jack Luis
Age range: 4–16
No. of pupils: 135
Fees: Day £5,200–£7,800

St Aubyn's School
Bunces Lane, Woodford Green, Essex IG8 9DU
Tel: 020 8504 1577
Headmaster: Leonard Blom BEd(Hons) BA NPQH
Age range: 3–13
No. of pupils: 510
Fees: Day £4,610–£10,449
(£) (✓)

St Mary's Hare Park School & Nursery
South Drive, Gidea Park, Romford, Essex RM2 6HH
Tel: 01708 761220
Head Teacher: Mrs K Karwacinski
Age range: 2–11
No. of pupils: 180
Fees: Day £4,485

Stratford College of Management
1-7 Hainault Street, Ilford, Essex IG1 4EL
Tel: 020 8553 0205
Head: Dr Raza
(16)

WOODFORD GREEN PREPARATORY SCHOOL
For further details see p. 87
Glengall Road, Woodford Green, Essex IG8 0BZ
Tel: 020 8504 5045
Email: admin@wgprep.co.uk
Website: www.wgprep.co.uk
Headmaster: Mr J P Wadge
Age range: 3–11
No. of pupils: 375
Fees: Day £2,995
(£) (✓)

Hertfordshire

LYONSDOWN SCHOOL
For further details see p. 82
3 Richmond Road, New Barnet, Barnet, Hertfordshire EN5 1SA
Tel: 020 8449 0225
Email: enquiries@lyonsdownschool.co.uk
Website: www.lyonsdownschool.co.uk
Head: Mrs L Maggs-Wellings BEd
Age range: B3–7 G3–11
No. of pupils: 205
Fees: Day £3,612–£9,186

Norfolk Lodge Montessori Nursery & Pre-Prep School
Dancers Hill Road, Barnet, Hertfordshire EN5 4RP
Tel: 020 8447 1565
Head Teacher: Mrs Mary Wales
Age range: 6 months–7 years
No. of pupils: 140
Fees: Day £2,200–£2,400

St Martha's School
Camlet Way, Hadley Wood, Barnet, Hertfordshire EN4 0NJ
Tel: 020 8449 6889
Headmaster: Mr Matthew Burke
Age range: G11–18
No. of pupils: 220 VIth40
Fees: Day £4,625
(👤) (A) (£) (✓) (16)

Susi Earnshaw Theatre School
68 High Street, Barnet, Hertfordshire EN5 5SJ
Tel: 020 8441 5010
Headteacher: Mr David Earnshaw
Age range: 11–16
No. of pupils: 60
Fees: Day £10,500
(£)

**The Royal Masonic
School for Girls**
Rickmansworth Park,
Rickmansworth,
Hertfordshire WD3 4HF
Tel: 01923 773168
Headmistress: Mrs Diana
Rose MA(Cantab)
Age range: G4–18
No. of pupils: 917 VIth188
Fees: Day £9,000–£14,700 WB
£15,750–£23,760 FB £16,050–£25,050

Kent

Ashgrove School
116 Widmore Road,
Bromley, Kent BR1 3BE
Tel: 020 8460 4143
Principal: Patricia Ash CertEd,
BSc(Hons), PhD, CMath, FIMA
Age range: 4–11
Fees: Day £8,460

**BABINGTON HOUSE
SCHOOL**
For further details see p. 80
Grange Drive, Chislehurst,
Kent BR7 5ES
Tel: 020 8467 5537
Email: enquiries@
babingtonhouse.com
Website:
www.babingtonhouse.com
Headmaster: Mr Tim Lello
MA, FRSA, NPQH
Age range: B3–11 & 16–18 G3–18
No. of pupils: 354

Beckenham College
The Clockhouse Business Centre,
Unit 2, Thayers Farm Road,
Beckenham, Kent BR3 4LZ
Tel: 020 8650 3321
Principal: Mrs E Wakeling
Age range: 16+
Fees: Day £100–£3,500

**Benedict House
Preparatory School**
1-5 Victoria Road, Sidcup,
Kent DA15 7HD
Tel: 020 8300 7206
Headmistress: Mrs Gemma Chikola
Age range: 3–11
Fees: Day £2,145–£2,395

Bickley Park School
24 Page Heath Lane, Bickley,
Bromley, Kent BR1 2DS
Tel: 020 8467 2195
Headmaster: Mr Paul Ashley
Age range: B3–13 G3–4
No. of pupils: 370
Fees: Day £6,525–£11,925

Bird College
The Centre, 27 Station Road,
Sidcup, Kent DA15 7EB
Tel: 020 8300 6004/3031
Principal & Chief Executive: Ms
Shirley Coen BA(Hons), FSRA
Fees: Day £0

Bishop Challoner School
228 Bromley Road, Shortlands,
Bromley, Kent BR2 0BS
Tel: 020 8460 3546
Headteacher: Ms Paula Anderson
Age range: 3–18
No. of pupils: 412 VIth32
Fees: Day £6,441–£9,036

**Breaside Preparatory
School**
41-43 Orchard Road,
Bromley, Kent BR1 2PR
Tel: 020 8460 0916
Headmistress: Mrs Karen Nicholson
BEd, NPQH, Diploma in Early Years
Age range: 2–11
No. of pupils: 304
Fees: Day £9,450–£9,525

**BROMLEY HIGH
SCHOOL GDST**
For further details see p. 81
Blackbrook Lane, Bickley,
Bromley, Kent BR1 2TW
Tel: 020 8781 7000/1
Email: bhs@bro.gdst.net
Website:
www.bromleyhigh.gdst.net
Head: Mrs A M Drew
BA(Hons), MBA (Dunelm)
Age range: G4–18
No. of pupils: 912 VIth125
Fees: Day £12,423–£15,405

Darul Uloom London
Foxbury Avenue, Perry Street,
Chislehurst, Kent BR7 6SD
Tel: 020 8295 0637
Principal: Mufti Mustafa
Age range: B11–18
No. of pupils: 160
Fees: FB £2,400

Farringtons School
Perry Street, Chislehurst,
Kent BR7 6LR
Tel: 020 8467 0256
Head: Mrs Dorothy Nancekievill
Age range: 3–18
No. of pupils: 681 VIth94
Fees: Day £10,680–£13,560
WB £25,530 FB £27,120

**Merton Court
Preparatory School**
38 Knoll Road, Sidcup,
Kent DA14 4QU
Tel: 020 8300 2112
Headmaster: Mr Dominic
Price BEd, MBA
Age range: 3–11
Fees: Day £8,115–£8,910

**St Christopher's
The Hall School**
49 Bromley Road,
Beckenham, Kent BR3 5PA
Tel: 020 8650 2200
Headmaster: Mr A Velasco
MEd, BH(Hons), PGCE
Age range: 3–11
No. of pupils: 305
Fees: Day £2,250–£6,630

St David's College
Beckenham Road, West
Wickham, Kent BR4 0QS
Tel: 020 8777 5852
Principal: Mrs J Foulger
Age range: 4–11
No. of pupils: 155
Fees: Day £6,015–£6,165

West Lodge School
36 Station Road, Sidcup,
Kent DA15 7DU
Tel: 020 8300 2489
Head Teacher: Mrs Susan Webb
Age range: 3–11
No. of pupils: 163
Fees: Day £5,205–£8,700

Wickham Court School
Schiller International,
Layhams Road, West
Wickham, Kent BR4 9HW
Tel: 020 8777 2942
Head: Mrs Barbara Hunter
Age range: 2–16
No. of pupils: 121
Fees: Day £4,481–£6,900

Middlesex

360 GSP College
6th Floor, Wembley Point,
1 Harrow Road, Wembley,
Middlesex HA9 6DE
Tel: 020 8672 4151/0845
6034709
Head: Mr Yassin Sayfoo

Acorn House College
39-47 High Street, Southall,
Middlesex UB1 3HF
Tel: 020 8571 9900
Principal: Mr John Wilson
Age range: 13–19
No. of pupils: 121 VIth85
Fees: Day £5,200–£14,600

ACS Hillingdon
International School
Hillingdon Court, 108 Vine
Lane, Hillingdon, Uxbridge,
Middlesex UB10 0BE
Tel: +44 (0) 1895 259 771
Head of School: Linda LaPine
Age range: 4–18
No. of pupils: 520
Fees: Day £17,090–£22,550

Alpha Preparatory School
21 Hindes Road, Harrow,
Middlesex HA1 1SH
Tel: 020 8427 1471
Head: C.J.W Trinidad
BSc(Hons), PGCE
Age range: 3–11
No. of pupils: 170
Fees: Day £3,150–£9,900

Ashton House School
50-52 Eversley Crescent,
Isleworth, Middlesex TW7 4LW
Tel: 020 8560 3902
Headteacher: Mrs M
Grundberg MA, PGCE
Age range: 3–11
Fees: Day £9,300–£10,200

Athelstan House School
36 Percy Road, Hampton,
Middlesex TW12 2LA
Tel: 020 8979 1045
Headmistress: Elsa Woolf
Age range: 3–7

Buckingham College
Preparatory School
458 Rayners Lane, Pinner,
Middlesex HA5 5DT
Tel: 020 8866 2737
Headmaster: Mr L S Smith BA(Hons),
MSc, LCP, PGDE, CertEd
Age range: B4–11
Fees: Day £7,560–£9,900

Buxlow Preparatory School
5/6 Castleton Gardens,
Wembley, Middlesex HA9 7QJ
Tel: 020 8904 3615
Headmistress: Mrs Ann Baines
Age range: 4–11
Fees: Day £6,885

Denmead School
41-43 Wensleydale Road,
Hampton, Middlesex TW12 2LP
Tel: 020 8979 1844
Headmaster: Mr M T
McKaughan BEd
Age range: 3–11
Fees: Day £4,995–£11,580

Edgware Jewish Girls
– Beis Chinuch
Yeshurun Synagogue,
Fernhurst Gardens, Edgware,
Middlesex HA8 7PH
Tel: 020 8951 0239
Headteacher: Mr M Cohen
Age range: G3–7

Halliford School
Russell Road, Shepperton,
Middlesex TW17 9HX
Tel: 01932 223593
Headmaster: Mr Simon
G Wilson BSc LRAM
Age range: B11–18 G16–18
No. of pupils: 426
Fees: Day £13,800

Hampton School
Hanworth Road, Hampton,
Middlesex TW12 3HD
Tel: 020 8979 5526
Headmaster: Mr Kevin
Knibbs MA (Oxon)
Age range: B11–18
No. of pupils: 1130 VIth330
Fees: Day £12,870

Harrow School
5 High Street, Harrow on the
Hill, Middlesex HA1 3HT
Tel: 020 8872 8000
Head Master: Mr Jim Hawkins
Age range: B13–18
No. of pupils: 830 VIth320
Fees: FB £33,285

Harrow Secretarial
College & Computer
Training Centre
68 Station Road, Harrow,
Middlesex HA1 2SQ
Tel: 020 8424 9900
Fees: Day £0

Holland House School
1 Broadhurst Avenue, Edgware,
Middlesex HA8 8TP
Tel: 020 8958 6979
Headmistress: Mrs Irinia
Tyk BA(Hons)
Age range: 4–11
Fees: Day £7,308

International School
of Business Studies
204-226 Imperial Drive, Rayners
Lane, Harrow, Middlesex HA2 7HH
Tel: 020 8872 4103
Head: Mr Dawar Aziz

Jack and Jill School
30 Nightingale Road, Hampton,
Middlesex TW12 3HX
Tel: 020 8979 3195
Principal: Miss K Papirnik BEd(Hons)
Age range: B2–5 G2–7
No. of pupils: 155
Fees: Day £2,409–£9,597

Kew House School
Kew House, 6 Capital Interchange
Way, London, Middlesex TW8 0EX
Tel: 0208 742 2038
Headmaster: Mr Mark Hudson
Age range: 11–18
Fees: Day £18,924

Kids Inc Day
Nursery – Enfield
8 Glyn Road, Southbury,
Enfield, Middlesex EN3 4JL
Tel: 020 8805 1144

Lady Nafisa Independent
Secondary School for Girls
83A Sunbury Road, Feltham,
Middlesex TW13 4PH
Tel: 020 8751 5610
Headteacher: Ms Fouzia Butt
Age range: G11–16

Menorah Grammar School
Abbots Road, Edgware,
Middlesex HA8 0QS
Tel: 020 8906 9756
Headteacher: Rabbi A M Goldblatt
Age range: B11–17
No. of pupils: 203

Merchant Taylors' School
Sandy Lodge, Northwood,
Middlesex HA6 2HT
Tel: 01923 820644
Head: Mr S J Everson MA (Cantab)
Age range: B11–18
No. of pupils: 865 VIth282
Fees: Day £16,660

Newland House School
32-34 Waldegrave Park,
Twickenham, Middlesex TW1 4TQ
Tel: 020 8865 1234
Headmaster: Mr D A Alexander
Age range: B4–13 G4–11
Fees: Day £9,300–£10,440

North London
Collegiate School
Canons, Canons Drive,
Edgware, Middlesex HA8 7RJ
Tel: +44 (0)20 8952 0912
Headmistress: Mrs Bernice McCabe
Age range: G4–18
No. of pupils: 1080
Fees: Day £5,214–£6,169

Northwood College
for Girls GDST
Maxwell Road, Northwood,
Middlesex HA6 2YE
Tel: 01923 825446
Head Mistress: Miss Jacqualyn
Pain MA, MA, MBA
Age range: G3–18
No. of pupils: 750 VIth100
Fees: Day £8,400–£13,800

Oak Heights
3 Red Lion Court, Alexandra Road,
Hounslow, Middlesex TW3 1JS
Tel: 020 8577 1827
Head: Mr S Dhillon
Age range: 11–16
No. of pupils: 48
Fees: Day £6,000

Orley Farm School
South Hill Avenue, Harrow,
Middlesex HA1 3NU
Tel: 020 8869 7600
Headmaster: Tim Calvey
Age range: 4–13
No. of pupils: 496
Fees: Day £12,834–£14,811

Pinner Day Nursery
485 Rayners Lane, Pinner,
Middlesex HA5 5DT
Tel: 020 8868 1260
Manager: Toni Ward BTEC, GNVQ
Age range: 0–4
No. of pupils: 27

Quainton Hall
School & Nursery
91 Hindes Road, Harrow,
Middlesex HA1 1RX
Tel: 020 8861 8861
Headmaster: S Ford BEd
(Hons), UWE Bristol
Age range: B2–13 G2–11
Fees: Day £9,075–£9,975

Radnor House
Pope's Villa, Cross Deep,
Twickenham, Middlesex TW1 4QG
Tel: 020 8891 6264
Head of School: Mr.
David Paton MA
🌐

Rambert School of Ballet & Contemporary Dance
Clifton Lodge, St Margaret's Drive,
Twickenham, Middlesex TW1 1QN
Tel: 020 8892 9960
Principal: R McKim
Age range: 16+
16⁺

Reddiford School
36-38 Cecil Park, Pinner,
Middlesex HA5 5HH
Tel: 020 8866 0660
Headteacher: Mrs J
Batt CortEd, NPQH
Age range: 3–11
No. of pupils: 320
Fees: Day £3,480–£8,340
£

Regal International College
542B High Road, Wembley,
Middlesex HA0 2AA
Tel: 020 8795 5335
Head: Mr S Sivakumar
16⁺

Regent College
Sai House, 167 Imperial Drive,
Harrow, Middlesex HA2 7HD
Tel: 020 8966 9900
Principal: Mr Selva
Pankaj MBA, FCMA
Age range: 11–19
No. of pupils: 167
Fees: Day £2,745–£12,995
16⁺ A 16⁺

Roxeth Mead School
Buckholt House, 25 Middle Road,
Harrow, Middlesex HA2 0HW
Tel: 020 8422 2092
Headmistress: Mrs A Isaacs
Age range: 3–7
No. of pupils: 54
Fees: Day £9,450

St Catherine's School
Cross Deep, Twickenham,
Middlesex TW1 4QJ
Tel: 020 8891 2898
Headmistress: Sister Paula
Thomas BEd(Hons), MA
Age range: G3–18
No. of pupils: 430
Fees: Day £9,915–£13,680
👤 A £ 🖊 16⁺

St Christopher's School
71 Wembley Park Drive,
Wembley, Middlesex HA9 8HE
Tel: 020 8902 5069
Headteacher: Mrs Alison McNeill
Age range: 4–11
No. of pupils: 72
Fees: Day £2,435–£2,560

St Helen's College
Parkway, Hillingdon, Uxbridge,
Middlesex UB10 9JX
Tel: 01895 234371
Joint Headteachers: Mr D A
Crehan & Mrs G R Crehan
Age range: 3–11
No. of pupils: 351
Fees: Day £5,160–£9,090
🖊

ST HELEN'S SCHOOL
For further details see p. 84
Eastbury Road, Northwood,
Middlesex HA6 3AS
Tel: +44 (0)1923 843210
Email: admissions@
sthelens.london
Website: www.sthelens.london
Headmistress: Dr Mary
Short BA, PhD
Age range: G3–18
No. of pupils: 1145 VIth165
👤 🎓 A £ IB 16⁺

St John's School
Potter Street Hill, Northwood,
Middlesex HA6 3QY
Tel: 020 8866 0067
Headmaster: Mr M S Robinson BSc
Age range: B3–13 years
No. of pupils: 350
Fees: Day £9,000–£13,250
👤 👤 £

St John's Senior School
North Lodge, The Ridgeway,
Enfield, Middlesex EN2 8BE
Tel: 020 8366 0035
Headmaster: Mr Andrew Tardios
LLB(Hons), BA(Hons), CertEd
Age range: 11–18 years
No. of pupils: 262 VIth72
Fees: Day £12,060
A 16⁺

St Martin's School
40 Moor Park Road, Northwood,
Middlesex HA6 2DJ
Tel: 01923 825740
Headmaster: Mr D J
Tidmarsh BSc(Wales)
Age range: B3–13
No. of pupils: 400
Fees: Day £1,450–£4,066
👤 👤 £ 🖊

Staines Preparatory School
3 Gresham Road, Staines upon
Thames, Middlesex TW18 2BT
Tel: 01784 450909
Head of School: Samantha
Sawyer BEd (Hons)
Age range: 3–11
No. of pupils: 396
Fees: Day £9,150–£10,500
£ 🖊

Tashbar of Edgeware
47-49 Mowbray Road, Edgware,
Middlesex HA8 8JL
Tel: 020 8958 5162
Headteacher: Mr N Jaffe
Age range: B3–11
No. of pupils: 88
👤

The Falcons Preparatory School for Boys
41 Few Foot Road, Richmond,
Middlesex TW9 2SS
Tel: 0844 225 2211
Headmaster: Mr Gordon Milne
Age range: B7–13
No. of pupils: 100
Fees: Day £12,660
👤 🖊

The Hall Pre-Preparatory School & Nursery
The Grange Country House,
Rickmansworth Road,
Northwood, Middlesex HA6 2RB
Tel: 01923 822807
Headmistress: Mrs S M Goodwin
Age range: 1–7
Fees: Day £3,120–£10,350
🖊

The John Lyon School
Middle Road, Harrow on the
Hill, Middlesex HA2 0HN
Tel: 020 8515 9400
Head: Miss Katherine
Haynes BA, NPQH
Age range: B11–18
No. of pupils: 579
👤 A £ 🖊 16⁺

The Lady Eleanor Holles School
Hanworth Road, Hampton,
Middlesex TW12 3HF
Tel: 020 8979 1601
Head Mistress: Mrs
Heather Hanbury
Age range: G7–18
No. of pupils: 875 VIth170
Fees: Day £13,050–£16,200
👤 A £ 🖊 16⁺

The Mall School
185 Hampton Road, Twickenham,
Middlesex TW2 5NQ
Tel: 020 8614 1082
Headmaster: Mr D C Price BSc, MA
Age range: B4–13
No. of pupils: 320
Fees: Day £10,281–£11,934
👤 £ 🖊

The Noam Primary School
8-10 Forty Avenue, Wembley,
Middlesex HA9 8JW
Tel: 020 8908 9491
Headteacher: Mrs Sarah Simmonds
Age range: 3–11
No. of pupils: 154

The St Michael Steiner School
Park Road, Hanworth Park,
London, Middlesex TW13 6PN
Tel: 0208 893 1299
Age range: 3–16 (17 from Jul 2014)
No. of pupils: 101
Fees: Day £5,800–£8,900
£ 🖊

Twickenham Preparatory School
Beveree, 43 High Street,
Hampton, Middlesex TW12 2SA
Tel: 020 8979 6216
Head: Mr D Malam BA(Hons)
(Southampton), PGCE(Winchester)
Age range: B4–13 G4–11
No. of pupils: 272
Fees: Day £9,345–£10,110
£ 🖊

Surrey

Al-Khair School
109-117 Cherry Orchard Road,
Croydon, Surrey CR0 6BE
Tel: 020 8662 8664
Headteacher: Mr Usman Qureshi
Age range: 5–16
No. of pupils: 126

Broomfield House School
Broomfield Road, Kew Gardens,
Richmond, Surrey TW9 3HS
Tel: 020 8940 3884
Headteacher: Mr N O York
BA(Hons), MA, MPhil, FRSA
Age range: 3–11
No. of pupils: 160
Fees: Day £5,054–£11,787
🖊

Cambridge Tutors College
Water Tower Hill, Croydon,
Surrey CR0 5SX
Tel: 020 8688 5284/7363
Principal: Mr M Eagers
Age range: 15–19
No. of pupils: 215 VIth200
Fees: Day £19,800
16⁺ A 🏠 £ 16⁺

Canbury School
Kingston Hill, Kingston upon
Thames, Surrey KT2 7LN
Tel: 020 8549 8622
Headmistress: Ms Louise Clancy
Age range: 11–16
No. of pupils: 65
Fees: Day £14,490
£ 🖊

Collingwood School
3 Springfield Road, Wallington,
Surrey SM6 0BD
Tel: 020 8647 4607
Headmaster: Mr Chris Fenwick
Age range: 3–11
No. of pupils: 120
Fees: Day £3,600–£6,750

Croydon High School GDST
Old Farleigh Road, Selsdon,
South Croydon, Surrey CR2 8YB
Tel: 020 8260 7500
Head of Junior School:
Mrs Sophie Bradshaw
Age range: G3–18
No. of pupils: 600 VIth110

Cumnor House School
168 Pampisford Road, South
Croydon, Surrey CR2 6DA
Tel: 020 8660 3445
Head Master: Mr P J Clare-
Hunt MA(Ed) Cert Ed
Age range: B2–13
No. of pupils: 440
Fees: Day £2,945–£3,735

**Cumnor House
School for Girls**
1 Woodcote Lane, Purley,
Surrey CR8 3HB
Tel: 020 8660 3445
Headmaster: Mr Peter Kelly
Age range: G2–11
No. of pupils: 180
Fees: Day £2,945–£3,735

Educare Small School
12 Cowleaze Road, Kingston
upon Thames, Surrey KT2 6DZ
Tel: 020 8547 0144
Head Teacher: Mrs E Steinthal
Age range: 3–11
No. of pupils: 46
Fees: Day £4,800

Elmhurst School
44-48 South Park Hill Rd, South
Croydon, Surrey CR2 7DW
Tel: 020 8688 0661
Headmaster: Mr M J Apsley
BA(Hons), PGCE
Age range: B4–11
No. of pupils: 207
Fees: Day £6,300–£7,545

Folly's End Christian School
Folly's End Church, 5-9 Surrey
Street, Croydon, Surrey CR0 1RG
Tel: 020 8649 9121
Senior Leaders: Dave & Ze Markee
Age range: 3–11
Fees: Day £4,740

**Holy Cross Preparatory
School**
George Road, Kingston upon
Thames, Surrey KT2 7NU
Tel: 020 8942 0729
Headteacher: Mrs S Hair BEd(Hons)
Age range: G4–11
No. of pupils: 250
Fees: Day £9,960

**Homefield Preparatory
School**
Western Road, Sutton,
Surrey SM1 2TE
Tel: 020 8642 0965
Acting Headteacher:
Ms Sabine White
Age range: B3–13
No. of pupils: 400
Fees: Day £4,800–£11,130

Kew College
24-26 Cumberland Road,
Kew, Surrey TW9 3HQ
Tel: 020 8940 2039
Headteacher: Mrs Marianne Austin
BSc(Hons) MA(Hons) ACA PGCE
Age range: 3–11
No. of pupils: 296
Fees: Day £5,850–£9,150

**Kew Green
Preparatory School**
Layton House, Ferry Lane, Kew
Green, Richmond, Surrey TW9 3AF
Tel: 020 8948 5999
Headmaster: Mr J Peck
Age range: 4–11
No. of pupils: 260
Fees: Day £15,606

King's House School
68 King's Road, Richmond,
Surrey TW10 6ES
Tel: 020 8940 1878
Head: Mr Mark Turner
BA, PGCE, NPQH
Age range: B3–13 G3–4
No. of pupils: 449
Fees: Day £6,300–£14,910

Kingston Grammar School
70 London Rd, Kingston upon
Thames, Surrey KT2 6PY
Tel: 020 8456 5875
Head Master: Mr Stephen Lehec
Age range: 11–18
No. of pupils: 820
Fees: Day £17,430

Laleham Lea School
29 Peaks Hill, Purley, Surrey CR8 3JJ
Tel: 020 8660 3351
Headteacher: Mrs J Staunton
Age range: 3–11
Fees: Day £2,128–£6,405

**MARYMOUNT
INTERNATIONAL
SCHOOL LONDON**
For further details see p. 83
George Road, Kingston upon
Thames, Surrey KT2 7PE
Tel: +44 (0)20 8949 0571
Email: admissions@
marymountlondon.com
Website:
www.marymountlondon.com
Headmistress: Ms Sarah
Gallagher MA, HDip in Ed
Age range: G11–18
No. of pupils: 252 VIth115
Fees: Day £19,260–£22,035
WB £33,020–£35,765 FB
£34,615–£37,360

**Oakwood Independent
School**
Godstone Road, Purley,
Surrey CR8 2AN
Tel: 020 8668 8080
Headmaster: Mr Ciro
Candia BA(Hons), PGCE
Age range: 3–11
No. of pupils: 176
Fees: Day £5,280–£7,644

**OLD PALACE OF JOHN
WHITGIFT SCHOOL**
For further details see p. 86
Old Palace Road, Croydon,
Surrey CR0 1AX
Tel: 020 8686 7347
Email: info@oldpalace.
croydon.sch.uk
Website:
www.oldpalace.croydon.sch.uk
Head: Mrs. C Jewell
Age range: B3 months–4
years G3 months–19 years
No. of pupils: 740 VIth120
Fees: Day £10,086–£13,497

Old Vicarage School
48 Richmond Hill, Richmond,
Surrey TW10 6QX
Tel: 020 8940 0922
Headmistress: Mrs G D Linthwaite
Age range: G4–11
No. of pupils: 200
Fees: Day £12,630

Park Hill School
8 Queens Road, Kingston upon
Thames, Surrey KT2 7SH
Tel: 020 8546 5496
Principal: Mrs Marie Christie
Age range: 2–7
No. of pupils: 100
Fees: Day £4,320–£8,130

**Purley Language
College Ltd**
34 Brighton Road, Purley,
Surrey CR8 3AD
Tel: 020 8660 5060
Fees: Day £0

Reedham Park School
71A Old Lodge Lane,
Purley, Surrey CR8 4DN
Tel: 020 8660 6357
Headteacher: Ms Louise Shaw
BA(Hons), DipEurHum
Age range: 4–11
No. of pupils: 122
Fees: Day £3,540–£4,110

**Richmond The
American International
University in London**
Queen's Road, Richmond,
Surrey TW10 6JP
Tel: 020 8332 8200
President & CEO: Dr Norman Smith
Fees: Day £0

Rokeby School
George Road, Kingston upon
Thames, Surrey KT2 7PB
Tel: 020 8942 2247
Head: Mr J R Peck
Age range: B4–13
No. of pupils: 370
Fees: Day £3,974–£4,948

Royal Botanic Gardens
School of Horticulture, Kew,
Richmond, Surrey TW9 3AB
Tel: 020 8332 5545
Principal: Emma Fox BEd(Hons),
DipHort(Kew)(Hons)
Fees: Day £0

Royal Russell Junior School
Coombe Lane, Croydon,
Surrey CR9 5BX
Tel: 020 8651 5884
Junior School Headmaster:
Mr James C Thompson
Age range: 3–11
No. of pupils: 300
Fees: Day £3,660–£10,155

Royal Russell School
Coombe Lane, Croydon,
Surrey CR9 5BX
Tel: 020 8657 3669
Headmaster: Christopher
Hutchinson
Age range: 11–18
No. of pupils: 590 VIth180
Fees: Day £15,285 FB
£22,365–£30,240

Seaton House School
67 Banstead Road South,
Sutton, Surrey SM2 5LH
Tel: 020 8642 2332
Headmistress: Mrs Debbie Morrison
Higher Diploma in Education (RSA)
Age range: B3–5 G3–11
No. of pupils: 164
Fees: Day £2,187–£8,955

Shrewsbury House School
107 Ditton Road, Surbiton,
Surrey KT6 6RL
Tel: 020 8399 3066
Headmaster: Mr K Doble
BA, PDM, PGCE
Age range: B7–13
No. of pupils: 320
Fees: Day £13,680

St David's School
23/25 Woodcote Valley Road,
Purley, Surrey CR8 3AL
Tel: 020 8660 0723
Headmistress: Mrs Lindsay
Nash BEd(Hons)
Age range: 3–11
No. of pupils: 167
Fees: Day £2,985–£5,940

St James Senior Boys School
Church Road, Ashford,
Surrey TW15 3DZ
Tel: 01784 266930
Headmaster: Mr David Brazier
Age range: B11–18
No. of pupils: B385 VIth65
Fees: Day £16,320

Surbiton High School
13-15 Surbiton Crescent, Kingston
upon Thames, Surrey KT1 2JT
Tel: 020 8546 5245
Principal: Ann Haydon BSc(Hons)
Age range: G4–18
No. of pupils: 1210 VIth186
Fees: Day £6,390–£10,857

The Cedars School
Coombe Road, Lloyd Park,
Croydon, Surrey CR0 5RD
Tel: 020 8185 7770
Headmaster: Robert
Teague Bsc (Hons)
Age range: B11–18

The Royal Ballet School
White Lodge, Richmond,
Surrey TW10 5HR
Tel: 020 7836 8899
Director: Ms Gailene Stock AM
Age range: 11–19
No. of pupils: VIth80
Fees: Day £14,394–£18,946
FB £17,709–£25,588

The Secretary College
123 South End, Croydon,
Surrey CR0 1BJ
Tel: 0208 688 4440
Principal: Mr J E K Safo

The Study School
57 Thetford Road, New
Malden, Surrey KT3 5DP
Tel: 020 8942 0754
Head of School: Ms Donna
Brackstone-Drake
Age range: 3–11
No. of pupils: 134
Fees: Day £3,984–£8,973

Treetops Nursery
91 Pampisford Road, South
Croydon, Surrey CR2 6DH
Tel: +44 (0)20 8660 3445
Manager: Mrs Charlotte
Figueira BEd(Hons)
Age range: 2–4
No. of pupils: 200
Fees: Day £1,370–£2,945

Trinity School
Shirley Park, Croydon,
Surrey CR9 7AT
Tel: 020 8656 9541
Headmaster: M J Bishop MA, MBA
Age range: B10–18 G16–18
No. of pupils: VIth220
Fees: Day £14,460

Unicorn School
238 Kew Road, Richmond,
Surrey TW9 3JX
Tel: 020 8948 3926
Headmaster: Mr Kit Thompson
Age range: 3–11
Fees: Day £6,000–£11,010

Westbury House
80 Westbury Road, New
Malden, Surrey KT3 5AS
Tel: 020 8942 5885
Head of School: Rosalyn Holiday
Age range: 3–11
Fees: Day £1,043–£2,507

Whitgift School
Haling Park, South Croydon,
Surrey CR2 6YT
Tel: +44 (0)20 8633 9935
Headmaster: Dr Christopher Barnett
Age range: B10–18
No. of pupils: 1464
Fees: Day £17,340 WB
£27,924 FB £33,396

Schools in the South-East

KEY TO SYMBOLS

- 👤 *Boys' school*
- 👤 *Girls' school*
- 🌐 *International school*
- 16· *Tutorial or sixth form college*
- Ⓐ *A levels*
- 🏛 *Boarding accommodation*
- £ *Bursaries*
- IB *International Baccalaureate*
- ✎ *Learning support*
- 16· *Entrance at 16+*
- 🎓 *Vocational qualifications*
- (IAPS) *Independent Association of Prep Schools*
- (HMC) *The Headmasters' & Headmistresses' Conference*
- (ISA) *Independent Schools Association*
- (GSA) *Girls' School Association*
- (BSA) *Boarding Schools' Association*
- Ⓢ *Society of Heads*

Unless otherwise indicated, all schools are coeducational day schools. Single-sex and boarding schools will be indicated by the relevant icon.

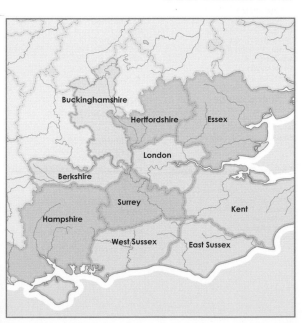

Berkshire

Alder Bridge School
Bridge House, Mill Lane, Padworth, Reading, Berkshire RG7 4JU
Tel: 0118 971 4471
Age range: 1–11
No. of pupils: 58
Fees: Day £3,420–£4,470

Bradfield College
Bradfield, Berkshire RG7 6AU
Tel: 0118 964 4516
Headmaster: Dr Christopher Stevens
Age range: 13–18
No. of pupils: 770 VIth310
Fees: Day £27,420 FB £34,275

Brigidine School Windsor
Queensmead, King\'s Road, Windsor, Berkshire SL4 2AX
Tel: 01753 863779
Headmistress: Mrs Elizabeth Robinson
Age range: B2–7 G3–18
No. of pupils: 300
Fees: Day £3,945–£11,865

Brockhurst & Marlston House Schools
Hermitage, Newbury, Berkshire RG18 9UL
Tel: 01635 200293
Joint Heads: Mr David Fleming & Mrs Caroline Riley
Age range: G3–13
No. of pupils: 275
Fees: Day £7,410–£12,450 WB £16,530 FB £16,530

Caversham School
16 Peppard Road, Caversham, Reading, Berkshire RG4 8JZ
Tel: 01189 478 684
Head: Mrs Jacqueline Lawson
Age range: 4–11
No. of pupils: 60
Fees: Day £6,750

Chiltern College
16 Peppard Road, Caversham, Reading, Berkshire RG4 8JZ
Tel: 0118 947 1847
Head: Christine Lawrence

Claires Court Junior Boys
Maidenhead Thicket, Maidenhead, Berkshire SL6 3QE
Tel: 01628 411490
Head: J M E Spanswick
Age range: B4–11
No. of pupils: 248
Fees: Day £7,965–£13,860

Claires Court Nursery, Girls and Sixth Form
1 College Avenue, Maidenhead, Berkshire SL6 6AW
Tel: 01628 411480
Head: Mr Paul Bevis
Age range: B16–18 G3–18
No. of pupils: 495 VIth111
Fees: Day £5,715–£14,580

Claires Court Senior Boys
Ray Mill Road East, Maidenhead, Berkshire SL6 8TE
Tel: 01628 411470
Headmaster: Mr J M Rayer BSc, PGCE
Age range: B11–16
No. of pupils: 335 VIth112
Fees: Day £13,860–£14,580

Crosfields School
Shinfield, Reading, Berkshire RG2 9BL
Tel: 0118 987 1810
Headmaster: Mr J P Wansey
Age range: 3–13
No. of pupils: 510
Fees: Day £6,600–£10,710

Dolphin School
Waltham Road, Hurst, Reading, Berkshire RG10 0FR
Tel: 0118 934 1277
Head: Mr Tom Lewis
Age range: 3–13
Fees: Day £8,340–£11,190

Eagle House School
Sandhurst, Berkshire GU47 8PH
Tel: 01344 772134
Headmaster: Mr A P N Barnard BA(Hons), PGCE
Age range: 3–13
No. of pupils: 395
Fees: Day £10,590–£16,575 FB £22,245

Elstree School
Woolhampton, Reading, Berkshire RG7 5TD
Tel: 0118 971 3302
Headmaster: Mr S Inglis
Age range: B3–13 G3–7
No. of pupils: 248
Fees: Day £17,775 FB £22,800

Eton College
Windsor, Berkshire SL4 6DW
Tel: 01753 671249
Head Master: Simon Henderson MA
Age range: B13–18
No. of pupils: 1300 VIth520
Fees: FB £33,270

Eton End PNEU School
35 Eton Road, Datchet, Slough, Berkshire SL3 9AX
Tel: 01753 541075
Headmistress: Mrs V M Pilgerstorfer BA(Hons), PGCE
Age range: B3–7 G3–11
No. of pupils: 245
Fees: Day £5,850–£6,900

Heathfield School
London Road, Ascot, Berkshire SL5 8BQ
Tel: 01344 898342
Head: Mrs Jo Heywood BSc(Hons), PGCE
Age range: G11–18
No. of pupils: 200 VIth80
Fees: Day £22,680–£23,310 FB £32,400–£33,300

Hemdean House School
Hemdean Road, Caversham, Reading, Berkshire RG4 7SD
Tel: 0118 947 2590
Headmistress: Mrs J Harris BSc
Age range: B3–11 G3–16
Fees: Day £5,280–£7,200

Herries Preparatory School
Dean Lane, Cookham Dean, Berkshire SL6 9BD
Tel: 01628 483350
Headmistress: Sophie Green
Age range: 3–11
Fees: Day £6,645–£8,985

Highfield Preparatory School
2 West Road, Maidenhead, Berkshire SL6 1PD
Tel: 01628 624918
Headteacher: Mrs J Leach
Age range: B3–5 G3–11
Fees: Day £897–£10,110

Holme Grange School
Heathlands Road, Wokingham, Berkshire RG40 3AL
Tel: 0118 978 1566
Headteacher: Mrs C Robinson
Age range: 3–16
No. of pupils: 357
Fees: Day £3,951–£13,170

Hurst Lodge
Bagshot Road, Ascot, Berkshire SL5 9JU
Tel: 01344 622154
Principal: Ms Victoria Smit
Age range: 3–18
No. of pupils: 202 VIth13
Fees: Day £6,420–£25,200 WB £19,905–£34,005

Impact International College
81 London Street, Reading, Berkshire RG1 4QA
Tel: 0118 956 0610
Head: Mr Alan Loveridge

Kids Inc Day Nursery – Crowthorne
59-61 Dukes Ride, Crowthorne, Berkshire RG45 6NS
Tel: 01344 780670

Lambrook School
Winkfield Row, Bracknell, Berkshire RG42 6LU
Tel: 01344 882717
Headmaster: Mr Jonathan Perry
Age range: 3–13
No. of pupils: 440
Fees: Day £9,078–£15,180 WB £16,803–£18,009 FB £17,433–£18,639

Leighton Park School
Shinfield Road, Reading, Berkshire RG2 7DE
Tel: 0118 987 9600
Head: Nigel Williams BA(Bristol), MA(London), PGCE
Age range: 11–18
No. of pupils: 474 VIth145
Fees: Day £16,524–£20,313 WB £22,524–£27,225 FB £25,614–£31,632

Long Close School
Upton Court Road, Upton, Slough, Berkshire SL3 7LU
Tel: 01753 520095
Head: Mr David Brazier
Age range: 2–16
No. of pupils: 283
Fees: Day £5,715–£10,080

Luckley House School
Luckley Road, Wokingham, Berkshire RG40 3EU
Tel: 0118 978 4175
Headmistress: Mrs Jane Tudor
Age range: G11–18
No. of pupils: 300 VIth50
Fees: Day £13,476 WB £21,858 FB £23,586

Ludgrove
Wokingham, Berkshire RG40 3AB
Tel: 0118 978 9881
Head of School: Mr Simon Barber
Age range: B8–13
No. of pupils: 190

LVS ASCOT (LICENSED VICTUALLERS' SCHOOL)
For further details see p. 93
London Road, Ascot,
Berkshire SL5 8DR
Tel: 01344 882770
Email: enquiries@lvs.
ascot.sch.uk
Website: www.lvs.ascot.sch.uk
Headmistress: Mrs Christine
Cunniffe BA (Hons), MMus, MBA
Age range: 4–18
No. of pupils: 870
Fees: Day £9,528–£17,079
FB £24,384–£30,006

Meadowbrook Montessori School
Malt Hill Road, Warfield,
Bracknell, Berkshire RG42 6JQ
Tel: 01344 890869
Director of Education: Mrs S Gunn
Age range: 3–11
No. of pupils: 78
Fees: Day £10,200

Newbold School
Popeswood Road, Binfield,
Bracknell, Berkshire RG42 4AH
Tel: 01344 421088
Headteacher: Mrs P Eastwood
Age range: 3–11
Fees: Day £3,000–£4,000

Our Lady's Preparatory School
The Avenue, Crowthorne,
Wokingham, Berkshire RG45 6PB
Tel: 01344 773394
Headmistress: Mrs Helene Robinson
Age range: 3 months–11 years
No. of pupils: 100
Fees: Day £5,328–£10,464

Padworth College
Padworth, Reading,
Berkshire RG7 4NR
Tel: 0118 983 2644
Principal: Mr John Aguilar
Age range: 13–19
No. of pupils: 116 VIth50
Fees: Day £14,250 FB £28,392

PANGBOURNE COLLEGE
For further details see p. 96
Pangbourne, Reading,
Berkshire RG8 8LA
Tel: 0118 984 2101
Email: registrar@
pangbourne.com
Website: www.pangbourne.com
Headmaster: Thomas
J C Garnier
Age range: 11–18
No. of pupils: 423 VIth148
Fees: Day £15,999–£22,548
FB £22,533–£31,890

Papplewick School
Windsor Road, Ascot,
Berkshire SL5 7LH
Tel: 01344 621488
Head: Mr T W Bunbury BA, PGCE
Age range: B6–13
No. of pupils: 195

Queen Anne's School
6 Henley Road, Caversham,
Reading, Berkshire RG4 6DX
Tel: 0118 918 7300
Headmistress: Mrs Julia Harrington
BA(Hons), PGCE, NPQH
Age range: G11–18
No. of pupils: 336 VIth100
Fees: Day £5,695 WB
£7,545–£7,975 FB £8,395

Queensland College London
Reading Campus, 80 London
Street, Reading, Berkshire RG1 4SJ
Tel: 0118 956 9111
Head: Alan McColm

Reading Blue Coat School
Holme Park, Sonning Lane, Sonning,
Reading, Berkshire RG4 6SU
Tel: 0118 944 1005
Headmaster: M J Windsor
Age range: B11–18 G16–18
No. of pupils: 710 VIth230
Fees: Day £13,470

Reddam House Bearwood
Bearwood Road, Wokingham,
Berkshire RG41 5BG
Tel: 0118 974 8300
Headmaster: Mr Donald Wilkinson
Age range: 0–18
No. of pupils: 487 VIth80
Fees: Day £13,890–£16,365
FB £24,360–£28,080

Redroofs School for the Performing Arts (Redroofs Theatre School)
26 Bath Road, Maidenhead,
Berkshire SL6 4JT
Tel: 01628 674092
Principal: June Rose
Age range: 8–18
No. of pupils: 100
Fees: Day £4,000

St Andrew's School
Buckhold, Pangbourne,
Reading, Berkshire RG8 8QA
Tel: 0118 974 4276
Headmaster: Dr D Livingstone
BSc, PhD, NPQH
Age range: 3–13
Fees: Day £4,050–£14,280
WB £16,950

St Bernard's Preparatory School
Hawtrey Close, Slough,
Berkshire SL1 1TB
Tel: 01753 521821
Head Teacher: Mrs M B
Smith CertEd, NPQH
Age range: 2–11

St Edward's School
64 Tilehurst Road, Reading,
Berkshire RG30 2JH
Tel: 0118 957 4342
Principal: G W Mottram
Age range: B4–13
No. of pupils: 170
Fees: Day £6,660–£8,550

St George's Ascot
Wells Lane, Ascot, Berkshire SL5 7DZ
Tel: 01344 629920
Headmistress: Mrs Rachel Owens
MA(Hons) (Oxon) PGCE NPQH
Age range: G11–18
No. of pupils: 280 VIth85
Fees: Day £20,250 WB
£29,325–£30,375 FB £31,125

St George's School Windsor Castle
Windsor, Berkshire SL4 1QF
Tel: 01753 865553
Head Master: Mr C F McDade
Age range: 3–13
Fees: Day £8,493–£14,097
WB £18,723 FB £19,203

St John's Beaumont Preparatory School
Priest Hill, Old Windsor,
Berkshire SL4 2JN
Tel: 01784 432428
Headmaster: Mr G E F
Delaney BA(Hons), PGCE
Age range: B3–13
No. of pupils: 310
Fees: Day £7,140–£13,320
WB £17,520 FB £20,250

St Joseph's College
Upper Redlands Road,
Reading, Berkshire RG1 5JT
Tel: 0118 966 1000
Head of College (Senior School): Mr Andrew Colpus
Age range: 3–18
No. of pupils: VIth46
Fees: Day £5,634–£9,630

St Mary's School Ascot
St Mary\'s Road, Ascot,
Berkshire SL5 9JF
Tel: 01344 296614
Headmistress: Mrs Mary
Breen BSc, MSc
Age range: G11–18
No. of pupils: 390 VIth120
Fees: Day £23,400 FB £32,850

St Piran's Preparatory School
Gringer Hill, Maidenhead,
Berkshire SL6 7LZ
Tel: 01628 594302
Headmaster: Mr J A Carroll
BA(Hons), BPhilEd, PGCE, NPQH
Age range: 3–11
Fees: Day £9,900–£14,550

Sunningdale School
Dry Arch Road, Sunningdale,
Berkshire SL5 9PY
Tel: 01344 620159
Headmaster: T A C N
Dawson MA, PGCE
Age range: B7–13
No. of pupils: 90
Fees: Day £13,950 FB £17,985

Telkyo School UK
Framewood Road, Wexham,
Slough, Berkshire SL2 4QS
Tel: 01753 663711
Headmaster: A Watanabe BA
Age range: 16–18

The Abbey School
Kendrick Road, Reading,
Berkshire RG1 5DZ
Tel: 0118 987 2256
Head: Mrs Rachel S E Dent
Age range: G3–18
No. of pupils: 1070
Fees: Day £15,090

The Marist Preparatory School
King\'s Road, Sunninghill,
Ascot, Berkshire SL5 7PS
Tel: 01344 626137
Headteacher: J Finlayson
Age range: G2–11
No. of pupils: 225
Fees: Day £8,700–£9,360

The Marist Schools
King\'s Road, Sunninghill,
Ascot, Berkshire SL5 7PS
Tel: 01344 624291
Head of Secondary School: Mr K McCloskey
Age range: G2–18
No. of pupils: 550 VIth60
Fees: Day £7,845–£10,695

The Oratory Preparatory School
Great Oaks, Goring Heath,
Reading, Berkshire RG8 7SF
Tel: 0118 984 4511
Headmaster: Mr J J Smith BA, PGCE
Age range: 3–13
No. of pupils: 400
Fees: Day £3,245–£11,475
WB £14,565 FB £15,825

The Oratory School
Woodcote, Reading,
Berkshire RG8 0PJ
Tel: 01491 683500
Head Master: Mr A J Wyles
BSc(Hons), MEd, PGCE, FRGS
Age range: B11–18
No. of pupils: 380 VIth120
Fees: Day £23,250 FB
£21,540–£31,950
🧍 🏃 Ⓐ 🏋 £ 16

The Vine Christian School
SORCF Christian Centre,
Basingstoke Road, Three Mile
Cross, Reading, Berkshire RG7 1AT
Tel: 0118 988 6464
Head: Mrs Joan Muirhead
Age range: 5–13
No. of pupils: 9

Upton House School
115 St Leonard's Road,
Windsor, Berkshire SL4 3DF
Tel: 01753 862610
Headmistress: Mrs Madeleine
Collins BA(Hons), PGCE(Oxford)
Age range: B2–7 G2–11
No. of pupils: 280
£ 🖊

Waverley School
Waverley Way, Finchampstead,
Wokingham, Berkshire RG40 4YD
Tel: 0118 973 1121
Principal: Mrs Jane Sculpher
Age range: 3–11
Fees: Day £3,300–£7,362
🖊

Wellington College
Duke's Ride, Crowthorne,
Berkshire RG45 7PU
Tel: +44 (0)1344 444000
Master: Mr Julian Thomas
Age range: 13–18
No. of pupils: 1045 VIth470
Fees: Day £26,130–
£30,030 FB £35,775
🏃 Ⓐ 🏋 £ ⒾⒷ 🖊 16

Buckinghamshire

Akeley Wood School
Akeley Wood, Buckingham,
Buckinghamshire MK18 5AE
Tel: 01280 814110
Headmaster: Dr Jerry
Grundy BA, PhD
Age range: 12 months–18 years
No. of pupils: 833 VIth119
Fees: Day £7,185–£10,575
Ⓐ £ 🖊 16

Ashfold School
Dorton House, Dorton, Aylesbury,
Buckinghamshire HP18 9NG
Tel: 01844 238237
Headmaster: Mr M O M Chitty BSc
Age range: 3–13
No. of pupils: 280 VIth28
Fees: Day £7,320–£12,900
WB £15,084
🏋 £ 🖊

Broughton Manor Preparatory School
Newport Road, Broughton, Milton
Keynes, Buckinghamshire MK10 9AA
Tel: 01908 665234
Headmaster: Mr Ross Urquhart
Age range: 2 months–11 years
No. of pupils: 250
Fees: Day £9,600
£

Caldicott
Crown Lane, Farnham Royal,
Buckinghamshire SL2 3SL
Tel: 01753 649301
Headmaster: Mr S J G
Doggart BA(Cantab)
Age range: B7–13
No. of pupils: 256
Fees: Day £13,080–
£14,148 FB £19,227
🧍 🏋 £ 🖊

Chesham Preparatory School
Two Dells Lane, Chesham,
Buckinghamshire HP5 3QF
Tel: 01494 782619
Headmaster: Mr Michael
Davies BA, PGCE
Age range: 3–13
No. of pupils: 392
Fees: Day £8,700–£12,300
🖊

Childfirst Day Nursery Aylesbury
Green End, off Rickford\'s Hill,
Aylesbury, Buckinghamshire
HP20 2SA
Tel: 01296 392516
Registrar: Mrs Carole Angood
Age range: 2 months–7 years
No. of pupils: 80
Fees: Day £6,276

Childfirst Pre School Aylesbury
35 Rickfords Hill, Aylesbury,
Buckinghamshire HP20 2RT
Tel: 01296 433224

Crown House School
19 London Road, High Wycombe,
Buckinghamshire HP11 1BJ
Tel: 01494 529927
Headmaster: Ben Kenyon
Age range: 4–11
No. of pupils: 120
Fees: Day £5,985–£6,570
🖊

Dair House School
Bishops Blake, Beaconsfield
Road, Farnham Royal,
Buckinghamshire SL2 3BY
Tel: 01753 643964
Headmaster: Mr Terry
Wintle BEd(Hons)
Age range: 3–11
No. of pupils: 104
Fees: Day £2,907–£8,526
£ 🖊

Davenies School
Station Road, Beaconsfield,
Buckinghamshire HP9 1AA
Tel: 01494 685400
Headmaster: C Rycroft
Age range: B4–13
No. of pupils: 325
Fees: Day £12,180–£15,540
🧍 £ 🖊

Fernwood School
Church Road, Aspley Heath, Milton
Keynes, Buckinghamshire MK17 8TJ
Tel: 01908 583541
Head: Mrs M E Denyer
Age range: 1–9
No. of pupils: 75

Filgrave School
Filgrave Village, Newport
Pagnell, Milton Keynes,
Buckinghamshire MK16 9ET
Tel: 01234 711534
Headteacher: Mrs H Schofield
BA(Hons), MA, PGCE
Age range: 2–7
No. of pupils: 27
Fees: Day £5,160
£ 🖊

Gateway School
1 High Street, Great Missenden,
Buckinghamshire HP16 9AA
Tel: 01494 862407
Headteacher: Mrs Sue
LaFarge BA(Hons), PGCE
Age range: 2–11
No. of pupils: 355
Fees: Day £10,002
🖊

Gayhurst School
Bull Lane, Gerrards Cross,
Buckinghamshire SL9 8RJ
Tel: 01753 882690
Headmaster: A J Sims MA(Cantab)
Age range: B3–13 G3–13
Fees: Day £9,882–£12,555
🧍 🏋 £ 🖊

Godstowe Preparatory School
Shrubbery Road, High Wycombe,
Buckinghamshire HP13 6PR
Tel: 01494 529273
Headmaster: Mr David Gainer
Age range: B3–7 G3–13
No. of pupils: 409
Fees: Day £8,505–£13,245
WB £19,455 FB £19,455
🏋 £ 🖊

Griffin House School
Little Kimble, Aylesbury,
Buckinghamshire HP17 0XP
Tel: 01844 346154
Headmaster: Mr Tim Walford
Age range: 3–11
No. of pupils: 100
Fees: Day £7,395–£7,695
£ 🖊

Heatherton House School
Copperkins Lane,
Chesham Bois, Amersham,
Buckinghamshire HP6 5QB
Tel: 01494 726433
Headteacher: Mrs
Debbie Isaachsen
Age range: B3–4 G3–11
Fees: Day £1,068–£12,330
🧍 🖊

High March School
23 Ledborough Lane, Beaconsfield,
Buckinghamshire HP9 2PZ
Tel: 01494 675186
Headmistress: Mrs S J Clifford
Age range: G3–11
No. of pupils: 292
Fees: Day £903–£12,510
🧍 £ 🖊

Maltman's Green School
Maltman's Lane, Gerrards Cross,
Buckinghamshire SL9 8RR
Tel: 01753 883022
Headmistress: Mrs Joanna
Pardon MA, BSc(Hons), PGCE
Age range: G3–11
No. of pupils: 425
Fees: Day £7,725–£11,460
🧍 £ 🖊

Milton Keynes Preparatory School
Tattenhoe Lane, Milton Keynes,
Buckinghamshire MK3 7EG
Tel: 01908 642111
Headmistress: Mrs Hilary Pauley BEd
Age range: 0–11
No. of pupils: 500
Fees: Day £3,858–£14,040
(£)

Pipers Corner School
Pipers Lane, Great
Kingshill, High Wycombe,
Buckinghamshire HP15 6LP
Tel: 01494 718 255
Headmistress: Mrs H J Ness-
Gifford BA(Hons), PGCE
Age range: G4–18
No. of pupils: VIth72
Fees: Day £7,230–£14,010
WB £18,750–£222,845 FB
£18,990–£23,085
(♠)(A)(♠)(£)(✎)(16·)(♠)

Sefton Park School
School Lane, Stoke Poges,
Buckinghamshire SL2 4QA
Tel: 01753 662167
Headteacher: Mr Timothy Thorpe
Age range: 11–16
No. of pupils: 120

St Mary's School
94 Packhorse Road, Gerrards
Cross, Buckinghamshire SL9 8JQ
Tel: 01753 883370
Headmistress: Mrs J A
Ross BA(Hons), NPQH
Age range: G3–18
No. of pupils: 320 VIth38
Fees: Day £3,420–£12,155
(♠)(A)(£)(✎)(16·)

St Teresa's Catholic School & Nursery
Aylesbury Road, Princes
Risborough, Buckinghamshire
HP27 0JW
Tel: 01844 345005
Head: Mr Simon Detre
Age range: 3–11
No. of pupils: 132
Fees: Day £5,775–£7,308
(✎)

Stowe School
Buckingham, Buckinghamshire
MK18 5EH
Tel: 01280 818000
Headmaster: Dr Anthony
Wallersteiner
Age range: 13–18
No. of pupils: 769 VIth318
Fees: Day £22,500 FB £30,975
(♠)(A)(♠)(£)(✎)(16·)

Swanbourne House School
Swanbourne, Milton Keynes,
Buckinghamshire MK17 0HZ
Tel: 01296 720264
Headmaster: Mr Simon
Hitchings MA (Oxon)
Age range: 3–13
No. of pupils: 361
Fees: Day £4,155–£15,780 FB £21,250
(♠)(£)(✎)

The Beacon School
Chesham Bois, Amersham,
Buckinghamshire HP6 5PF
Tel: 01494 433654
Headmaster: P Brewster
BSc(Hons), PGCE
Age range: B3–13
No. of pupils: 470
Fees: Day £4,695–£13,200
(♠)(£)(✎)

The Grove Independent School
Redland Drive, Loughton, Milton
Keynes, Buckinghamshire MK5 8HD
Tel: 01908 690590
Principal: Mrs Deborah Berkin
Age range: 3 months–13 years
No. of pupils: 210

The Webber Independent School
Soskin Drive, Stantonbury
Fields, Milton Keynes,
Buckinghamshire MK14 6DP
Tel: 01908 574740
Principal: Hilary Marsden
Age range: 3–18
No. of pupils: 300 VIth15
Fees: Day £3,894–£10,371
(A)(£)(✎)(16·)

Thornton College
Thornton, Milton Keynes,
Buckinghamshire MK17 0HJ
Tel: 01280 812610
Headmistress: Miss Agnes T Williams
Age range: B2–4+ G2–16
No. of pupils: 370
Fees: Day £6,300–£10,095 WB
£10,500–£13,305 FB £13,305–£16,545
(♠)(♠)(♠)(✎)

Thorpe House School
Oval Way, Gerrards Cross,
Buckinghamshire SL9 8QA
Tel: 01753 882474
Headmaster: Mr Terrence Ayres
Age range: B3–16
Fees: Day £9,000–£13,500
(♠)(£)(✎)

Walton Pre-Preparatory School & Nursery
The Old Rectory, Walton
Drive, Milton Keynes,
Buckinghamshire MK7 6BB
Tel: 01908 678403
Headmistress: Mrs M
Ramsbotham CertEd
Age range: 2 months–7 years
No. of pupils: 120
Fees: Day £8,316

Wycombe Abbey
High Wycombe,
Buckinghamshire HP11 1PE
Tel: +44 (0)1494 897008
Headmistress: Mrs Rhiannon J
Wilkinson MA (Oxon) MEd
Age range: G11–18
No. of pupils: 554
Fees: Day £26,775 FB £35,700
(♠)(♠)(A)(♠)(£)(✎)(16·)

Cambridgeshire

Kirkstone House School
Main Street, Baston, Peterborough,
Cambridgeshire PE6 9PA
Tel: 01778 560350
Head: Mrs C Jones BSocSc
Age range: 5–16
No. of pupils: 234
Fees: Day £5,688–£8,493
(£)(✎)

The Peterborough School
Thorpe Road, Peterborough,
Cambridgeshire PE3 6AP
Tel: 01733 343357
Headmaster: Mr A D
Meadows BSc(Hons)
Age range: 6 weeks–18 years
No. of pupils: 430
Fees: Day £9,893–£14,121
(♠)(A)(£)(✎)(16·)

East Sussex

Ashdown House School
Forest Row, East Sussex RH18 5JY
Tel: 01342 822574
Headmaster: Haydon Moore
Age range: 7–13
No. of pupils: 125
Fees: FB £23,250
(♠)

Bartholomews Tutorial College
22-23 Prince Albert Street,
Brighton, East Sussex BN1 1HF
Tel: 01273 205965/205141
Governor: W A Duncombe BSc
Age range: 15+
No. of pupils: 40 VIth30
Fees: Day £22,000 WB
£27,000 FB £29,000
(16·)(A)(✎)

Battle Abbey School
Battle, East Sussex TN33 0AD
Tel: 01424 772385
Headmaster: Mr R C Clark
BA(Hons), MA(Ed)
Age range: 2–18
No. of pupils: 286 VIth48
Fees: Day £6,630–£13,390 FB £23,190
(♠)(A)(♠)(£)(✎)(16·)

Bede's School
The Dicker, Upper Dicker,
Hailsham, East Sussex BN27 3QH
Tel: +44 (0)1323843252
Head: Dr Richard Maloney
Age range: 12–18+
No. of pupils: 800 VIth295
Fees: Day £15,450 FB £25,725
(♠)(A)(♠)(£)(✎)(16·)(♠)

Bellerbys College
44 Cromwell Road, Hove,
East Sussex BN3 3EU
Tel: 01273 339300
Principal: N Addison
Age range: 14–20
No. of pupils: 700 VIth610
Fees: FB £17,500–£21,000
16ᵗʰ Ⓐ ⬛

Bricklehurst Manor Preparatory
Bardown Road, Stonegate,
Wadhurst, East Sussex TN5 7EL
Tel: 01580 200448
Headteacher: Mrs C Flowers
Age range: 3–11
No. of pupils: 127
Fees: Day £980–£8,925
£ ✎

Brighton & Hove High School GDST
Montpelier Road, Brighton,
East Sussex BN1 3AT
Tel: 01273 280280
Head: Mrs Lorna Duggleby
Age range: G3–18
No. of pupils: 680 VIth70
Fees: Day £5,028–£8,898
♿ Ⓐ £ ✎ 16ᵗʰ

Brighton & Hove Montessori School
67 Stanford Avenue, Brighton,
East Sussex BN1 6FB
Tel: 01273 702485
Headteacher: Mrs Daisy
Cockburn AMI, MontDip
Age range: 2–11
Fees: Day £1,400–£5,900
✎

Brighton College
Eastern Road, Brighton,
East Sussex BN2 0AL
Tel: 01273 704200
Head Master: Richard Cairns MA
Age range: 3–18
No. of pupils: 945 VIth340
Fees: Day £4,890–£18,675 WB
£24,729–£25,884 FB £28,575–£30,141
🌐 Ⓐ ⬛ £ ✎ 16ᵗʰ

Brighton Steiner School
John Howard House, Roedean
Road, Brighton, East Sussex BN2 5RA
Tel: 01273 386300
**Chair of the College of
Teachers:** Carrie Rawle
Age range: 3–16
Fees: Day £6,540
£ ✎

Buckswood School
Broomham Hall, Rye
Road, Guestling, Hastings,
East Sussex TN35 4LT
Tel: 01424 813 813
Headteacher: Mr Mark Redsell
Age range: 10–19
No. of pupils: 420
🌐 Ⓐ ⬛ £ IB ✎ 16ᵗʰ

Buckswood St George's
Westwood House, 7-9
Holmesdale Gardens, Hastings,
East Sussex TN34 1LY
Tel: 01424 813696
College Director: Ian Godfrey
Age range: B16–19 G16–20
No. of pupils: VIth50
16ᵗʰ Ⓐ ⬛ £ IB 16ᵗʰ

Charters Ancaster College
Woodsgate Place, Gunters Lane,
Bexhill-on-Sea, East Sussex TN39 4EB
Tel: 01424 216670
Headmistress: Mrs Miriam Black
Age range: 2–13
No. of pupils: 125
Fees: Day £5,325–£6,750
£ ✎

Claremont Preparatory & Nursery School
Ebdens Hill, Baldslow, St Leonards-
on-Sea, East Sussex TN37 7PW
Tel: 01424 751555
Headmistress: Mrs Diane Durrant
Age range: 1–14
Fees: Day £5,000–£10,000
Ⓐ £ ✎

Claremont Senior & Sixth Form School
Bodiam, Nr Robertsbridge,
East Sussex TN32 5UJ
Tel: 01580 830396
Headmaster: Mr. Giles Perrin

Darvell School
Darvell Bruderhof, Robertsbridge,
East Sussex TN32 5DR
Tel: 01580 883300
Headteacher: Mr Arnold Meier
Age range: 4–16
No. of pupils: 121
✎

Deepdene School
195 New Church Road, Hove,
East Sussex BN3 4ED
Tel: 01273 418984
Heads: Mrs Nicola Gane
& Miss Elizabeth Brown
Age range: 6 months–11 years
Fees: Day £1,800–£6,870
£

Dharma School
The White House, Ladies Mile
Road, Patcham, Brighton,
East Sussex BN1 8TB
Tel: 01273 502055
Headmaster: Kevin Fossey BEd
Age range: 3–11
Fees: Day £3,000
£ ✎

Eastbourne College
Old Wish Road, Eastbourne,
East Sussex BN21 4JX
Tel: 01323 452323 (Admissions)
Headmaster: Mr S P Davies MA
Age range: 13–18
No. of pupils: 630 VIth273
Fees: Day £20,940–£21,300
FB £31,965–£32,325
🌐 Ⓐ ⬛ £ ✎ 16ᵗʰ

European School of Animal Osteopathy
25 Old Steine, Brighton,
East Sussex BN1 1EL
Tel: 01273 673332
Head: Jean-Yves Girard
16ᵗʰ

Greenfields School
Priory Road, Forest Row,
East Sussex RH18 5JD
Tel: 01342 822189
Headteacher: Mr G Hudson
Age range: 2–19
No. of pupils: 125
Fees: Day £500–£10,800
FB £19,170–£20,850
🌐 Ⓐ ⬛ ✎ 16ᵗʰ

Hove College
48 Cromwell Road, Hove,
East Sussex BN3 3ER
Tel: 01273 772577
Director: Mr John Veale
16ᵗʰ

K-BIS Theatre School
Clermont Hall, Cumberland Road,
Brighton, East Sussex BN1 6SL
Tel: 01273 566739
Principal: Mrs Marcia King LGSM
Age range: 5–18
No. of pupils: VIth7
Fees: Day £5,980
Ⓐ £ ✎ 16ᵗʰ 🎭

Lancing College Preparatory School at Hove
The Droveway, Hove,
East Sussex BN3 6LU
Tel: 01273 503452
Headmaster: A P Laurent
Age range: 3–13
No. of pupils: 181
Fees: Day £2,550–£10,155
£ ✎

Lewes New School
Talbot Terrace, Lewes,
East Sussex BN7 2DS
Tel: 01273 477074
Head Teacher: Lizzie Overton
Age range: 3–11
No. of pupils: 76
Fees: Day £3,300–£3,600
£ ✎

Lewes Old Grammar School
High Street, Lewes, East
Sussex BN7 1XS
Tel: 01273 472634
Headmaster: Mr Robert Blewitt
Age range: 3–18
No. of pupils: 463 VIth50
Fees: Day £5,550–£10,815
Ⓐ £ ✎ 16ᵗʰ

MAYFIELD SCHOOL
For further details see p. 94
The Old Palace, Mayfield,
East Sussex TN20 6PH
Tel: +44 (0)1435 874600
Email: registrar@
mayfieldgirls.org
Website: www.mayfieldgirls.org
Head: Ms Antonia Beary
MA, Mphil(Cantab), PGCE
Age range: G11–18
No. of pupils: 356 VIth100
Fees: Day £19,125 WB
£30,900 FB £30,900
♿ 🌐 Ⓐ ⬛ £ ✎ 16ᵗʰ

MICHAEL HALL SCHOOL
For further details see p. 98
Kidbrooke Park, Priory Road,
Forest Row, East Sussex RH18 5BG
Tel: 01342 822275
Email: info@michaelhall.co.uk
Website: www.michaelhall.co.uk
Age range: 3–19
Fees: Day £8,840–£12,120
FB £5,400–£7,610
🌐 Ⓐ ⬛ ✎ 16ᵗʰ

Moira House Girls School
Upper Carlisle Road, Eastbourne,
East Sussex BN20 7TE
Tel: 01323 644144
Principal: Mrs L A Watson
MA(Ed), MInstD
Age range: G2–18
No. of pupils: 360 VIth105
Fees: Day £6,300–£14,655 WB
£19,260–£24,060 FB £20,715–£26,550
♿ 🌐 Ⓐ ⬛ £ ✎ 16ᵗʰ

ROEDEAN SCHOOL
For further details see p. 99
Roedean Way, Brighton,
East Sussex BN2 5RQ
Tel: 01273 667500
Email: info@roedean.co.uk
Website: www.roedean.co.uk
Headmaster: Mr. Oliver Bond
BA(Essex), PGCE, NPQH
Age range: G11–18
No. of pupils: 440 VIth177
Fees: Day £14,970–£19,470
WB £26,730–£29,820 FB
£28,860–£34,950
♿ 🌐 Ⓐ ⬛ £ ✎ 16ᵗʰ

Sacred Heart School
Mayfield Lane, Durgates,
Wadhurst, East Sussex TN5 6DQ
Tel: 01892 783414
Headteacher: Mrs H Blake
BA(Hons), PGCE
Age range: 3–11
Fees: Day £2,235–£6,225
£ ✎

Skippers Hill Manor Prep School
Five Ashes, Mayfield, East Sussex TN20 6HR
Tel: 01825 830234
Headmaster: T W Lewis BA(Exon), PGCE(London)
Age range: 3–13
Fees: Day £3,852–£12,930
£ ✎

St Andrew's Preparatory School
Meads, Eastbourne, East Sussex BN20 7RP
Tel: 01323 733203
Headmaster: Gareth Jones BA(Hons), PGCE
Age range: 1–13
Fees: Day £8,880–£15,465 FB £21,960
⚱ £ ✎

St Bede's Preparatory School
Duke's Drive, Eastbourne, East Sussex BN20 7XL
Tel: 01323 734222
Head: Mr Nicholas Bevington
Age range: 3 months–13 years
No. of pupils: 395
⚱ £ ✎

St Christopher's School
33 New Church Road, Hove, East Sussex BN3 4AD
Tel: 01273 735404
Headmaster: Mr Julian Withers
Age range: 4–13
Fees: Day £6,570–£8,688
£ ✎

The Academy of Creative Training
8-10 Rock Place, Brighton, East Sussex BN2 1PF
Tel: 01273 818266
16

The Drive Prep School
101 The Drive, Hove, East Sussex BN3 3JE
Tel: 01273 738444
Head Teacher: Mrs S Parkinson CertEd, CertPerfArts
Age range: 7–16
Fees: Day £3,885–£7,500
✎

Torah Academy
31 New Church Road, Hove, East Sussex BN3 4AD
Tel: 01273 328675
Principal: P Ffune
Age range: 4–11
✎

Vinehall School
Robertsbridge, East Sussex TN32 5JL
Tel: 01580 880413
Headmaster: Richard Follett
Age range: 2–13
No. of pupils: 260
Fees: Day £8,913–£16,620 FB £19,545–£21,675
⚱ £ ✎

Walsh Manor School
Walshes Road, Crowborough, East Sussex TN6 3RB
Tel: 01342 318229
Headteacher: Mrs Angela Paris
Age range: 10–16
No. of pupils: 22

Windlesham School
190 Dyke Road, Brighton, East Sussex BN1 5AA
Tel: 01273 553645
Headmistress: Mrs Aoife Bennett-Odlum
Age range: 3–11
No. of pupils: 233
Fees: Day £5,100–£7,200
£ ✎

Windmill Hill Tennis and Golf Academy
Windmill Hill, Hailsham, East Sussex BN27 4RZ
Tel: 08700 339 997
Managing Director: Steven P Jones
Fees: Day £0
16

Essex

Alleyn Court Preparatory School
Wakering Road, Southend-on-Sea, Essex SS3 0PW
Tel: 01702 582553
Headmaster: Mr Gareth Davies BA(Hons), PGCE
Age range: 2–11
Fees: Day £2,607–£10,881
£ ✎

Bliss College
211 Olympic House, 28-42 Clements Road, Ilford, Essex IG1 1BA
Tel: 020 8553 7975
Head: Mrs Shani Varghese
16

Braeside School for Girls
130 High Road, Buckhurst Hill, Essex IG9 5SD
Tel: 020 8504 1133
Head Teacher: Mrs G Haddon BA(Hons), PGCE
Age range: G3–16
No. of pupils: 199
Fees: Day £5,175–£10,875
⚱

Brentwood Pre-Preparatory School
Shenfield Road, Brentwood, Essex CM15 8BD
Tel: 01277 243239
Headmistress: Mrs S E Wilson BEd, CertEd
Age range: 3–7
Fees: Day £5,130
✎

Brentwood Preparatory School
Middleton Hall Lane, Brentwood, Essex CM15 8EQ
Tel: 01277 243333
Headmaster: Mr Jason Whiskerd
Age range: 3–11
Fees: Day £5,889–£11,640
✎

Brentwood School
Middleton Hall Lane, Brentwood, Essex CM15 8EE
Tel: 01277 243243
Headmaster: Mr Ian Davies
Age range: 3–18
No. of pupils: 1550
Fees: Day £16,635 FB £32,649
🌐 Ⓐ ⚱ £ Ⓘ🅑 ✎ 16

Chigwell School
High Road, Chigwell, Essex IG7 6QF
Tel: 020 8501 5700
Headmaster: Mr M E Punt MA, MSc
Age range: 4–18
No. of pupils: 915 VIth185
Fees: Day £10,200–£16,020 FB £26,730–£26,730
🌐 Ⓐ ⚱ £ ✎ 16

Colchester High School
Wellesley Road, Colchester, Essex CO3 3HD
Tel: 01206 573389
Principal: David Young BA(Hons), PGCE
Age range: 2–16
No. of pupils: 486
Fees: Day £3,300–£10,000
£ ✎

Coopersale Hall School
Flux's Lane, off Stewards Green Road, Epping, Essex CM16 7PE
Tel: 01992 577133
Headmistress: Miss Kaye Lovejoy
Age range: 2–11
No. of pupils: 275
Fees: Day £3,645–£7,275

Crowstone Preparatory School
121-123 Crowstone Road, Westcliff-on-Sea, Southend-on-Sea, Essex SS0 8LH
Tel: 01702 346758
Headmaster: J P Thayer
Age range: 3–11
No. of pupils: 133
Fees: Day £2,655

Dame Bradbury's School
Ashdon Road, Saffron Walden, Essex CB10 2AL
Tel: 01799 522348
Headmistress: Ms Tracy Handford
Age range: 3–11
No. of pupils: 254
Fees: Day £2,000–£10,950
£ ✎

East 15 Acting School
Hatfields, Rectory Lane, Loughton, Essex IG10 3RY
Tel: 020 8508 5983
Director: John Baraldi
Fees: Day £0
16

Elm Green Preparatory School
Parsonage Lane, Little Baddow, Chelmsford, Essex CM3 4SU
Tel: 01245 225230
Principal: Ms Ann Milner
Age range: 4–11
No. of pupils: 220
Fees: Day £7,449
✎

Empire College London
Forest House, 16-20 Clements Road, Ilford, Essex IG1 1BA
Tel: 020 8553 2683
Head: Ms Aaiesha Tak
16

Felsted Preparatory School
Felsted, Great Dunmow, Essex CM6 3JL
Tel: 01371 822610
Headmistress: Mrs Jenny Burrett BA(Dunelm), MEd(Cantab), PGCE
Age range: 4–13
No. of pupils: 460
Fees: Day £6,390–£13,965 FB £17,850
⚱ £ ✎

Felsted School
Felsted, Great Dunmow, Essex CM6 3LL
Tel: +44 (0) 1371 822605
Headmaster: Dr Michael Walker
Age range: 13–18
No. of pupils: 516 VIth236
Fees: Day £18,480 WB £22,377 FB £24,705
🌐 Ⓐ ⚱ £ Ⓘ🅑 ✎ 16

FKS Schools
Edwards House, Braintree Road,
Felsted, Essex CM6 3DS
Tel: 01371 820638
Headmistress: Mrs A Woods
Age range: 4–11
No. of pupils: 161
Fees: Day £6,219–£6,864

Friends' School
Mount Pleasant Road, Saffron
Walden, Essex CB11 3EB
Tel: 01799 525351
Head: Ms Anna Chaudhri MA
Age range: 3–18
No. of pupils: 390 VIth50
Fees: Day £2,375–£5,305 WB
£6,615–£7,690 FB £7,190–£8,590

Gosfield School
Cut Hedge Park, Halstead Road,
Gosfield, Halstead, Essex CO9 1PF
Tel: 01787 474040
Principal: Dr Sarah Welch
Age range: 4–18
No. of pupils: VIth21
Fees: Day £4,740–£13,695 WB
£15,465–£17,310 FB £17,985–£23,130

Great Warley School
Warley Street, Great Warley,
Brentwood, Essex CM13 3LA
Tel: 01277 233288
Head: Mrs B Harding
Age range: 3–11
Fees: Day £2,250–£3,500

**Guru Gobind Singh
Khalsa College**
Roding Lane, Chigwell,
Essex IG7 6BQ
Tel: 020 8559 9160
Principal: Mr Amarjit Singh
Toor BSc(Hons), BSc, BT
Age range: 3–17
Fees: Day £3,900

Heathcote School
Eves Corner, Danbury,
Chelmsford, Essex CM3 4QB
Tel: 01245 223131
Head Teacher: Miss H Petersen
Age range: 2–11
Fees: Day £4,830–£7,245

Herington House School
1 Mount Avenue, Hutton,
Brentwood, Essex CM13 2NS
Tel: 01277 211595
Principal: Mr R Dudley-Cooke
Age range: 3–11
No. of pupils: 129
Fees: Day £4,365–£8,670

**Holmwood House
Preparatory School**
Chitts Hill, Lexden, Colchester,
Essex CO3 9ST
Tel: 01206 574305
Headmaster: Alexander Mitchell
Age range: 4–13
No. of pupils: 302
Fees: Day £7,920–£14,079
WB £18,258

Hutton Manor School
428 Rayleigh Road, Hutton,
Brentwood, Essex CM13 1SD
Tel: 01277 245585
Head: Mr P Pryke
Age range: 3–11
Fees: Day £2,975–£3,995

**Kids Inc Day Nursery –
Beehive Lane Ilford**
229-231 Beehive Lane,
Ilford, Essex IG4 5EB
Tel: 020 8550 7400

**Kids Inc Day Nursery
– Loughton**
29 Old Station Road,
Loughton, Essex IG10 4PE
Tel: 020 8502 4488

**Kids Inc Day Nursery
– York Road Ilford**
81-85 York Road, Ilford,
Essex IG1 3AF
Tel: 020 8478 6510

Littlegarth School
Horkesley Park, Nayland,
Colchester, Essex CO6 4JR
Tel: 01206 262332
Headmaster: Mr Peter H Jones
Age range: 2–11 years
No. of pupils: 318
Fees: Day £2,700–£3,140

**London Academy of
Management Sciences**
9th Floor Wentworth House,
350 Eastern Avenue,
Ilford, Essex IG2 6NN
Tel: 020 8554 9169
Head: Mr Asif Siddiqui

**London College
of Business**
6A Monteagle Court, Wakering
Road, Barking, Essex IG11 8PD
Tel: 020 8591 2222
Head: Mr Zenon Adamek

**London College of
Business & Finance**
8th Floor, Crown House, Cambridge
Road, Barking, Essex IG11 8NW
Tel: 020 8507 8883
Head: Mr Sandeep Jethwa

Loyola Preparatory School
103 Palmerston Road,
Buckhurst Hill, Essex IG9 5NH
Tel: 020 8504 7372
Headmaster: Mr P G M
Nicholson CertEd, BEd(Hons)
Age range: B3–11
No. of pupils: 195
Fees: Day £8,820

**Maldon Court
Preparatory School**
Silver Street, Maldon,
Essex CM9 4QE
Tel: 01621 853529
Headteacher: Mrs L Guest
Age range: 3–11
Fees: Day £7,305

New Hall School
The Avenue, Boreham,
Chelmsford, Essex CM3 3HS
Tel: 01245 467588
Principal: Mrs Katherine Jeffrey
MA, BA, PGCE, MA(Ed Mg), NPQH
Age range: Coed 3-11,
Single 11-16, Coed 16–18
No. of pupils: 1175 VIth197
Fees: Day £8,742–£18,042 WB
£17,670–£25,815 FB £19,521–£27,099

Oaklands School
8 Albion Hill, Loughton,
Essex IG10 4RA
Tel: 020 8508 3517
Headmistress: Mrs Cheryl Macnair
Age range: B2 –7 G2 –11
No. of pupils: 243
Fees: Day £3,795–£7,650

Oxford House School
2-4 Lexden Road, Colchester,
Essex CO3 3NE
Tel: 01206 576686
Headteacher: Mrs E Hill
Age range: 2 –11
No. of pupils: 152
Fees: Day £4,305–£8,565

Saint Pierre School
16 Leigh Road, Leigh-on-Sea,
Southend-on-Sea, Essex SS9 1LE
Tel: 01702 474164
Headmaster: Mr Chris Perkins
Age range: 2 –11+
Fees: Day £2,062–£6,186

**St Anne's Preparatory
School**
New London Road, Chelmsford,
Essex CM2 0AW
Tel: 01245 353488
Head: Mrs S Robson
Age range: 3–11
No. of pupils: 160
Fees: Day £6,300–£6,600

St Cedd's School
178a New London Road,
Chelmsford, Essex CM2 0AR
Tel: 01245 392810
Head: Dr Pamela Edmonds
Age range: 3–11
No. of pupils: 400
Fees: Day £8,550–£9,300

St John's School
Stock Road, Billericay,
Essex CM12 0AR
Tel: 01277 623070
Head Teacher: Mrs F
Armour BEd(Hons)
Age range: 3–16
No. of pupils: 392
Fees: Day £4,470–£10,650

**St Margaret's
Preparatory School**
Gosfield Hall Park, Gosfield,
Halstead, Essex CO9 1SE
Tel: 01787 472134
Principal: Mrs E Powling
Age range: 2 –11
No. of pupils: 250
Fees: Day £45.50–£2,975

St Mary's School
Lexden Road, Colchester,
Essex CO3 3RB
Tel: 01206 572544   Admissions:
01206 216420
Principal: Mrs H K Vipond
MEd, BSc(Hons), NPQH
Age range: B3–4 G3–16
No. of pupils: 430
Fees: Day £7,464–£11,340

**St Michael's
Church Of England
Preparatory School**
198 Hadleigh Road, Leigh-on-Sea,
Southend-on-Sea, Essex SS9 2LP
Tel: 01702 478719
Head: Steve Tompkins
BSc(Hons), PGCE, MA, NPQH
Age range: 3–11
No. of pupils: 271
Fees: Day £3,510–£6,990

St Nicholas School
Hillingdon House, Hobbs Cross
Road, Harlow, Essex CM17 0NJ
Tel: 01279 429910
Headmaster: Mr K M
Knight BEd, MA, NPQH
Age range: 4–16
No. of pupils: 400
Fees: Day £7,470–£9,660

**St Philomena's
Catholic School**
Hadleigh Road, Frinton-on-
Sea, Essex CO13 9HQ
Tel: 01255 674492
Headmistress: Mrs B
McKeown DipEd
Age range: 3–11
Fees: Day £5,670–£6,750

The Daiglen School
68 Palmerston Road, Buckhurst
Hill, Essex IG9 5LG
Tel: 020 8504 7108
Headteacher: Mrs M Bradfield
Age range: 3–11
No. of pupils: 130
Fees: Day £6,360

Thorpe Hall School
Wakering Road, Southend-
on-Sea, Essex SS1 3RD
Tel: 01702 582340
Headmaster: Mr Andrew Hampton
Age range: 2–16 years
No. of pupils: 359
Fees: Day £7,695–£10,620
£ ✎

Trinity School
Brizes Park, Ongar Road, Kelvedon
Hatch, Brentwood, Essex CM15 0DG
Tel: 01277 374123
Headmaster: Reverend
M S B Reid BD
Age range: 4–18
Ⓐ

Ursuline Preparatory School
Old Great Ropers, Great
Ropers Lane, Warley,
Brentwood, Essex CM13 3HR
Tel: 01277 227152
Headmistress: Mrs
Pauline Wilson MSc
Age range: 3–11
Fees: Day £2,610–£4,950
✎

Widford Lodge School
Widford Road, Chelmsford,
Essex CM2 9AN
Tel: 01245 352581
Headmaster: Mr Simon Trowell
Age range: 2–11
Fees: Day £5,400–£7,050
✎

Hampshire

Allbrook School
The Old School, Pitmore
Road, Allbrook, Eastleigh,
Hampshire SO50 4LW
Tel: 023 8061 6316
Head of Studies: Mrs Hilary Luider
Age range: 11–16
No. of pupils: 79
✎ 16+

Alton Convent School
Anstey Lane, Alton,
Hampshire GU34 2NG
Tel: 01420 82070
Head: Graham Maher
Age range: B0–11 G0–18
No. of pupils: 563 VIth53
Fees: Day £8,655–£12,285
Ⓐ £ 16+

Ballard School
Fernhill Lane, New Milton,
Hampshire BH25 5SU
Tel: 01425 626900
Headmaster: Mr Alastair Reid
Age range: 18 months–16 years
No. of pupils: 500
Fees: Day £2,370–£4,265
£ ✎

Bedales School
Church Road, Steep, Petersfield,
Hampshire GU32 2DG
Tel: 01730 711733
Head: Keith Budge MA
Age range: 13–18
No. of pupils: 463 VIth192
Fees: Day £8,825 FB £11,230
🌐 Ⓐ ♠ £ ✎ 16+

Boundary Oak School
Roche Court, Fareham,
Hampshire PO17 5BL
Tel: 01329 280955/820373
Head: Mrs Hazel Kellett
Age range: 2–13
No. of pupils: 120
Fees: Day £7,500–£12,510 WB
£5,370 FB £7,095–£19,605
♠ £ ✎

Brockwood Park & Inwoods School
Brockwood Park, Bramdean,
Hampshire SO24 0LQ
Tel: +44 (0)1962 771744
Co-Principals: Mr Adrian Sydenham
& Dr Gopal Krishnamurthy
Age range: 4–19
No. of pupils: 92
Fees: Day £3,150 FB £17,270
🌐 Ⓐ ♠ £ ✎ 16+

Brookham School
Highfield Lane, Liphook,
Hampshire GU30 7LQ
Tel: 01428 722005
Headteacher: Mrs Sophie Baber
Age range: 3–8
No. of pupils: 141
Fees: Day £10,125–£13,350
✎

Churcher's College
Petersfield, Hampshire GU31 4AS
Tel: 01730 263033
Headmaster: Mr Simon
Williams MA, BSc
Age range: 4–18
No. of pupils: 1067 VIth224
Fees: Day £7,605–£11,955
Ⓐ £ ✎ 16+

Clay Hill School
Clay Hill, Lyndhurst,
Hampshire SO43 7DE
Tel: 023 8028 3633
Head of School: Mrs. Helen Sharpe
Age range: 5–19

Daneshill School
Stratfield Turgis, Basingstoke,
Hampshire RG27 0AR
Tel: 01256 882707
Headmaster: S V Spencer
CertEd, DipPhysEd
Age range: 3–13
Fees: Day £3,900–£9,150
✎

Ditcham Park School
Ditcham Park, Petersfield,
Hampshire GU31 5RN
Tel: 01730 825659
Headteacher: A P N Rowley
BSc (Hons), PGCE
Age range: 4–16
No. of pupils: 366
Fees: Day £6,957–£11,610
£ ✎

Dunhurst (Bedales Junior School)
Petersfield, Hampshire GU32 2DP
Tel: 01730 300200
Head: Jane Grubb
Age range: 8–13
No. of pupils: 199
Fees: Day £16,635 FB £21,255
♠ £ ✎

Durlston Court
Becton Lane, Barton-on-Sea, New
Milton, Hampshire BH25 7AQ
Tel: 01425 610010
Head of School: Mr Richard May
Age range: 2–13
No. of pupils: 304
Fees: Day £3,540–£12,255
£ ✎

Farleigh School
Red Rice, Andover,
Hampshire SP11 7PW
Tel: 01264 710766
Headmaster: Father Simon Everson
Age range: 3–13
Fees: Day £3,870–£14,085
FB £16,515–£18,345
♠ £ ✎

Farnborough Hill
Farnborough Road, Farnborough,
Hampshire GU14 8AT
Tel: 01252 545197
Headmistress: Mrs S Buckle
BSc, MA, PGCE, NPQH
Age range: G11–18
No. of pupils: 563 VIth80
Fees: Day £12,120
♣ Ⓐ £ ✎ 16+

Forres Sandle Manor
Fordingbridge, Hampshire SP6 1NS
Tel: 01425 653181
Headmaster: Mr M N
Hartley BSc(Hons)
Age range: 3–13
No. of pupils: 264
Fees: Day £3,150–£14,205
WB £19,380 FB £19,380
♠ £ ✎

GEMS Sherfield School
Sherfield-on-Loddon, Hook,
Hampshire RG27 0HU
Tel: +44 (0)1256 884 800
Headmaster: Mr Dick Jaine
Age range: 3 months–18 years
No. of pupils: 445 VIth16
Fees: Day £7,350–£13,890 FB £20,946
🌐 ♠ £ ✎ 16+ 🔊

Glenhurst School
16 Beechworth Road, Havant,
Hampshire PO9 1AX
Tel: 023 9248 4054
Principal: Mrs E M Haines
Age range: 3 months–8 years
Fees: Day £4,500
✎

Hampshire Collegiate School
Embley Park, Romsey,
Hampshire SO51 6ZE
Tel: 01794 512206
Principal: Mrs Emma-Kate Henry
Age range: 2–18
No. of pupils: 683
🌐 Ⓐ ♠ £ ✎ 16+

Highfield School
Liphook, Hampshire GU30 7LQ
Tel: 01428 728000
Headmaster: Mr Philip Evitt MA
Age range: 8–13
Fees: Day £17,025–£19,575
FB £21,450–£23,550
♠ £ ✎

King Edward VI School
Wilton Road, Southampton,
Hampshire SO15 5UQ
Tel: 023 8070 4561
Head Master: Mr A J
Thould MA(Oxon)
Age range: 11–18
No. of pupils: 975 VIth260
Fees: Day £14,355
Ⓐ £ ✎ 16+

Kingscourt School
Catherington Lane, Catherington,
Hampshire PO8 9NJ
Tel: 023 9259 3251
Headmistress: Mrs J L Easton
Age range: 2–11
Fees: Day £5,430

Lord Wandsworth College
Long Sutton, Hook,
Hampshire RG29 1TB
Tel: 01256 862201
Head of School: Mr Adam Williams
Age range: 11–18 years
No. of pupils: 550
Fees: Day £19,110–£20,940
WB £25,350–£28,350 FB
£26,100–£29,700
🌐 Ⓐ ♠ £ ✎ 16+

Mayville High School
35/37 St Simon\'s Road, Southsea, Portsmouth, Hampshire PO5 2PE
Tel: 023 9273 4847
Headteacher: Mrs L Owens B.Ed
Age range: 6 months–16 years
No. of pupils: 479
Fees: Day £5,481–£8,040

Meoncross School
Burnt House Lane, Stubbington, Fareham, Hampshire PO14 2EF
Tel: 01329 662182
Headmistress: Mrs Sarah Ebery BSc (Hons), MEd
Age range: 2–18
No. of pupils: 405
Fees: Day £7,365–£10,485

Moyles Court School
Moyles Court, Ringwood, Hampshire BH24 3NF
Tel: 01425 472856
Headmaster: Mr Dean
Age range: 3–16
Fees: Day £3,285–£4,650 FB £6,690–£7,740

New Forest Small School
1 Southampton Road, Lyndhurst, Hampshire SO43 7BU
Tel: 02380 284 415
Headteacher: Mr Nicholas Alp
Age range: 3–16

Portsmouth High School GDST
Kent Road, Southsea, Portsmouth, Hampshire PO5 3EQ
Tel: 023 9282 6714
Headmistress: Mrs Jane Prescott BSc NPQH
Age range: G3–18
No. of pupils: 421
Fees: Day £2,542–£4,248

Prince's Mead School
Worthy Park House, Kings Worthy, Winchester, Hampshire SO21 1AN
Tel: 01962 888000
Headmistress: Miss Penelope Kirk
Age range: 4–11
No. of pupils: 270
Fees: Day £9,600–£14,640

Ringwood Waldorf School
Folly Farm Lane, Ashley, Ringwood, Hampshire BH24 2NN
Tel: 01425 472664
Age range: 3–18
No. of pupils: 235
Fees: Day £3,622–£7,825

Rookwood School
Weyhill Road, Andover, Hampshire SP10 3AL
Tel: 01264 325900
Headmistress: Mrs L Whetstone MA
Age range: 3–16
Fees: Day £7,770–£12,780 FB £19,545–£22,875

Salesian College
Reading Road, Farnborough, Hampshire GU14 6PA
Tel: 01252 893000
Headmaster: Mr P A Wilson BA(Hons), MA, CertEd
Age range: B11–18 G16–18
No. of pupils: 650 VIth140
Fees: Day £9,000

Sherborne House School
Lakewood Road, Chandlers Ford, Eastleigh, Hampshire SO53 1EU
Tel: 023 8025 2440
Head Teacher: Mrs Heather Hopson-Hill
Age range: 3–11
No. of pupils: 293
Fees: Day £1,044–£8,730

St John's College
Grove Road South, Southsea, Portsmouth, Hampshire PO5 3QW
Tel: 023 9281 5118
Headmaster: Mr Timothy Bayley
Age range: 2–18
No. of pupils: 600 VIth86
Fees: Day £8,460–£11,100 FB £23,970–£25,770

St Mary's College
57 Midanbury Lane, Bitterne Park, Southampton, Hampshire SO18 4DJ
Tel: 023 8067 1267
Head of School: Mrs. Owen
Age range: 3–16
No. of pupils: 470
Fees: Day £1,750–£2,350

St Neot's School
St Neot's Road, Eversley, Hook, Hampshire RG27 0PN
Tel: 0118 973 2118
Head of School: Mrs Deborah Henderson
Age range: 3 months–13 years
No. of pupils: 300
Fees: Day £1,494–£14,850

St Nicholas' School
Redfields House, Redfields Lane, Church Crookham, Fleet, Hampshire GU52 0RF
Tel: 01252 850121
Headmistress: Mrs A V Whatmough BA, CertEd
Age range: B3–7 G3–16
No. of pupils: 370

St Swithun's Junior School
Alresford Road, Winchester, Hampshire SO21 1HA
Tel: 01962 835750
Headmistress: Mrs P Grimes BA(Hons)
Age range: B3–7 G3–11
No. of pupils: 183
Fees: Day £1,415–£3,650

St Swithun's School
Alresford Road, Winchester, Hampshire SO21 1HA
Tel: 01962 835700
Headmistress: Jane Gandee MA(Cantab)
Age range: G11–18
No. of pupils: G525 VIth85
Fees: Day £17,640 FB £28,290

St Winifred's School
17-19 Winn Road, Southampton, Hampshire SO17 1EJ
Tel: 023 8055 7352
Head Teacher: Mr M Brogan BEd,CertSpNeeds
Age range: 3–11
Fees: Day £6,330

Stockton House School
Stockton Avenue, Fleet, Hampshire GU51 4NS
Tel: 01252 616323
Early Years Manager: Mrs Jenny Bounds BA EYPS
Age range: 2–5
Fees: Day £25.50–£70

The Gregg School
Townhill Park House, Cutbush Lane, Southampton, Hampshire SO18 2GF
Tel: 023 8047 2133
Headteacher: Mrs S Sellers PGDip, MSc, BSc(Hons), NPQH, PGCE
Age range: 11–16
Fees: Day £10,680

The Grey House School
Mount Pleasant, Hartley Wintney, Hampshire RG27 8PW
Tel: 01252 842353
Head: Mrs C E Allen BEd(Cantab)
Age range: 4–11+
Fees: Day £7,365–£8,994

The King's School
Basingstoke Community Church, Sarum Hill, Basingstoke, Hampshire RG21 8SR
Tel: 01256 467092
Headteacher: Mr David Robotham
Age range: 7–16
No. of pupils: 172

The King's School
Lakesmere House, Allington Lane, Fair Oak, Eastleigh, Southampton, Hampshire SO50 7DB
Tel: 023 8060 0986
Head of School: Mrs H Bowden BA (Hons), PGCE
Age range: 3–16
No. of pupils: 256
Fees: Day £3,900–£6,840

The Pilgrims' School
3 The Close, Winchester, Hampshire SO23 9LT
Tel: 01962 854189
Headmaster: Mr Tom Burden
Age range: B4–13
No. of pupils: 250
Fees: Day £17,685 FB £22,335

The Portsmouth Grammar School
High Street, Portsmouth, Hampshire PO1 2LN
Tel: +44 (0)23 9236 0036
Headmaster: J E Priory MA
Age range: 2–18
No. of pupils: 1645 VIth298
Fees: Day £8,379–£13,059

The Stroud School
Highwood House, Highwood Lane, Romsey, Hampshire SO51 9ZH
Tel: 01794 513231
Headmaster: Mr Alastair J L Dodds MA(Cantab)
Age range: 3–13
Fees: Day £9,060–£14,775

Twyford School
Twyford, Winchester, Hampshire SO21 1NW
Tel: 01962 712269
Headmaster: Dr S J Bailey BEd, PhD, FRSA
Age range: 3–13
Fees: Day £4,845–£16,410 WB £20,670

Walhampton
Walhampton, Lymington, Hampshire SO41 5ZG
Tel: 01590 613 300
Headmaster: Mr Titus Mills
Age range: 2–13
No. of pupils: 353
Fees: Day £8,025–£15,555 FB £20,790

Wessex Tutors
44 Shirley Road, Southampton, Hampshire SO15 3EU
Tel: 023 8033 4719
Principal: Mrs J E White BA(London)
Age range: 14–21
Fees: Day £800–£10,000

West Hill Park Preparatory School
Titchfield, Fareham, Hampshire PO14 4BS
Tel: 01329 842356
Headmaster: A P Ramsay BEd(Hons), MSc
Age range: 2–13
No. of pupils: 288
Fees: Day £8,985–£14,985 FB £13,785–£19,785

Winchester College
College Street, Winchester,
Hampshire SO23 9NA
Tel: 01962 621247
Headmaster: R D
Townsend MA, DPhil
Age range: B13–18
No. of pupils: 690 VIth280
Fees: FB £35,610

Woodhill School, Botley
Brook Lane, Botley, Southampton,
Hampshire SO30 2ER
Tel: 01489 781112
Head Teacher: Mrs M Dacombe
Age range: 3–11
No. of pupils: 100
Fees: Day £2,199–£4,965

Yateley Manor School
51 Reading Road, Yateley,
Hampshire GU46 7UQ
Tel: 01252 405500
Headmaster: Mr R J Williams
MA(Hons)Edinburgh, PGCE Bedford
Age range: 3–13
No. of pupils: 453
Fees: Day £4,500–£12,150

Hertfordshire

Abbot's Hill School
Bunkers Lane, Hemel Hempstead,
Hertfordshire HP3 8RP
Tel: 01442 240333
Headmistress: Mrs E Thomas
BA (Hons), PGCE, NPQH
Age range: B3–5 G3–16
Fees: Day £9,159–£16,332

Aldenham School
Elstree, Hertfordshire WD6 3AJ
Tel: 01923 858122
Headmaster: James C Fowler MA
Age range: 3–18
No. of pupils: 700 VIth158
Fees: Day £13,626–£19,500
FB £18,768–£28,410

Aldwickbury School
Wheathampstead Road,
Harpenden, Hertfordshire AL5 1AD
Tel: 01582 713022
Headmaster: Mr V W Hales
Age range: B4–13
No. of pupils: 330
Fees: Day £2,002–£3,012
WB £3,800–£3,884

Beechwood Park School
Markyate, St Albans,
Hertfordshire AL3 8AW
Tel: 01582 840333
Headmaster: Mr E Balfour
Age range: 3–13
Fees: Day £9,765–£14,640
WB £18,120

Berkhamsted School
Overton House, 131 High Street,
Berkhamsted, Hertfordshire HP4 2DJ
Tel: 01442 358001
Principal: Mr Richard
Backhouse MA(Cantab)
Age range: 3–18 years
No. of pupils: 1680 VIth361
Fees: Day £10,065–£19,095
WB £25,565 FB £30,415

**Bhaktivedanta
Manor School**
Hilfield Lane, Aldenham, Watford,
Hertfordshire WD25 8EZ
Tel: 01923 851000 Ext:241
Headteacher: Mrs. Wendy Harrison
Age range: 4–12
No. of pupils: 40
Fees: Day £1,680

Bishop's Stortford College
10 Maze Green Road, Bishop's
Stortford, Hertfordshire CM23 2PJ
Tel: 01279 838575
Headmaster: Mr Jeremy Gladwin
Age range: 13–18
No. of pupils: VIth249
Fees: Day £17,496–£17,655 WB
£25,950–£26,109 FB £26,208–£27,405

**Bishop's Stortford
College Prep School**
Maze Green Road, Bishop's
Stortford, Hertfordshire CM23 2PH
Tel: 01279 838607
Head of Prep School:
Mr Bill Toleman
Age range: 4–13
Fees: Day £8,088–£12,489 WB
£18,114–£19,671 FB £18,312–£20,691

**Champneys International
College of Health & Beauty**
Chesham Road, Wigginton,
Tring, Hertfordshire HP23 6HY
Tel: 01442 291333
College Principal: Ms Pam Clegg
Age range: 16+
No. of pupils: 61
Fees: Day £3,000–£9,050

**Charlotte House
Preparatory School**
88 The Drive, Rickmansworth,
Hertfordshire WD3 4DU
Tel: 01923 772101
Head: Miss P Woodcock
Age range: G3–11
No. of pupils: 140
Fees: Day £6,900–£11,100

Duncombe School
4 Warren Park Road, Bengeo,
Hertford, Hertfordshire SG14 3JA
Tel: 01992 414100
Headmaster: Mr Jeremy
Phelan M.A. (Ed)
Age range: 2–11
No. of pupils: 325
Fees: Day £9,075–£12,585

Edge Grove School
Aldenham Village,
Hertfordshire WD25 8NL
Tel: 01923 855724
Headmaster: Mr Ben Evans
Age range: 3–13
Fees: Day £11,100–£114,835 WB
£15,870–£19,305 FB £15,870–£19,305

Egerton Rothesay School
Durrants Lane, Berkhamsted,
Hertfordshire HP4 3UJ
Tel: 01442 865275
Headteacher: Mr Colin Parker
BSc(Hons), Dip.Ed (Oxon),
PGCE, C.Math MIMA
Age range: 6–19
No. of pupils: 143
Fees: Day £14,310–£20,370

**Haberdashers'
Aske's School**
Butterfly Lane, Elstree,
Borehamwood,
Hertfordshire WD6 3AF
Tel: 020 8266 1700
Headmaster: Mr P B Hamilton MA
Age range: B5–18
No. of pupils: 1402 VIth310
Fees: Day £10,641–£14,103

**Haberdashers' Aske's
School for Girls**
Aldenham Road,
Elstree, Borehamwood,
Hertfordshire WD6 3BT
Tel: 020 8266 2300
Headmistress: Miss Biddie
A O'Connor MA (Oxon)
Age range: G4–18
No. of pupils: 1185
Fees: Day £13,269–£15,516

HAILEYBURY
For further details see p. 92
Haileybury, Hertford,
Hertfordshire SG13 7NU
Tel: +44 (0)1992 706353
Email: registrar@haileybury.com
Website: www.haileybury.com
The Master: J S Davies
MA(Cantab)
Age range: 11–18
No. of pupils: 759 VIth301
Fees: Day £15,435–£23,220
FB £19,605–£30,900

Haresfoot School
Chesham Road, Berkhamsted,
Hertfordshire HP4 2SZ
Tel: 01442 872742
Principal: Mrs Carole
Hawkins BA, PGCE
Age range: 0–11
Fees: Day £1,845–£7,770

Heath Mount School
Woodhall Park, Watton-at-Stone,
Hertford, Hertfordshire SG14 3NG
Tel: 01920 830230
Headmaster: Mr R Middleton
MSc, BEd(Hons)
Age range: 3–13
Fees: Day £2,715–£9,315
WB £12,630–£12,960

High Elms Manor School
High Elms Manor, High Elms Lane,
Watford, Hertfordshire WD25 0JX
Tel: 01923681103
Headmistress: Mrs Sheila O'Neill
MontDipDist, TCert, BA, AMI Dip
Age range: 2–12
No. of pupils: 90
Fees: Day £11,220

Howe Green House School
Great Hallingbury, Bishop's
Stortford, Hertfordshire CM22 7UF
Tel: 01279 657706
Head of School: Mrs Deborah Mills
Age range: 2–11
Fees: Day £5,946–£9,444

Immanuel College
87/91 Elstree Road, Bushey,
Hertfordshire WD23 4EB
Tel: 020 8950 0604
Headmaster: Mr Philip Skelker MA
Age range: 11–18
No. of pupils: 520 VIth127
Fees: Day £10,995

Kingshott
St Ippolyts, Hitchin,
Hertfordshire SG4 7JX
Tel: 01462 432009
Headmaster: Mr Iain Gilmour
Age range: 3–13
No. of pupils: 372
Fees: Day £4,770–£10,350

Little Acorns Montessori School
Lincolnsfield Centre,
Bushey Hall Drive, Bushey,
Hertfordshire WD23 2ER
Tel: 01923 230705
Head of School: Lola
Davies BPA, AMIDip
Age range: 2–6
No. of pupils: 28
Fees: Day £2,120

Lochinver House School
Heath Road, Little Heath, Potters
Bar, Hertfordshire EN6 1LW
Tel: 01707 653064
Headmaster: Ben Walker
BA(Hons), PGCE, CELTA
Age range: B4–13
No. of pupils: 349
Fees: Day £9,000–£11,826

Lockers Park
Lockers Park Lane, Hemel
Hempstead, Hertfordshire HP1 1TL
Tel: 01442 251712
Headmaster: Mr C R Wilson
Age range: B4–13 G4–7
No. of pupils: 150

Longwood School
Bushey Hall Drive, Bushey,
Hertfordshire WD23 2QG
Tel: 01923 253715
Head Teacher: Mrs Muriel Garman
Age range: 3–11
Fees: Day £4,590–£5,790

Manor Lodge School
Rectory Lane, Ridge Hill, Shenley,
Hertfordshire WD7 9BG
Tel: 01707 642424
Headmaster: Mr G Dunn CertEd
Age range: 3–11
No. of pupils: 425
Fees: Day £9,975–£11,235

Merchant Taylors' Prep
Moor Farm, Sandy Lodge
Road, Rickmansworth,
Hertfordshire WD3 1LW
Tel: 01923 825648
Headmaster: Dr T D Lee BEd(Hons)
Age range: B4–13
No. of pupils: 300
Fees: Day £2,613–£9,414

Princess Helena College
Preston, Hitchin,
Hertfordshire SG4 7RT
Tel: 01462 443888
Headmistress: Mrs Sue
Wallace-Woodroffe
Age range: G11–18
No. of pupils: 194 VIth35
Fees: Day £15,225–£18,585
FB £21,705–£26,985

Queenswood
Shepherd's Way, Brookmans Park,
Hatfield, Hertfordshire AL9 6NS
Tel: 01707 602500
Principal: Mrs P C Edgar
BA(Hons)London, PGCE
Age range: G11–18
No. of pupils: 400 VIth120
Fees: Day £19,485–£21,825
FB £26,295–£28,665

Radlett Preparatory School
Kendal Hall, Watling Street,
Radlett, Hertfordshire WD7 7LY
Tel: 01923 856812
Principal: Mr G White BEd (Hons)
Age range: 4–11
Fees: Day £7,140–£7,250

Rudolf Steiner School
Langley Hill, Kings Langley,
Hertfordshire WD4 9HG
Tel: 01923 262500
Age range: 3–19
No. of pupils: 405
Fees: Day £2,985–£7,800

Sherrardswood School
Lockleys, Welwyn,
Hertfordshire AL6 0BJ
Tel: 01438 714282
Headmistress: Mrs L Corry
Age range: 2–18
No. of pupils: 357
Fees: Day £6,720–£12,750

St Albans High School for Girls
Townsend Avenue, St Albans,
Hertfordshire AL1 3SJ
Tel: 01727 853800
Headmistress: Mrs Jenny
Brown MA (Oxon)
Age range: G4–18
No. of pupils: 940 VIth170

St Albans School
Abbey Gateway, St Albans,
Hertfordshire AL3 4HB
Tel: 01727 855521
Headmaster: Mr JWJ Gillespie
MA(Cantab), FRSA
Age range: B11–18 G16–18
No. of pupils: 870
Fees: Day £16,818

St Albans Tutors
69 London Road, St Albans,
Hertfordshire AL1 1LN
Tel: 01727 842348
Principals: Mr. A N Jemal
& Mr Elvis Cotena
Age range: 15+
Fees: Day £3,400

St Christopher School
Barrington Road, Letchworth,
Hertfordshire SG6 3JZ
Tel: 01462 650 850
Head: Richard Palmer
Age range: 3–18
No. of pupils: 511 VIth78
Fees: Day £3,375–£14,505
FB £15,600–£25,470

St Columba's College
King Harry Lane, St Albans,
Hertfordshire AL3 4AW
Tel: 01727 855185
Headmaster: David R Buxton
Age range: B4–18
No. of pupils: 860 VIth150
Fees: Day £8,235–£10,416

St Columba's College Prep School
King Harry Lane, St Albans,
Hertfordshire AL3 4AW
Tel: 01727 862616
Head of Prep: Mrs Ruth Loveman
Age range: B4–11
Fees: Day £9,702–£12,087

St Edmund's College & Prep School
Old Hall Green, Nr Ware,
Hertfordshire SG11 1DS
Tel: 01920 824247
Head: Paulo Durán BA MA
Age range: 3–18
No. of pupils: 799 VIth135
Fees: Day £9,465–£14,955 WB
£19,830–£22,575 FB £21,855–£24,990

St Edmund's Prep
Old Hall Green, Ware,
Hertfordshire SG11 1DS
Tel: 01920 824239
Head: Mr Steven Cartwright
BSc (Surrey)
Age range: 3–11
No. of pupils: 185
Fees: Day £8,484–£12,252

St Francis' College
Broadway, Letchworth Garden
City, Hertfordshire SG6 3PJ
Tel: 01462 670511
Headmistress: Mrs B Goulding
Age range: G3–18
No. of pupils: 460 VIth75
Fees: Day £8,670–£13,830 WB
£19,425–£22,875 FB £24,195–£27,645

St Hilda's School
28 Douglas Road, Harpenden,
Hertfordshire AL5 2ES
Tel: 01582 712307
Headmaster: Mr Dan Sayers
Age range: G3–11 years
No. of pupils: 165
Fees: Day £5,715–£9,975

St Hilda's School
High Street, Bushey,
Hertfordshire WD23 3DA
Tel: 020 8950 1751
Headmistress: Mrs Tracy
Handford MA
Age range: B2–4 G2–11
No. of pupils: 142
Fees: Day £4,635–£8,685

St John's Preparatory School
The Ridgeway, Potters Bar,
Hertfordshire EN6 5QT
Tel: 01707 657294
Headmistress: Mrs C
Tardios BA(Hons)
Age range: 4–11
No. of pupils: 184
Fees: Day £8,190–£8,730

St Joseph's In The Park
St Mary's Lane, Hertingfordbury,
Hertford, Hertfordshire SG14 2LX
Tel: 01992 581378
Headmaster: Mr Neil Jones
Age range: 3–11
No. of pupils: 161
Fees: Day £5,298–£14,247

St Margaret's School, Bushey
Merry Hill Road, Bushey,
Hertfordshire WD23 1DT
Tel: 020 8416 4400
Head: Mrs Rose Hardy
MA(Oxon), MEd, FRSA
Age range: G4–18 years
No. of pupils: 450 VIth100
Fees: Day £14,730 WB
£20,220–£23,670 FB £27,600

Stanborough School
Stanborough Park, Garston,
Watford, Hertfordshire WD25 9JT
Tel: 01923 673268
Head Teacher: Ms Lorraine Dixon
Age range: 3–19
No. of pupils: 300 VIth20
Fees: Day £3,660–£5,500
WB £12,834–£15,846

Stormont
The Causeway, Potters Bar,
Hertfordshire EN6 5HA
Tel: 01707 654037
Head of School: Mrs Sharon Martin
Age range: G4–11
Fees: Day £10,215–£10,680

The Christian School (Takeley)
Dunmow Road, Brewers End,
Takeley, Bishop's Stortford,
Hertfordshire CM22 6QH
Tel: 01279 871182
Headmaster: M E Humphries
Age range: 5–16
Fees: Day £3,720

The King's School
Elmfield, Ambrose Lane,
Harpenden, Hertfordshire AL5 4DU
Tel: 01582 767566
Principal: Mr Clive John
Case BA, HDE
Age range: 5–16
Fees: Day £4,380

The Purcell School, London
Aldenham Road, Bushey,
Hertfordshire WD23 2TS
Tel: 01923 331100
Headteacher: Mr. Stephen Yeo
Age range: 8–18
No. of pupils: 167 VIth70
Fees: WB £22,452 FB £28,716

Tring Park School for the Performing Arts
Tring Park, Tring,
Hertfordshire HP23 5LX
Tel: 01442 824255
Principal: Mr Stefan Anderson
MA, ARCM, ARCT
Age range: 8–19
No. of pupils: 340 VIth217
Fees: Day £13,785–£21,960
FB £23,250–£32,880

Westbrook Hay Prep School
London Road, Hemel Hempstead,
Hertfordshire HP1 2RF
Tel: 01442 256143
Headmaster: Keith D
Young BEd(Hons)
Age range: 3–13
No. of pupils: 300
Fees: Day £9,225–£13,275

York House School
Redheath, Sarratt Road,
Croxley Green, Rickmansworth,
Hertfordshire WD3 4LW
Tel: 01923 772395
Headmaster: Jon Gray BA(Ed)
Age range: 3–13
No. of pupils: 240
Fees: Day £10,845

Kent

Ashford School
East Hill, Ashford, Kent TN24 8PB
Tel: 01233 739030
Head: Mr M R Buchanan
BSc(Hons), CertEd, NPQH, CPhys
Age range: 3 months–18 years
No. of pupils: 835 VIth170
Fees: Day £8,400–£16,200
WB £28,500 FB £32,400

Beech Grove School
Beech Grove Bruderhof,
Sandwich Road, Nonington,
Dover, Kent CT15 4HH
Tel: 01304 842980
Head: Mr Benjamin Shirky
Age range: 4–14
No. of pupils: 63

Beechwood Sacred Heart
12 Pembury Road, Tunbridge
Wells, Kent TN2 3QD
Tel: 01892 532747
Headmaster: Mr Aaron
Lennon BA(Hons)
Age range: 3–18
No. of pupils: 400 VIth70
Fees: Day £9,060–£15,936
WB £23,460 FB £26,460

Benenden School
Cranbrook, Kent TN17 4AA
Tel: 01580 240592
Headmistress: Mrs S Price
Age range: G11–18
No. of pupils: 543
Fees: FB £31,410

Bethany School
Curtisden Green, Goudhurst,
Cranbrook, Kent TN17 1LB
Tel: 01580 211273
Headmaster: Mr Francie
Healy BSc, HDipEd, NPQH
Age range: 11–18 years
No. of pupils: 345 VIth112
Fees: Day £15,483–£16,986 WB
£23,967–£26,283 FB £25,842–£28,917

Bronte School
Mayfield, 7 Pelham Road,
Gravesend, Kent DA11 0HN
Tel: 01474 533805
Headmaster: Mr R Dyson
Age range: 4–11
No. of pupils: 120
Fees: Day £7,950

Bryony School
Marshall Road, Rainham,
Gillingham, Kent ME8 0AJ
Tel: 01634 231511
Joint Heads: D E and
Mrs M P Edmunds
Age range: 2–11
No. of pupils: 174
Fees: Day £4,551–£5,451

Canterbury Steiner School
Garlinge Green, Chartham,
Canterbury, Kent CT4 5RU
Tel: 01227 738285
Age range: 3–18
Fees: Day £3,246–£4,405.50

CATS College Canterbury
68 New Dover Road,
Canterbury, Kent CT1 3LQ
Tel: +44 (0)1227866540
Principal: Jonathan Ullmer
MBE, MA, LRAM, FCollP,
ACP, Dip Arts, NPQH
Age range: 14–18
No. of pupils: 400

Chartfield School
45 Minster Road, Westgate
on Sea, Kent CT8 8DA
Tel: 01843 831716
Head & Proprietor: Miss L P Shipley
Age range: 4–11
No. of pupils: 50
Fees: Day £2,580–£3,000

Cobham Hall School
Cobham, Kent DA12 3BL
Tel: 01474 823371
Headmaster: Mr Paul Mitchell BSc
Age range: G11–18
No. of pupils: 180

COMBE BANK SCHOOL
For further details see p. 91
Combe Bank Drive,
Sevenoaks, Kent TN14 6AE
Tel: 01959 563720
Email: enquiries@
combebank.co.uk
Website:
www.combebank.co.uk
Head: Mr David Paton
BComm (Hons) PGCE MA
Age range: 2.5–18
No. of pupils: 250

Derwent Lodge School for Girls
Somerhill, Tonbridge, Kent TN11 0NJ
Tel: 01732 352124
Headmistress: Mrs S Michau
MA(Oxon), PGCE
Age range: G7–11
No. of pupils: 134
Fees: Day £12,675

Dover College
Effingham Crescent,
Dover, Kent CT17 9RH
Tel: 01304 205969 Ext:201
Headmaster: Gerry Holden
Age range: 3–18
No. of pupils: 340 VIth100
Fees: Day £6,750–£14,250 WB
£18,900–£22,200 FB £20,700–£27,900

Dulwich Preparatory School
Coursehorn, Cranbrook,
Kent TN17 3NP
Tel: 01580 712179
Headmaster: Mr Paul
David BEd(Hons)
Age range: 3–13
No. of pupils: 535
Fees: Day £4,890–£14,400

Elliott Park School
18-20 Marina Drive, Minster,
Sheerness, Kent ME12 2DP
Tel: 01795 873372
Head: Mr R Barson
Age range: 4–11
No. of pupils: 60
Fees: Day £3,897

European School of Osteopathy
Boxley House, The Street, Boxley,
Maidstone, Kent ME14 3DZ
Tel: 01622 671 558
Principal: Mr Renzo Molinari DO

Fosse Bank School
Mountains, Noble Tree
Road, Hildenborough,
Tonbridge, Kent TN11 8ND
Tel: 01732 834212
Headmistress: Mrs Lovatt-Young
Age range: 3–11
No. of pupils: 124
Fees: Day £1,560–£10,671

Gad's Hill School
Higham, Rochester,
Medway, Kent ME3 7PA
Tel: 01474 822366
Headmaster: Mr D G Craggs
BSc, MA, NPQH, FCollP, FRSA
Age range: 3–16
No. of pupils: 370
Fees: Day £6,000–£7,600

Haddon Dene School
57 Gladstone Road,
Broadstairs, Kent CT10 2HY
Tel: 01843 861176
Head: Mrs E Rowe
Age range: 3–11
No. of pupils: 200
Fees: Day £4,950–£6,135

Hilden Grange School
62 Dry Hill Park Road,
Tonbridge, Kent TN10 3BX
Tel: 01732 351169
Headmaster: Mr J Withers BA(Hons)
Age range: 3–13
Fees: Day £9,780–£12,950

Hilden Oaks School & Nursery
38 Dry Hill Park Road,
Tonbridge, Kent TN10 3BU
Tel: 01732 353941
Headmistress: Mrs S A Webb
Age range: 0–11 B0–11 G0–11
Fees: Day £7,980–£10,710

Holmewood House School
Langton Green, Tunbridge
Wells, Kent TN3 0EB
Tel: 01892 860006
Headmaster: Mr J D B
Marjoribanks BEd
Age range: 3–13
No. of pupils: 473
Fees: Day £5,900–£16,455

Kent College
Whitstable Road, Canterbury,
Kent CT2 9DT
Tel: 01227 763231
Head Master: Dr D J Lamper
Age range: 3–18
No. of pupils: 702
Fees: Day £15,669–£17,259
FB £23,529–£32,316

Kent College Nursery, Infant & Junior School
Vernon Holme, Harbledown,
Canterbury, Kent CT2 9AQ
Tel: 01227 762436
Headmaster: Mr A J Carter
Age range: 3–11
No. of pupils: 190
Fees: Day £8,805–£9,615
WB £14,196 FB £18,400

Kent College Pembury
Old Church Road, Pembury,
Tunbridge Wells, Kent TN2 4AX
Tel: +44 (0)1892 822006
Headmistress: Mrs Sally-Anne
Huang MA(Oxon), MSc, PGCE
Age range: G3–18
No. of pupils: 650 VIth102
Fees: Day £7,887–£17,322
FB £21,471–£27,924

Kids Inc Day Nursery – Bluewater
West Village, Bluewater,
Greenhithe, Kent DA9 9SE
Tel: 01322 386624

King's Preparatory School, Rochester
King Edward Road, Rochester,
Medway, Kent ME1 1UB
Tel: 01634 888577
Headmaster: Mr R Overend
Age range: 4–13
No. of pupils: 228
Fees: Day £7,125–£10,380 FB £16,005

King's School, Rochester
Satis House, Boley Hill,
Rochester, Kent ME1 1TE
Tel: 01634 888555
Headmaster: Dr I R Walker BA,
PhD, LTh, ABIA, FCollP, FRSA
Age range: 13–18
No. of pupils: 688 VIth113
Fees: Day £7,655–£14,400
FB £17,145–£24,210

Linton Park School
3 Eccleston Road, Tovil,
Maidstone, Kent ME17 4HT
Tel: 01622 740820
Headteacher: Mr C Allen
Age range: 7–18
No. of pupils: 134

Lorenden Preparatory School
Painter's Forstal, Faversham,
Kent ME13 0EN
Tel: 01795 590030
Headmistress: Mrs R Simmonds
Age range: 3–11
No. of pupils: 100
Fees: Day £7,374–£10,680

Marlborough House School
High Street, Hawkhurst,
Kent TN18 4PY
Tel: 01580 753555
Headmaster: Mr David N
Hopkins MA(Oxon), PGCE
Age range: 2–13
No. of pupils: 334
Fees: Day £2,808–£14,700

Meredale Independent Primary School
Solomon Road, Rainham,
Gillingham, Kent ME8 8EB
Tel: 01634 231405
Headteacher: Miss
Michelle Ingledew
Age range: 3–11
No. of pupils: 53
Fees: Day £5,100

Northbourne Park School
Betteshanger, Deal, Kent CT14 0NW
Tel: 01304 611215/218
Headmaster: Mr Edward Balfour
Age range: 3–13
No. of pupils: 185
Fees: Day £11,400–£13,740 WB
£16,140–£16,140 FB £119,200–£19,200

Rochester Independent College
Star Hill, Rochester,
Medway, Kent ME1 1XF
Tel: 01634 828115
Principals: Alistair Brownlow,
Brian Pain, Pauline Bailey
Age range: 11–19
No. of pupils: 306 VIth233
Fees: Day £12,000–£16,500 WB
£25,650–£27,300 FB £27,450–£29,100

Rose Hill School
Coniston Avenue, Tunbridge
Wells, Kent TN4 9SY
Tel: 01892 525591
Headmaster: Mr D
Westcombe BA, PGCE
Age range: 3–13
Fees: Day £3,040–£4,130

Russell House School
Station Road, Otford,
Sevenoaks, Kent TN14 5QU
Tel: 01959 522352
Headmistress: Mrs Alison Cooke
Age range: 2–11
Fees: Day £4,650–£9,840

Sackville School
Tonbridge Rd, Hildenborough,
Tonbridge, Kent TN11 9HN
Tel: 01732 838888
Headteacher: Mr John
Hewitt BA MBA
Age range: 11–18
No. of pupils: 184 VIth35
Fees: Day £13,620

Saint Ronan's School
Water Lane, Hawkhurst,
Kent TN18 5DJ
Tel: 01580 752271
Headmaster: William Trelawny-
Vernon BSc(Hons)
Age range: 3–13
No. of pupils: 300
Fees: Day £6,951–£11,892

Sevenoaks Preparatory School
Godden Green, Sevenoaks,
Kent TN15 0JU
Tel: 01732 762336
Headmaster: Mr Luke Harrison
Age range: 2–13
No. of pupils: 388
Fees: Day £3,552–£11,910

Sevenoaks School
High Street, Sevenoaks,
Kent TN13 1HU
Tel: +44 (0)1732 455133
Head: Dr Katy Ricks MA, DPhil
Age range: 11–18
No. of pupils: 1054 VIth423
Fees: Day £20,763–£23,571
FB £33,156–£35,964

Shernold School
Hill Place, Queens Avenue,
Maidstone, Kent ME16 0ER
Tel: 01622 752868
Headmistress: Mrs L Dack
Age range: 3–11
No. of pupils: 142
Fees: Day £3,525–£4,200

Solefield School
Solefield Road, Sevenoaks,
Kent TN13 1PH
Tel: 01732 452142
Headmaster: Mr D A
Philps BSc(Hons)
Age range: B4–13
No. of pupils: 180
Fees: Day £9,990–£12,060

Somerhill Pre-Prep
Somerhill, Five Oak Green Road,
Tonbridge, Kent TN11 0NJ
Tel: 01732 352124
Headmistress: Mrs J Ruth
Sorensen BEd(Hons), CertEd
Age range: 3–7
No. of pupils: 245

Spring Grove School
Harville Road, Wye,
Ashford, Kent TN25 5EZ
Tel: 01233 812337
Headmaster: Mr Bill Jones
Age range: 2–11
No. of pupils: 194
Fees: Day £2,050–£3,125

St Andrew's School
24-28 Watts Avenue, Rochester,
Medway, Kent ME1 1SA
Tel: 01634 843479
Principal: Mrs E Steinmann-Gilbert
Age range: 2–11
No. of pupils: 367
Fees: Day £6,672–£7,059

St Christopher's School
New Dover Road,
Canterbury, Kent CT1 3DT
Tel: 01227 462960
The Master: Mr D Evans
Age range: 3–11
Fees: Day £7,600

St Edmund's Junior School
St Thomas Hill, Canterbury,
Kent CT2 8HU
Tel: 01227 475600
Master: R G Bacon
BA(Hons)(Durham)
Age range: 3–13
No. of pupils: 230
Fees: Day £6,969–£14,211
WB £18,969 FB £20,817

St Edmund's School
St Thomas\' Hill, Canterbury,
Kent CT2 8HU
Tel: 01227 475601
Head: Louise Moelwyn-Hughes
Age range: 3–18
No. of pupils: 535
Fees: Day £18,651 FB £29,781

St Faith's at Ash School
5 The Street, Ash, Canterbury,
Kent CT3 2HH
Tel: 01304 813409
Headmaster: Mr Lawrence Groves
Age range: 2–11
No. of pupils: 225
Fees: Day £6,435–£8,100

**St Joseph's Convent
Prep School**
46 Old Road East, Gravesend,
Kent DA12 1NR
Tel: 01474 533012
Head Teacher: Mrs Carola Timney
Age range: 3–11
No. of pupils: 146
Fees: Day £6,655

St Lawrence College
Ramsgate, Kent CT11 7AE
Tel: 01843 572931
Principal: Mr Antony Spencer
Age range: 3–18
No. of pupils: VIth140
Fees: Day £7,047–£17,436
FB £23,640–£31,452

**St Michael's
Preparatory School**
Otford Court, Otford,
Sevenoaks, Kent TN14 5SA
Tel: 01959 522137
Headteacher: Mrs Jill Aisher
Age range: 2–13
No. of pupils: 472
Fees: Day £2,064–£12,555

Steephill School
Off Castle Hill, Fawkham,
Longfield, Kent DA3 7BG
Tel: 01474 702107
Head: Mrs C Birtwoll
BSc, MBA, PGCE
Age range: 3–11
No. of pupils: 131
Fees: Day £6,860

**Sutton Valence
Preparatory School**
Underhill, Chart Sutton,
Maidstone, Kent ME17 3RF
Tel: 01622 842117
Head: Mr C Gibbs BA(Hons),
HDE(1st Class)
Age range: 3–11
No. of pupils: 375
Fees: Day £1,630–£9,135

Sutton Valence School
North Street, Sutton
Valence, Kent ME17 3HL
Tel: 01622 845200
Headmaster: Mr B C W Grindlay
MA(Cantab), MusB, FRCO, CHM
Age range: 11–18
No. of pupils: VIth170
Fees: Day £5,020–£6,660 WB
£7,930–£10,310 FB £7,930–£10,310

The Granville School
2 Bradbourne Park Road,
Sevenoaks, Kent TN13 3LJ
Tel: 01732 453039
Headmistress: Mrs J
Scott BEd(Cantab)
Age range: B3–4 G3–11
No. of pupils: 190
Fees: Day £4,695–£12,120

**The Junior King's
School, Canterbury**
Milner Court, Sturry,
Canterbury, Kent CT2 0AY
Tel: 01227 714000
Headmaster: Mr Peter
Wells BEd(Hons)
Age range: 3–13
Fees: Day £8,610–£14,610 FB £19,830

**THE KING'S SCHOOL,
CANTERBURY**
For further details see p. 100
The Precincts, Canterbury,
Kent CT1 2ES
Tel: 01227 595501
Email: info@kings-school.co.uk
Website:
www.kings-school.co.uk
Head: Mr P Roberts
Age range: 13–18
No. of pupils: 824 VIth380
Fees: Day £26,055 FB £34,440

The Mead School
16 Frant Road, Tunbridge
Wells, Kent TN2 5SN
Tel: 01892 525837
Headmistress: Mrs A
Culley CertEd(Oxon)
Age range: 3–11
No. of pupils: 188
Fees: Day £3,900–£9,945

The New Beacon School
Brittains Lane, Sevenoaks,
Kent TN13 2PB
Tel: 01732 452131
Headmaster: Mr M Piercy BA(Hons)
Age range: B4–13
No. of pupils: 400
Fees: Day £9,405–£12,135

TONBRIDGE SCHOOL
For further details see p. 103
Tonbridge, Kent TN9 1JP
Tel: 01732 365555
Email: admissions@
tonbridge-school.org
Website:
www.tonbridge-school.co.uk
Headmaster: T H P Haynes
Age range: B13–18
No. of pupils: 778 VIth317
Fees: Day £27,216 FB £36,288

**Walthamstow Hall Pre-
Prep and Junior School**
Sevenoaks, Kent TN13 3LD
Tel: 01732 451334
Headmistress: Mrs Jill
Milner MA(Oxford)
Age range: G2–11
No. of pupils: 218
Fees: Day £1,230–£9,990

Walthamstow Hall School
Sevenoaks, Kent TN13 3UL
Tel: 01732 451334
Headmistress: Mrs J
Milner MA(Oxford)
Age range: G2–18
No. of pupils: 500 VIth80
Fees: Day £8,070–£13,710

Wellesley House
114 Ramsgate Road,
Broadstairs, Kent CT10 2DG
Tel: 01843 862991
Headmaster: Mr S T P
O'Malley MA(Hons), PGCE
Age range: 7–13
No. of pupils: 133
Fees: Day £14,985–
£17,850 FB £22,575

Yardley Court
Somerhill, Five Oak Green Road,
Tonbridge, Kent TN11 0NJ
Tel: 01732 352124
Headmaster: J T Coakley
MA, BA(Hons), PGCE
Age range: B7–13
No. of pupils: 260
Fees: Day £13,150

Surrey

Aberdour School
Brighton Road, Burgh Heath,
Tadworth, Surrey KT20 6AJ
Tel: 01737 354119
Headmaster: Mr Simon Collins
Age range: 2–13
No. of pupils: 255
Fees: Day £3,990–£10,605

**ACS Cobham
International School**
Heywood, Portsmouth Road,
Cobham, Surrey KT11 1BL
Tel: +44 (0) 1932 867251
Head of School: Mr A Eysele
Age range: 2–18
No. of pupils: 1460
Fees: Day £10,690–£25,050
FB £36,240–£43,730

**ACS Egham
International School**
Woodlee, London Road,
Egham, Surrey TW20 0HS
Tel: +44 (0) 1784 430 800
Head of School: Jeremy Lewis
Age range: 3–18
No. of pupils: 620
Fees: Day £7,010–£23,430

Aldro School
Shackleford, Godalming,
Surrey GU8 6AS
Tel: 01483 810266
Headmaster: Mr D W N
Aston BA(Hons), PGCE
Age range: B7–13
No. of pupils: 220
Fees: Day £14,610 FB £18,795

Amesbury
Hazel Grove, Hindhead,
Surrey GU26 6BL
Tel: 01428 604322
Headmaster: Mr Nigel Taylor MA
Age range: 2–13
No. of pupils: 325
Fees: Day £9,060–£13,875
£ ⊘

Barfield School
Runfold, Farnham, Surrey GU10 1PB
Tel: 01252 782271
Head: James Reid
Age range: 2–13
No. of pupils: 280
Fees: Day £5,055–£13,020
£

Barrow Hills School
Roke Lane, Witley, Godalming,
Surrey GU8 5NY
Tel: 01428 683639/682634
Headmaster: Mr M
Unsworth BEng, PGCE
Age range: 3–13
No. of pupils: 261
Fees: Day £7,995–£12,720
£ ⊘

Belmont Preparatory School
Feldemore, Holmbury St Mary,
Dorking, Surrey RH5 6LQ
Tel: 01306 730852
Headmistress: Mrs Helen Skrine
BA, PGCE, NPQH, FRSA
Age range: 2–13
No. of pupils: 227
Fees: Day £6,120–£10,428
WB £15,345
⊞ £ ⊘

Bishopsgate School
Bishopsgate Road, Englefield
Green, Egham, Surrey TW20 0YJ
Tel: 01784 432109
Headmaster: Mr Andrew
Cowell BEd, CPSE
Age range: 3–13
Fees: Day £4,500–£12,726
£ ⊘

Box Hill School
Old London Road, Mickleham,
Dorking, Surrey RH5 6EA
Tel: 01372 373382
Headmaster: Mr Corydon Lowde
Age range: 11–18
No. of pupils: 425 VIth96
Fees: Day £16,140–£17,170
WB £24,600–£25,800 FB
£29,970–£35,850
🌐 ⊞ £ IB ⊘ 16+

Bramley School
Chequers Lane, Walton-on-the-
Hill, Tadworth, Surrey KT20 7ST
Tel: 01737 812004
Headmistress: Mrs P Burgess
Age range: G3–11
No. of pupils: 110
Fees: Day £3,858–£8,418
⚥ £ ⊘

Cambridge Management College
4-8 Castle Street, Oakington,
Kingston upon Thames,
Surrey KT11SS
Tel: 08003166282
Principal: Dr Peter Holmes
16+

Caterham School
Harestone Valley, Caterham,
Surrey CR3 6YA
Tel: 01883 343028
Head: Mr C. W. Jones MA(Cantab)
Age range: 11–18
No. of pupils: VIth321
🌐 A ⊞ £ ⊘ 16+

Charterhouse
Godalming, Surrey GU7 2DX
Tel: 01483 291500
Headmaster: Mr Richard
Pleming MA
Age range: B13–18 G16–18
No. of pupils: 803 VIth422
Fees: Day £29,361 FB £35,529
🌐 A ⊞ £ IB ⊘ 16+

Chinthurst School
Tadworth Street, Tadworth,
Surrey KT20 5QZ
Tel: 01737 812011
Headmaster: Mr David
Williams BA (Hons), PGCE
Age range: B3–13
No. of pupils: 120
Fees: Day £3,800–£10,650
⚥ £ ⊘

City of London Freemen's School
Ashtead Park, Ashtead,
Surrey KT21 1ET
Tel: 01372 277933
Headmaster: Mr Philip
MacDonald MA(Oxon)
Age range: 7–18
No. of pupils: 877 VIth213
Fees: Day £10,872–
£14,598 FB £23,238
🌐 A ⊞ £ ⊘ 16+

Claremont Fan Court School
Claremont Drive, Esher,
Surrey KT10 9LY
Tel: 01372 467841
Head of Senior School: Mr
Jonathan Insall-Reid
Age range: 2–18
No. of pupils: 736 VIth90
Fees: Day £4,845–£16,035
A £ ⊘ 16+

Cornerstone School
22 West Hill, Epsom, Surrey KT19 8JD
Tel: 01372 742940
Headmaster: Mr G R Davies BEd
Age range: 5–16

Coworth-Flexlands School
Valley End, Chobham,
Woking, Surrey GU24 8TE
Tel: 01276 855707
Headmistress: Mrs Anne Sweeney
Age range: B3–7 G3–11
No. of pupils: 145
Fees: Day £3,885–£10,185
⊘

Cranleigh Preparatory School
Horseshoe Lane, Cranleigh,
Surrey GU6 8QH
Tel: 01483 274199
Headmaster: Mr M T Wilson BSc
Age range: 7–13
No. of pupils: 290
Fees: Day £11,385 FB £14,025
⊞

Cranleigh School
Horseshoe Lane, Cranleigh,
Surrey GU6 8QQ
Tel: +44 (0) 1483 273666
Headmaster: Mr Martin
Reader MA, MPhil, MBA
Age range: 7–18 (including
Prep School)
No. of pupils: 631 VIth253
Fees: Day £27,855 FB £34,170
🌐 A ⊞ £ ⊘ 16+

Cranmore School
Epsom Road, West Horsley,
Surrey KT24 6AT
Tel: 01483 280340
Headmaster: Mr Michael
Connolly BSc, BA, MA, MEd
Age range: 2–13
No. of pupils: 475
£ ⊘

Danes Hill School
Leatherhead Road, Oxshott,
Surrey KT22 0JG
Tel: 01372 842509
Headmaster: Mr W Murdock BA
Age range: 3–13
No. of pupils: 872
Fees: Day £1,682–£4,662
£ ⊘

Danesfield Manor School
Rydens Avenue, Walton-on-
Thames, Surrey KT12 3JB
Tel: 01932 220930
Principal: Mrs Helen Chalmers
Age range: 2–11
No. of pupils: 170
Fees: Day £8,400
⊘

Downsend School
Ashtead Lodge, 22 Oakfield
Road, Ashtead, Surrey KT21 2RE
Tel: 01372 385439
Head Teacher: Mrs K Barrett
Age range: 2–6
No. of pupils: 66
Fees: Day £2,190–£8,250

Downsend School
Epsom Lodge, 6 Norman Avenue,
Epsom, Surrey KT17 3AB
Tel: 01372 385438
Head Teacher: Miss J Birchall
Age range: 2–6
No. of pupils: 110
Fees: Day £2,325–£11,640
⊘

Downsend School
Leatherhead Lodge, Epsom Road,
Leatherhead, Surrey KT22 8ST
Tel: 01372 372123
Headteacher: Mrs Gill Brooks
Age range: 2–6
Fees: Day £6,780–£8,250

Downsend School
1 Leatherhead Road,
Leatherhead, Surrey KT22 8TJ
Tel: 01372 372197
Headmaster: Mr Ian Thorpe
Age range: 2–13
No. of pupils: 740
Fees: Day £13,455
⊘

Drayton House School
35 Austen Road, Guildford,
Surrey GU1 3NP
Tel: 01483 504707
Headmistress: Mrs J Tyson-Jones
Froebel Cert.Ed. London University
Age range: 3 months–7 years
Fees: Day £4,420–£12,500
⊘

Duke of Kent School
Peaslake Road, Ewhurst,
Surrey GU6 7NS
Tel: 01483 277313
Head: Mrs Judith Fremont-Barnes
Age range: 3–16
No. of pupils: 234
Fees: Day £4,860–£14,130 WB
£13,350–£16,770 FB £15,735–£18,855
🌐 ⊞ £ ⊘

Dunottar School
High Trees Road, Reigate,
Surrey RH2 7EL
Tel: 01737 761945
Head: Mrs Rowena Cole
Age range: 11–18
No. of pupils: 200 VIth40
Fees: Day £14,700
A £ 16+

Edgeborough
Frensham, Farnham,
Surrey GU10 3AH
Tel: 01252 792495
Headmaster: Mr C J Davies BA
Age range: 2–13
No. of pupils: 285
Fees: Day £9,105–£14,850
WB £16,752–£18,282
⊞ £ ⊘

Emberhurst School
94 Ember Lane, Esher,
Surrey KT10 8EN
Tel: 020 8398 2933
Headmistress: Mrs P Chadwick BEd
Age range: 2+–7+
No. of pupils: 70
Fees: Day £2,265–£6,495

Epsom College
Epsom, Surrey KT17 4JQ
Tel: 01372 821234
Headmaster: Mr Jay A Piggot MA
Age range: 13–18
No. of pupils: 730
Fees: Day £21,255 FB £31,098
🌐 A ⊞ £ ⊘ 16+

Essendene Lodge School
Essendene Road, Caterham,
Surrey CR3 5PB
Tel: 01883 348349
Head Teacher: Mrs J Wermig
Age range: 2–11
No. of pupils: 153
Fees: Day £2,775–£5,550
£ ⊘

Ewell Castle School
Church Street, Ewell, Epsom,
Surrey KT17 2AW
Tel: 020 8393 1413
Principal: Peter Harris
Age range: B3–18 G3-11–16-18
No. of pupils: 531
Fees: Day £6,750–£13,020
(A)(£)(⚲)(16)

Feltonfleet School
Cobham, Surrey KT11 1DR
Tel: 01932 862264
Headmaster: P C Ward
Age range: 3–13
No. of pupils: 356
Fees: Day £7,680–£11,250
WB £15,750
(🏫)(£)(⚲)

Focus School – Hindhead Campus
Tilford Road, Hindhead,
Surrey GU26 6SJ
Tel: 01428 601800
Head: Mr S Hardy
Age range: 8–18
No. of pupils: 90

Frensham Heights
Rowledge, Farnham,
Surrey GU10 4EA
Tel: 01252 792561
Headmaster: Mr Andrew
Fisher BA, MEd, FRSA
Age range: 3–18
No. of pupils: 497 VIth105
Fees: Day £5,205–£15,300
FB £19,485–£22,680
(🏊)(A)(🏫)(£)(⚲)(16)

Glenesk School
Ockham Road North, East
Horsley, Surrey KT24 6NS
Tel: 01483 282329
Headmistress: Mrs S Christie-Hall
Age range: 2–7
Fees: Day £1,350–£8,112
(£)(⚲)

Greenacre School for Girls
Sutton Lane, Banstead,
Surrey SM7 3RA
Tel: 01737 352114
Headmistress: Mrs L E Redding
Age range: G3–18
No. of pupils: 320 VIth30
Fees: Day £8,898–£15,282
(🏊)(A)(£)(⚲)(16)

Greenfield
Brooklyn Road, Woking,
Surrey GU22 7TP
Tel: 01483 772525
Headmistress: Mrs Tania Botting BEd
Age range: 3–11
No. of pupils: 179
Fees: Day £4,284–£9,450
(£)(⚲)

Guildford High School
London Road, Guildford,
Surrey GU1 1SJ
Tel: 01483 561440
Headmistress: Mrs F J
Boulton BSc, MA
Age range: G4–18
No. of pupils: 980 VIth160
Fees: Day £9,591–£15,564
(🏊)(A)(£)(16)

Guildford Secretarial & Business College
17 Chapel Street, Guildford,
Surrey GU1 3UL
Tel: 01483 564885
Corporate Training Manager:
Mrs V Alexander
Fees: Day £0
(16)

Hall Grove School
London Road, Bagshot,
Surrey GU19 5HZ
Tel: 01276 473059
Headmaster: Mr A R
Graham BSc, PGCE
Age range: 3–13
Fees: Day £8,880–£12,480
(🏫)

Halstead Preparatory School
Woodham Rise, Woking,
Surrey GU21 4EE
Tel: 01483 772682
Headmistress: Mrs P Austin
Age range: G3–11
No. of pupils: 220
Fees: Day £2,673–£12,162
(🏊)(£)(⚲)

Hampton Court House
Hampton Court Road, East
Molesey, Surrey KT8 9BS
Tel: 020 8943 0889
Headmaster: Mr Guy Holloway
Age range: 3–16
No. of pupils: VIth20
Fees: Day £7,842–£10,017
(A)(£)

Haslemere Preparatory School
The Heights, Hill Road,
Haslemere, Surrey GU27 2JP
Tel: 01428 642350
Head: Mr P Wenham
MA(Cantab), PGCE
Age range: B3–13 G3–4
No. of pupils: 191
Fees: Day £2,199–£3,145
(🏊)(£)(⚲)

Hawley Place School
Fernhill Road, Blackwater,
Camberley, Surrey GU17 9HU
Tel: 01276 32028
Head of School: Mr Michael Stone
Age range: B2–11 G2–16
No. of pupils: 370
Fees: Day £4,446–£11,400
(£)(⚲)

Hazelwood School
Wolf's Hill, Limpsfield,
Oxted, Surrey RH8 0QU
Tel: 01883 712194
Head: Mrs Maxine Shaw
Age range: 2–13
No. of pupils: 399
Fees: Day £3,585–£11,100
(£)(⚲)

Hoe Bridge School
Hoe Place, Old Woking Road,
Woking, Surrey GU22 8JE
Tel: 01483 760018 &
01483 772194
Head: Mr N Arkell BSc
Age range: 2–14
Fees: Day £5,355–£14,080
(£)(⚲)

Hurtwood House
Holmbury St Mary, Dorking,
Surrey RH5 6NU
Tel: 01483 279000
Principal: Mr Cosmo Jackson
Age range: 16–18
No. of pupils: 300
Fees: FB £30,600–£35,100
(16)(A)(🏫)

International School of London (ISL) Surrey
Old Woking Road, Woking,
Surrey GU22 8HY
Tel: +44 (0)1483 750409
**Campus Principal & Head of
Secondary:** Richard Parker
Age range: 2–18 years
No. of pupils: 252
Fees: Day £17,700–£21,900
(🌐)(£)(IB)(⚲)

Kids Inc Day Nursery – Guildford
Railton Road, Queen Elizabeth
Park, Guildford, Surrey GU2 9LX
Tel: 01483 237999

King Edward's Witley
Godalming, Surrey GU8 5SG
Tel: +44 (0)1428 686700
Acting Headmaster:
Paul Crissell MA
Age range: 2–18
Fees: Day £19,950 FB £29,145
(🌐)(🏫)(£)(IB)(⚲)(16)

Kingswood House School
56 West Hill, Epsom, Surrey KT19 8LG
Tel: 01372 723590
Headmaster: Mr Peter R
Brooks MA, BEd(Hons)
Age range: B3–13 G3–7
No. of pupils: 210
Fees: Day £7,440–£9,825
(🏊)(£)(⚲)

Lanesborough
Maori Road, Guildford,
Surrey GU1 2EL
Tel: 01483 880650
Head: Mrs Clare Turnbull BA(Hons)
Age range: B3–13
No. of pupils: 350
Fees: Day £7,437–£10,026
(🏊)(£)(⚲)

Lingfield Notre Dame School
Lingfield, Surrey RH7 6PH
Tel: 01342 833176
Headmaster: Mr R Bool
Age range: 2–18
No. of pupils: 886 VIth120
Fees: Day £8,900–£12,000
(A)(£)(⚲)(16)

Longacre School
Shamley Green, Guildford,
Surrey GU5 0NQ
Tel: 01483 893225
Headmistress: Ms Alexia
Bracewell MA, BA(Hons), QTS
Age range: 2–11
No. of pupils: 237
(⚲)

Lyndhurst School
36 The Avenue, Camberley,
Surrey GU15 3NE
Tel: 01276 22895
Head: Mr A Rudkin BEd(Hons)
Age range: 2–11
Fees: Day £9,690–£11,655
(£)(⚲)

Manor House School
Manor House Lane, Little Bookham,
Leatherhead, Surrey KT23 4EN
Tel: 01372 458538
Headmistress: Miss Zara Axton
Age range: G2–16
No. of pupils: 360
Fees: Day £750–£4,070
(🏊)(£)(⚲)

Maple House School
23 Parchmore Road, Thornton
Heath, Surrey CR7 8LY
Tel: 020 8653 1827
Headteacher: Mrs Pauline Khoo
Age range: 5–10
No. of pupils: 97
(⚲)

Micklefield School
10/12 Somers Road, Reigate,
Surrey RH2 9DU
Tel: 01737 242615
Headmistress: Mrs L Rose
BEd(Hons), CertEd, Dip PC
Age range: 3–11
No. of pupils: 272
Fees: Day £2,565–£9,030
(⚲)

Milbourne Lodge School
Arbrook Lane, Esher,
Surrey KT10 9EG
Tel: 01372 462737
Head: Mrs Judy Waite
Age range: 4–13
No. of pupils: 236
Fees: Day £10,845–£13,500
(£)

New Life Christian Primary School
Cairo New Road, Croydon,
Surrey CR0 1XP
Tel: 020 8680 7671 Ext:327

Notre Dame School
Cobham, Surrey KT11 1HA
Tel: 01932 869990
Principal: Mr David Plummer
B.Ed. (Hons.), Dip HE, FRSA
Age range: 2–18
No. of pupils: 600

Oakhyrst Grange School
160 Stanstead Road,
Caterham, Surrey CR3 6AF
Tel: 01883 343344
Headmaster: Mr A Gear
Age range: 4–11
No. of pupils: 142
Fees: Day £1,107–£2,450

Parkside School
The Manor, Stoke d'Abernon,
Cobham, Surrey KT11 3PX
Tel: 01932 862749
Headmaster: Mr David
Aylward BEd(Hons), MA
Age range: B2 –13 G2 –4
No. of pupils: 382
Fees: Day £1,089–£13,350

Prior's Field
Priorsfield Road, Godalming,
Surrey GU7 2RH
Tel: 01483 810551
Head of School: Mrs T Kirnig
Age range: G11–18
No. of pupils: 450
Fees: Day £15,855 FB £25,575

Priory Preparatory School
Bolters Lane, Banstead,
Surrey SM7 2AJ
Tel: 01737 366920
Headmaster: Graham D
Malcom MA, BEd, FRSA
Age range: B2–13
No. of pupils: 200
Fees: Day £4,650–£10,350

Redehall Preparatory School
Redehall Road, Smallfield,
Horley, Surrey RH6 9QL
Tel: 01342 842987
Headmistress: Mrs J Wright
Age range: 3–11
Fees: Day £1,620

Reed's School
Sandy Lane, Cobham,
Surrey KT11 2ES
Tel: 01932 869001
Headmaster: Mr Mark
Hoskins BA MA MSc
Age range: B11–18 G16–18
No. of pupils: 650 VIth230
Fees: Day £16,938–£21,184
FB £22,582–£28,023

Reigate Grammar School
Reigate Road, Reigate,
Surrey RH2 0QS
Tel: 01737 222231
Headmaster: Mr Shaun Fenton
MA (Oxon) M Ed (Oxon)
Age range: 11–18
No. of pupils: 947 VIth246
Fees: Day £16,590

Reigate St Mary's Prep & Choir School
Chart Lane, Reigate,
Surrey RH2 7RN
Tel: 01737 244880
Headmaster: Mr Marcus
Culverwell MA
Age range: 3–11
No. of pupils: 280

Ripley Court School
Rose Lane, Ripley, Surrey GU23 6NE
Tel: 01483 225217
Headmaster: Mr A J Gough
Age range: 3–13
No. of pupils: 281
Fees: Day £8,745–£12,960

ROWAN PREPARATORY SCHOOL
For further details see p. 102
6 Fitzalan Road, Claygate,
Surrey KT10 0LX
Tel: 01372 462627
Email: school.registrar@
rowanprepschool.co.uk
Website:
www.rowanprepschool.co.uk
Headteacher: Mrs Susan Clarke
Age range: G2–11
No. of pupils: 330
Fees: Day £3,366–£4,465

Royal Grammar School, Guildford
High Street, Guildford,
Surrey GU1 3BB
Tel: 01483 880600
Headmaster: Dr J M Cox BSc, PhD
Age range: B11–18
No. of pupils: 900
Fees: Day £15,300–£16,050

Royal School of Needlework
Apartment 12A, Hampton
Court Palace, East Molesey,
Surrey KT8 9AU
Tel: 020 8943 1432
Principal: Mrs E Elvin
Age range: 17–30
No. of pupils: 24
Fees: Day £0

Rydes Hill Preparatory School
Rydes Hill House, Aldershot Road,
Guildford, Surrey GU2 8BP
Tel: 01483 563160
Headmistress: Mrs Stephanie
Bell MA(Oxon)
Age range: B3–7 G3–11
No. of pupils: 200
Fees: Day £897–£3,771

Shrewsbury Lodge School
22 Milbourne Lane, Esher,
Surrey KT10 9EA
Tel: 01372 462781
Head: Mrs Gill Hope
Age range: 3–7
Fees: Day £2,475–£3,945

Sir William Perkins's School
Guildford Road, Chertsey,
Surrey KT16 9BN
Tel: 01932 574900
Head: Mr C Muller
Age range: G11–18 years
No. of pupils: 605 VIth140
Fees: Day £14,163

St Catherine's School
Bramley, Guildford, Surrey GU5 0DF
Tel: 01483 893363
Headmistress: Mrs A M
Phillips MA(Cantab)
Age range: G4–18
No. of pupils: 900
Fees: Day £7,695–£15,660 FB £25,770

St Christopher's School
6 Downs Road, Epsom,
Surrey KT18 5HE
Tel: 01372 721807
Headteacher: Mrs A C
Thackray MA, BA(Hons)
Age range: 3–7
No. of pupils: 137
Fees: Day £1,250–£2,450

St Edmund's School
Portsmouth Road, Hindhead,
Surrey GU26 6BH
Tel: 01428 604808
Headmaster: Mr A J Walliker
MA(Cantab), MBA, PGCE
Age range: 2–13
Fees: Day £2,160–£13,842

St George's College
Weybridge Road, Addlestone,
Weybridge, Surrey KT15 2QS
Tel: 01932 839300
Headmistress: Mrs Rachel Owens
Age range: 11–18
No. of pupils: 909 VIth250
Fees: Day £15,120–£17,235

St George's Junior School
Thames Street, Weybridge,
Surrey KT13 8NL
Tel: 01932 839400
Head Master: Mr Antony Hudson
Age range: 3–11 years
No. of pupils: 647
Fees: Day £4,680–£12,120

St Hilary's School
Holloway Hill, Godalming,
Surrey GU7 1RZ
Tel: 01483 416551
Headmistress: Mrs Jane
Whittingham BEdCert,
ProfPracSpLD
Age range: B2–7 G2–11
No. of pupils: 155
Fees: Day £9,375–£13,800

St Ives School
Three Gates Lane, Haslemere,
Surrey GU27 2ES
Tel: 01428 643734
Headteacher: Mrs S E
Cattaneo CertEd
Age range: B3–4 G3–11
No. of pupils: 149
Fees: Day £6,600–£9,225

St John's School
Epsom Road, Leatherhead,
Surrey KT22 8SP
Tel: 01372 373000
Headmaster: Martin A R Collier
Age range: 13 (11 in 2016)–18
No. of pupils: 656
Fees: Day £22,275 WB £28,125

St Teresa's Effingham (Preparatory School)
Effingham, Surrey RH5 6ST
Tel: 01372 453456
Headmaster: Mr. Mike Farmer
Age range: B2–4 G2–11
No. of pupils: 100
Fees: Day £735–£11,235
WB £19,845 FB £21,780

St Teresa's Effingham (Senior School)
Beech Avenue, Effingham,
Surrey RH5 6ST
Tel: 01372 452037
Head: Mr Michael Farmer
Age range: G2–18
No. of pupils: 450 VIth90
Fees: Day £14,190–£14,730
WB £22,800–£23,340 FB
£22,800–£23,340

St. Andrew's School
Church Hill House, Horsell,
Woking, Surrey GU21 4QW
Tel: 01483 760943
Headmaster: Mr A Perks
Age range: 3–13
No. of pupils: 303
Fees: Day £3,492–£13,710

Surbiton Preparatory School
3 Avenue Elmers, Surbiton,
Surrey KT6 4SP
Tel: 020 8390 6640
Head of Surbiton High, Junior Girls' & Bo: Ms C Bufton BA(Hons)
Age range: B4–11
No. of pupils: 135
Fees: Day £6,783–£9,246

Sutton High School GDST
55 Cheam Road, Sutton,
Surrey SM1 2AX
Tel: 020 8642 0594
Headmistress: Mrs Katharine Crouch
Age range: G3–18
No. of pupils: 600 VIth60
Fees: Day £9,153–£15,450

Tante Marie Culinary Academy
Woodham House, Carlton Road,
Woking, Surrey GU21 4HF
Tel: 01483 726957
Principal: Mr Andrew Maxwell
Age range: 16–60
No. of pupils: 72
Fees: Day £20,750

TASIS The American School in England
Coldharbour Lane, Thorpe,
Surrey TW20 8TE
Tel: +44 (0)1932 582316
Head: Dr Mindy Hong
Age range: 3–18
No. of pupils: 740
Fees: Day £6,810–£22,070
FB £38,350

The Hawthorns School
Pendell Court, Bletchingley,
Redhill, Surrey RH1 4QJ
Tel: 01883 743048
Headmaster: Mr A E Floyd BSc(Hons), PGCE
Age range: 2–13
No. of pupils: 535
Fees: Day £1,920–£12,600

The Royal School, Haslemere
Farnham Lane, Haslemere,
Surrey GU27 1BE
Tel: 01428 603052
Principal: Mrs Anne Lynch BEd, PGCE, FRSA
Age range: B6 weeks–16 years G6 weeks–18 years
No. of pupils: 500
Fees: Day £3,026–£5,619 WB £7,741–£8,290 FB £8,893–£9,442

Tormead School
27 Cranley Road, Guildford,
Surrey GU1 2JD
Tel: 01483 575101
Headmistress: Mrs Christina Foord
Age range: G4–18
No. of pupils: 760 VIth120
Fees: Day £5,520–£11,565

Warlingham Park School
Chelsham Common,
Warlingham, Surrey CR6 9PB
Tel: 01883 626844
Headmaster: Mr M R Donald BSc
Age range: 3–11
No. of pupils: 110
Fees: Day £3,660–£7,410

Weston Green School
Weston Green Road, Thames Ditton, Surrey KT7 0JN
Tel: 020 8398 2778
Head: Mrs Lucia Harvey CertEd
Age range: 4–8
Fees: Day £4,574–£7,800

Westward Preparatory School
47 Hersham Road, Walton-on-Thames, Surrey KT12 1LE
Tel: 01932 220911
Headmistress: Mrs P Robertson CertEd
Age range: 3–12
No. of pupils: 140
Fees: Day £4,560–£5,655

Woldingham School
Marden Park, Woldingham,
Surrey CR3 7YA
Tel: 01883 349431
Headmistress: Mrs Jayne Triffitt MA(Oxon)
Age range: G11–18
No. of pupils: 530 VIth150
Fees: Day £23,700 FB £28,410

Woodcote House School
Snows Ride, Windlesham,
Surrey GU20 6PF
Tel: 01276 472115
Headmaster: Mr Henry Knight
Age range: B7–13
No. of pupils: 100
Fees: Day £14,025 FB £18,900

World Federation of Hairdressing & Beauty Schools
PO Box 367, Coulsdon,
Surrey CR5 2TP
Tel: 01737 551355

Yehudi Menuhin School
Stoke Road, Stoke d'Abernon,
Cobham, Surrey KT11 3QQ
Tel: 01932 864739
Headmaster: Dr. Richard J Hillier MA(Cantab), PhD
Age range: 7–19
No. of pupils: 80 VIth36
Fees: FB £41,928

West Sussex

ARDINGLY COLLEGE
For further details see p. 90
College Road, Ardingly,
Haywards Heath, West Sussex RH17 6SQ
Tel: +44 (0)1444 893000
Email: registrar@ardingly.com
Website: www.ardingly.com
Headmaster: Mr Ben Figgis
Age range: 13–18
No. of pupils: 548
Fees: Day £21,960–£23,160 FB £29,715–£31,425

Ardingly College Preparatory School
Haywards Heath, West Sussex RH17 6SQ
Tel: 01444 893200
Headmaster: Mr Chris Calvey BEd
Age range: 2–13
Fees: Day £5,925–£13,950

Ashton Park School
Brinsbury Campus East, Stane Street, North Heath, Pulborough, West Sussex RH20 1DJ
Tel: 01798 875836
Head: Mr G Holding
Age range: 11–16
No. of pupils: 66

Brambletye
Brambletye, East Grinstead,
West Sussex RH19 3PD
Tel: 01342 321004
Headmaster: Will Brooks
Age range: 2–13
No. of pupils: 280
Fees: Day £16,500 FB £22,800

Burgess Hill Girls
Keymer Road, Burgess Hill,
West Sussex RH15 0EG
Tel: 01444 241050
Head: Mrs Kathryn Bell BSc (Hons), PGCE
Age range: B2.5–4 G2.5–18
No. of pupils: 550 VIth87
Fees: Day £7,200–£16,200 FB £25,500–£28,200

Chichester High Schools Sixth Form
Kingsham Road, Chichester,
West Sussex PO19 8AE
Tel: +44 1243 832 546

Christ's Hospital
Horsham, West Sussex RH13 0YP
Tel: 01403 211293
Head Master: John R Franklin BA, MEd(Admin)
Age range: 11–18
No. of pupils: 870
Fees: Day £15,750–£19,800 FB £32,100

Conifers School
Egmont Road, Midhurst,
West Sussex GU29 9BG
Tel: 01730 813243
Headmistress: Mrs Emma Smyth
Age range: 2–13
No. of pupils: 104
Fees: Day £6,030–£8,400

Copthorne Prep School
Effingham Lane, Copthorne,
West Sussex RH10 3HR
Tel: 01342 712311
Headmaster: Mr C Jones
Age range: 2–13
No. of pupils: 366
Fees: Day £7,785–£13,185 WB £15,030

Cottesmore School
Buchan Hill, Pease Pottage,
West Sussex RH11 9AU
Tel: 01293 520648
Head: T F Rogerson
Age range: 4–13
No. of pupils: 150
Fees: Day £4,800–£12,600 WB £16,875 FB £18,750

Cumnor House School
Danehill, Haywards Heath,
West Sussex RH17 7HT
Tel: 01825 790347
Headmaster: C St J Heinrich BA
Age range: 4–13
No. of pupils: 368
Fees: Day £8,100–£18,210 FB £18,210

Dorset House School
The Manor, Church Lane, Bury,
Pulborough, West Sussex RH20 1PB
Tel: 01798 831456
Headmaster: R C M
Brown MA, PGCE
Age range: 3–13
No. of pupils: 135
Fees: Day £7,290–£14,595
WB £15,810–17,685

Farlington School
Strood Park, Horsham,
West Sussex RH12 3PN
Tel: 01403 254967
Headmistress: Ms Louise
Higson BSc, PGCE
Age range: G3–18
No. of pupils: 345 VIth53
Fees: Day £7,050–£16,470 WB
£21,585–£26,310 FB £22,785–£27,510

Great Ballard School
Eartham, Chichester,
West Sussex PO18 0LR
Tel: 01243 814236
Head: Mr Richard Evans
Age range: 2–13
No. of pupils: 125
Fees: Day £7,800–£13,650
WB £15,000 FB £21,000

Great Walstead School
East Mascalls Lane,
Lindfield, Haywards Heath,
West Sussex RH16 2QL
Tel: 01444 483528
Headmaster: Mr C Baty
NPQH, BEd(Waikato NZ)
Age range: 2–13
No. of pupils: 421
Fees: Day £7,500–£14,475

Handcross Park School
Handcross, Haywards Heath,
West Sussex RH17 6HF
Tel: 01444 400526
Headmaster: Mr Graeme
Owton BEd(Hons)
Age range: 2–13
No. of pupils: 339
Fees: Day £2,860–£5,640 WB
£4,750–£6,610 FB £5,340–£7,200

Hurstpierpoint College
College Lane, Hurstpierpoint,
West Sussex BN6 9JS
Tel: 01273 833636
Headmaster: Mr. T J Manly BA, MSc
Age range: 4–18
No. of pupils: 1083
Fees: Day £20,925 WB £26,385
FB £29,520–£31,125

Hurstpierpoint College Prep School
Hurstpierpoint, West Sussex BN6 9JS
Tel: 01273 834975
Head: Mr I D Pattison BSc
Age range: 4–13
No. of pupils: 360

Lancing College
Lancing, West Sussex BN15 0RW
Tel: 01273 465805
Head Master: Mr Dominic
T Oliver MPhil
Age range: 13–18
No. of pupils: 550 VIth255
Fees: Day £7,710 WB
£10,970 FB £10,970

Lancing College Preparatory School at Worthing
Broadwater Road, Worthing,
West Sussex BN14 8HU
Tel: 01903 201123
Head of School: Mrs Heather Beeby
Age range: 2–13
No. of pupils: 177
Fees: Day £540–£8,400

Lavant House
West Lavant, Chichester,
West Sussex PO18 9AB
Tel: 01243 527211
Headteacher: Mrs Nicola
Walker BSC (Hons), MEdm
NPQH, MBA, PGCE
Age range: G4–18
No. of pupils: VIth20

Oakwood School
Chichester, West Sussex PO18 9AN
Tel: 01243 575209
Headteacher: Mrs Gill Proctor
Age range: 3–11
No. of pupils: 247
Fees: Day £2,760–£8,880

Our Lady of Sion School
Gratwicke Road, Worthing,
West Sussex BN11 4BL
Tel: 01903 204063
Headmaster: Mr M Scullion MA, BEd
Age range: 2–18
No. of pupils: 528 VIth55
Fees: Day £5,715–£9,150

Pennthorpe School
Church Street, Horsham,
West Sussex RH12 3HJ
Tel: 01403 822391
Headmaster: Mr Matthew
King BA(Hons)
Age range: 2–13
No. of pupils: 362
Fees: Day £1,392–£12,690

Rikkyo School in England
Guildford Road, Rudgwick,
Horsham, West Sussex RH12 3BE
Tel: 01403 822107
Headmaster: Mr Roger Munechika
Age range: 10–18
No. of pupils: 116
Fees: FB £15,000–£21,600

Seaford College
Lavington Park, Petworth,
West Sussex GU28 0NB
Tel: 01798 867392
Headmaster: J P Green MA BA
Age range: 6–18
No. of pupils: 690 VIth173
Fees: Day £9,930–£19,380 WB
£19,320–£26,130 FB £29,985

Shoreham College
St Julians Lane, Shoreham-by-
Sea, West Sussex BN43 6YW
Tel: 01273 592681
Headmaster: Mr R Taylor-West
Age range: 3–16 years
No. of pupils: 375
Fees: Day £8,550–£13,350

Slindon College
Slindon House, Slindon, Arundel,
West Sussex BN18 0RH
Tel: 01243 814320
Headmaster: Mr D Quick
Age range: B8–18
No. of pupils: 80 VIth17
Fees: Day £6,900 WB
£9,845 FB £9,845

Sompting Abbotts Preparatory School for Boys and Girls
Church Lane, Sompting,
West Sussex BN15 0AZ
Tel: 01903 235960
Principal: Mrs P M Sinclair
Age range: 2–13
No. of pupils: 185
Fees: Day £7,860–£10,095

Tavistock & Summerhill School
Summerhill Lane, Lindfield,
Haywards Heath, West
Sussex RH16 1RP
Tel: 01444 450256
Headmaster: Mr Andrew
Giles MEd, BSc, PGCE
Age range: 3–13
No. of pupils: 150
Fees: Day £5,700–£10,350

The Prebendal School
54 West Street, Chichester,
West Sussex PO19 1RT
Tel: 01243 772220
Head Master: Mr T R Cannell
Age range: 3–13
No. of pupils: 200
Fees: Day £7,500–£14,250
WB £18,450 FB £19,350

The Towers Convent School
Convent of the Blessed Sacrement,
Henfield Road, Upper Beeding,
Steyning, West Sussex BN44 3TF
Tel: 01903 812185
Headmistress: Mrs Clare Trelfa
Age range: B2–8 G2–16
No. of pupils: 320
Fees: Day £7,320–£10,200

Westbourne House School
Shopwyke, Chichester,
West Sussex PO20 2BH
Tel: 01243 782739
Headmaster: Mr Martin Barker
Age range: 2.5–13 years
No. of pupils: 458
Fees: Day £9,360–£15,840 FB £19,410

Windlesham House School
Washington, Pulborough,
West Sussex RH20 4AY
Tel: 01903 874700
Headmaster: Mr Richard
Foster BEd(Hons)
Age range: 4–13
No. of pupils: 350

Worth School
Paddockhurst Road, Turners Hill,
Crawley, West Sussex RH10 4SD
Tel: +44 (0)1342 710200
Head Master: Gino
Carminati MA, FRSA
Age range: 11–18
No. of pupils: 580 VIth222
Fees: Day £20,235 FB £27,849

International Schools in London and the South-East

International schools

London

Central London

CATS College London
43-45 Bloomsbury Square, London WC1A 2RA
Tel: 02078 411580
Principal: Mr Mark Love
Age range: 14–20
No. of pupils: VIth235
Fees: Day £16,460–£35,740
FB £33,560–£52,840

ÉCOLE JEANNINE MANUEL - LONDON
For further details see p. 50
43-45 Bedford Square, , London WC1B 3DN
Tel: 020 3829 5970
Email: contact@jmanuel.uk.net
Website: www.ecole jeanninemanuel.org.uk
Principal: Pauline Prévot
Age range: 3–14 years
No. of pupils: 190

North London

DWIGHT SCHOOL LONDON
For further details see p. 52
6 Friern Barnet Lane, London N11 3LX
Tel: +44 (0)20 8920 0600
Email: admissions@ dwightlondon.org
Website: www.dwightlondon.org
Head: Mrs Alison Cobbin BA, Dip Ed, MBA
Age range: 2–18+

North-West London

City of Westminster College
The Cockpit Theatre (Perfoming Arts, Sound & Lighting), Gateforth Street, London NW8 8EH
Tel: 020 7258 2920
Principal: Mr Robin Shreeve

College Francais Bilingue De Londres
87 Holmes Road, Kentish Town, , London NW5 3AX
Tel: +44 (0) 20 7993 7400
Principal: Mr François-Xavier Gabet
Age range: 5–15
No. of pupils: 210

INTERNATIONAL COMMUNITY SCHOOL
For further details see p. 57
4 York Terrace East, Regents Park, London NW1 4PT
Tel: +44 20 7935 1206
Email: admissions@ics.uk.net
Website: www.icschool.co.uk
Head of School: Ms Rose Threlfall
Age range: 3–18
No. of pupils: 260
Fees: Day £16,650–£22,100

Mill Hill School
The Ridgeway, Mill Hill Village, London NW7 1QS
Tel: 020 8959 1176
Head: Dr Dominic Luckett
Age range: 13–18
No. of pupils: 689 VIth259
Fees: Day £13,860 FB £21,900

Southbank International School - Hampstead
16 Netherhall Gardens, London NW3 5TH
Tel: 020 7243 3803
Principal: Shirley Harwood
Age range: 3–11

The American School in London
One Waverley Place, London NW8 0NP
Tel: 020 7449 1221
Head: Mrs Coreen Hester
Age range: 4–18
No. of pupils: 1350
Fees: Day £21,950–£25,650

South-East London

Dulwich College
London SE21 7LD
Tel: 020 8693 3601
Master: Dr J A F Spence
Age range: B7–18
No. of pupils: 1589 VIth470
Fees: Day £18,231 WB £35,679 FB £38,052

St Dunstan's College
Stanstead Road, London SE6 4TY
Tel: 020 8516 7200
Headmistress: Mrs J D Davies BSc
Age range: 3–18
No. of pupils: 870

South-West London

Centre Academy London
92 St John's Hill, Battersea, London SW11 1SH
Tel: 020 7738 2344
Principal: Dr. Duncan Rollo BA, MA, PhD
Age range: 9–19
Fees: Day £27,600–£40,100

Duff Miller College
59 Queen's Gate, South Kensington, London SW7 5JP
Tel: 020 7225 0577
Principal: C Kraft BSc, BPS
Age range: 14–19
No. of pupils: 370
Fees: Day £3,800–£19,300 FB £17,400–£37,600

Ecole Charles De Gaulle - Wix
Clapham Common North Side, London SW4 0AJ
Tel: +44 20 7738 0287
Headteacher: Mr Blanchard
Age range: 5–11
No. of pupils: 100

Ecole Marie D'Orliac
60 Clancarty Road, London SW6 3AA
Tel: +44 7736 020 58 63
Principal: Mr Olivier Rauch
Age range: 4–11
No. of pupils: 50

King's College School
Southside, Wimbledon Common, London SW19 4TT
Tel: 020 8255 5300
Head Master: A D Halls MA
Age range: B11–18 G16–18
No. of pupils: 855 VIth396
Fees: Day £19,830

Lycee Francais Charles de Gaulle
35 Cromwell Road, London SW7 2DG
Tel: 020 7584 6322
Headteacher: Mr Olivier Rauch
Age range: 3–18
No. of pupils: 4007
Fees: Day £4,521–£10,791

St Paul's School
Lonsdale Road, Barnes, London SW13 9JT
Tel: 020 8748 9162
High Master: Prof Mark Bailey
Age range: B13–18
No. of pupils: 897
Fees: Day £19,674 FB £29,466

Wandsworth Preparatory School
The Old Library, 2 Allfarthing Lane, London SW18 2PQ
Tel: 0208 870 4133

Westminster School
17 Dean's Yard, Westminster, London SW1P 3PF
Tel: 020 7963 1003
Headmaster: Mr Patrick Derham
Age range: B13–18 G16–18
No. of pupils: 744
Fees: Day £24,276–£26,322 FB £35,058

West London

Bales College
742 Harrow Road, Kensal Town, London W10 4AA
Tel: 020 8960 5899
Principal: William Moore
Age range: 11–19
No. of pupils: 90
Fees: Day £7,950–£8,550 FB £16,050

City of Westminster College
25 Paddington Green, London W2 1NB
Tel: 020 7723 8826
Principal: Mr Robin Shreeve

DLD COLLEGE
For further details see p. 48
199 Westminster Bridge Road, London SE1 7FX
Tel: 020 7935 8411
Email: dld@dld.org
Website: www.dldcollege.co.uk
Principal: Ms. Rachel Borland MA
No. of pupils: 485
Fees: Day £17,800–£19,900 FB £15,000–£21,000

Ecole Francaise Jacques Prevert
59 Brook Green, London W6 7BE
Tel: 020 7602 6871
Principal: P Possenti
Age range: 4–11

Halcyon London International School
33 Seymour Place, , London W1H 5AU
Tel: 020 7258 1169
Principal: Duncan Partridge

Instituto Espanol Canada Blanch
317a Portobello Road,
Kensington, London W10 5SZ
Tel: +44 (0) 20 8969 2664
Principal: Mr A Vitria
Age range: 4–19
No. of pupils: 405
🌐

International School of London (ISL) London
139 Gunnersbury Avenue,
Ealing, London W3 8LG
Tel: +44 (0)20 8992 5823
Middle & Lower School Principal:
Andrew Mitchell
Age range: 3–18 years
No. of pupils: 480
Fees: Day £18,000–£24,600
🌐 (IB) ✏ (16·)

King Fahad Academy
Bromyard Avenue, Acton,
London W3 7HD
Tel: 020 8743 0131
Acting Head of Primary School: Ms
Julie Benafif
Age range: 3–18
No. of pupils: 446
Fees: Day £3,000
🌐 (A) (£) (IB) (16·)

Southbank International School - Kensington
36-38 Kensington Park
Road, London W11 3BU
Tel: 020 7243 3803
Principal: Siobhan McGrath
Age range: 3–11
🌐 (IB) ✏

Southbank International School - Westminster
63-65 Portland Place,
London W1B 1QR
Tel: 020 7243 3803
Principal: Justine Oliver
Age range: 11–18/19
🌐 (IB) ✏ (16·)

Southbank International School – Fitzrovia
17 Conway Street, London W1T 6BN
Tel: +44 2076 312600
🌐

The Godolphin and Latymer School
Iffley Road, Hammersmith,
London W6 0PG
Tel: +44 (0)20 8741 1936
Head Mistress: Mrs R Mercer BA
Age range: G11–18
No. of pupils: 812
Fees: Day £19,224
🏃 🌐 (A) (£) (IB) ✏ (16·)

Berkshire

Bradfield College
Bradfield, Berkshire RG7 6AU
Tel: 0118 964 4516
Headmaster: Dr Christopher
Stevens
Age range: 13–18
No. of pupils: 770 VIth310
Fees: Day £27,420 FB £34,275
🌐 (A) (🏫) (£) (IB) ✏ (16·)

Eton College
Windsor, Berkshire SL4 6DW
Tel: 01753 671249
Head Master: Simon Henderson MA
Age range: B13–18
No. of pupils: 1300 VIth520
Fees: FB £33,270
🏃 🌐 (A) (🏫) (£) ✏ (16·)

Heathfield School
London Road, Ascot,
Berkshire SL5 8BQ
Tel: 01344 898342
Head: Mrs Jo Heywood BSc(Hons),
PGCE
Age range: G11–18
No. of pupils: 200 VIth80
Fees: Day £22,680–£23,310
FB £32,400–£33,300
🏃 🌐 (A) (🏫) (£) ✏ (16·)

Hurst Lodge
Bagshot Road, Ascot,
Berkshire SL5 9JU
Tel: 01344 622154
Principal: Ms Victoria Smit
Age range: 3–18
No. of pupils: 202 VIth13
Fees: Day £6,420–£25,200
WB £19,905–£34,005
🌐 (A) (£) (16·) 🐾

Leighton Park School
Shinfield Road, Reading,
Berkshire RG2 7DE
Tel: 0118 987 9600
Head: Nigel Williams BA(Bristol),
MA(London), PGCE
Age range: 11–18
No. of pupils: 474 VIth145
Fees: Day £16,524–£20,313 WB
£22,524–£27,225 FB £25,614–£31,632
🌐 (A) (🏫) (£) (IB) ✏ (16·)

Luckley House School
Luckley Road, Wokingham,
Berkshire RG40 3EU
Tel: 0118 978 4175
Headmistress: Mrs Jane Tudor
Age range: G11–18
No. of pupils: 300 VIth50
Fees: Day £13,476 WB
£21,858 FB £23,586
🏃 🌐 (A) (🏫) (£) ✏ (16·)

LVS ASCOT (LICENSED VICTUALLERS' SCHOOL)
For further details see p. 93
London Road, Ascot,
Berkshire SL5 8DR
Tel: 01344 882770
Email: enquiries@lvs.
ascot.sch.uk
Website: www.lvs.ascot.sch.uk
Headmistress: Mrs Christine
Cunniffe BA (Hons), MMus, MBA
Age range: 4–18
No. of pupils: 870
Fees: Day £9,528–£17,079
FB £24,384–£30,006
🌐 (A) (🏫) (£) ✏ (16·)

Padworth College
Padworth, Reading,
Berkshire RG7 4NR
Tel: 0118 983 2644
Principal: Mr John Aguilar
Age range: 13–19
No. of pupils: 116 VIth50
Fees: Day £14,250 FB £28,392
🌐 (A) (🏫) (£) (16·)

PANGBOURNE COLLEGE
For further details see p. 96
Pangbourne, Reading,
Berkshire RG8 8LA
Tel: 0118 984 2101
Email: registrar@
pangbourne.com
Website:
www.pangbourne.com
Headmaster: Thomas J C
Garnier
Age range: 11–18
No. of pupils: 423 VIth148
Fees: Day £15,999–£22,548
FB £22,533–£31,890
🌐 (A) (🏫) (£) (IB) ✏ (16·)

Queen Anne's School
6 Henley Road, Caversham,
Reading, Berkshire RG4 6DX
Tel: 0118 918 7300
Headmistress: Mrs Julia Harrington
BA(Hons), PGCE, NPQH
Age range: G11–18
No. of pupils: 336 VIth100
Fees: Day £5,695 WB
£7,545–£7,975 FB £8,395
🏃 🌐 (A) (🏫) (£) (16·)

Reddam House Bearwood
Bearwood Road, Wokingham,
Berkshire RG41 5BG
Tel: 0118 974 8300
Headmaster: Mr Donald Wilkinson
Age range: 0–18
No. of pupils: 487 VIth80
Fees: Day £13,890–£16,365
FB £24,360–£28,080
🌐 (A) (🏫) (£) ✏ (16·)

St George's Ascot
Wells Lane, Ascot, Berkshire SL5 7DZ
Tel: 01344 629920
Headmistress: Mrs Rachel Owens
MA(Hons) (Oxon) PGCE NPQH
Age range: G11–18
No. of pupils: 280 VIth85
Fees: Day £20,250 WB
£29,325–£30,375 FB £31,125
🏃 🌐 (A) (🏫) (£) (16·)

St Mary's School Ascot
St Mary\'s Road, Ascot,
Berkshire SL5 9JF
Tel: 01344 296614
Headmistress: Mrs Mary Breen
BSc, MSc
Age range: G11–18
No. of pupils: 390 VIth120
Fees: Day £23,400 FB £32,850
🏃 🌐 (A) (🏫) (£) (16·)

The Abbey School
Kendrick Road, Reading,
Berkshire RG1 5DZ
Tel: 0118 987 2256
Head: Mrs Rachel S E Dent
Age range: G3–18
No. of pupils: 1070
Fees: Day £15,090
🏃 🌐 (A) (£) (IB) ✏ (16·)

The Oratory School
Woodcote, Reading,
Berkshire RG8 0PJ
Tel: 01491 683500
Head Master: Mr A J Wyles
BSc(Hons), MEd, PGCE, FRGS
Age range: B11–18
No. of pupils: 380 VIth120
Fees: Day £23,250 FB
£21,540–£31,950
🏃 🌐 (A) (🏫) (£) (16·)

Wellington College
Duke's Ride, Crowthorne,
Berkshire RG45 7PU
Tel: +44 (0)1344 444000
Master: Mr Julian Thomas
Age range: 13–18
No. of pupils: 1045 VIth470
Fees: Day £26,130–
£30,030 FB £35,775
🌐 (A) (£) (IB) ✏ (16·)

Buckinghamshire

Stowe School
Buckingham, Buckinghamshire
MK18 5EH
Tel: 01280 818000
Headmaster: Dr Anthony
Wallersteiner
Age range: 13–18
No. of pupils: 769 VIth318
Fees: Day £22,500 FB £30,975

Thornton College
Thornton, Milton Keynes,
Buckinghamshire MK17 0HJ
Tel: 01280 812610
Headmistress: Miss Agnes T Williams
Age range: B2–4+ G2–16
No. of pupils: 370
Fees: Day £6,300–£10,095 WB
£10,500–£13,305 FB £13,305–£16,545

Wycombe Abbey
High Wycombe,
Buckinghamshire HP11 1PE
Tel: +44 (0)1494 897008
Headmistress: Mrs Rhiannon J
Wilkinson MA (Oxon) MEd
Age range: G11–18
No. of pupils: 554
Fees: Day £26,775 FB £35,700

East Sussex

Battle Abbey School
Battle, East Sussex TN33 0AD
Tel: 01424 772385
Headmaster: Mr R C Clark
BA(Hons), MA(Ed)
Age range: 2–18
No. of pupils: 286 VIth48
Fees: Day £6,630–£13,390 FB £23,190

Bede's School
The Dicker, Upper Dicker,
Hailsham, East Sussex BN27 3QH
Tel: +44 (0)1323843252
Head: Dr Richard Maloney
Age range: 12–18+
No. of pupils: 800 VIth295
Fees: Day £15,450 FB £25,725

Brighton College
Eastern Road, Brighton,
East Sussex BN2 0AL
Tel: 01273 704200
Head Master: Richard Cairns MA
Age range: 3–18
No. of pupils: 945 VIth340
Fees: Day £4,890–£18,675 WB
£24,729–£25,884 FB £28,575–£30,141

Buckswood School
Broomham Hall, Rye
Road, Guestling, Hastings,
East Sussex TN35 4LT
Tel: 01424 813 813
Headteacher: Mr Mark Redsell
Age range: 10–19
No. of pupils: 420

Eastbourne College
Old Wish Road, Eastbourne,
East Sussex BN21 4JX
Tel: 01323 452323 (Admissions)
Headmaster: Mr S P Davies MA
Age range: 13–18
No. of pupils: 630 VIth273
Fees: Day £20,940–£21,300
FB £31,965–£32,325

Greenfields School
Priory Road, Forest Row,
East Sussex RH18 5JD
Tel: 01342 822189
Headteacher: Mr G Hudson
Age range: 2–19
No. of pupils: 125
Fees: Day £500–£10,800
FB £19,170–£20,850

MAYFIELD SCHOOL
For further details see p. 94
The Old Palace, Mayfield,
East Sussex TN20 6PH
Tel: +44 (0)1435 874600
Email: registrar@
mayfieldgirls.org
Website: www.mayfieldgirls.org
Head: Ms Antonia Beary MA,
Mphil(Cantab), PGCE
Age range: G11–18
No. of pupils: 356 VIth100
Fees: Day £19,125 WB
£30,900 FB £30,900

MICHAEL HALL SCHOOL
For further details see p. 98
Kidbrooke Park, Priory Road,
Forest Row, East Sussex RH18 5BG
Tel: 01342 822275
Email: info@michaelhall.co.uk
Website: www.michaelhall.co.uk
Age range: 3–19
Fees: Day £8,840–£12,120
FB £5,400–£7,610

Moira House Girls School
Upper Carlisle Road, Eastbourne,
East Sussex BN20 7TE
Tel: 01323 644144
Principal: Mrs L A Watson MA(Ed),
MInstD
Age range: G2–18
No. of pupils: 360 VIth105
Fees: Day £6,300–£14,655 WB
£19,260–£24,060 FB £20,715–£26,550

ROEDEAN SCHOOL
For further details see p. 99
Roedean Way, Brighton,
East Sussex BN2 5RQ
Tel: 01273 667500
Email: info@roedean.co.uk
Website: www.roedean.co.uk
Headmaster: Mr. Oliver Bond
BA(Essex), PGCE, NPQH
Age range: G11–18
No. of pupils: 440 VIth177
Fees: Day £14,970–£19,470
WB £26,730–£29,820 FB
£28,860–£34,950

Essex

Brentwood School
Middleton Hall Lane,
Brentwood, Essex CM15 8EE
Tel: 01277 243243
Headmaster: Mr Ian Davies
Age range: 3–18
No. of pupils: 1550
Fees: Day £16,635 FB £32,649

Chigwell School
High Road, Chigwell, Essex IG7 6QF
Tel: 020 8501 5700
Headmaster: Mr M E Punt MA, MSc
Age range: 4–18
No. of pupils: 915 VIth185
Fees: Day £10,200–£16,020
FB £26,730–£26,730

Felsted School
Felsted, Great Dunmow,
Essex CM6 3LL
Tel: +44 (0) 1371 822605
Headmaster: Dr Michael Walker
Age range: 13–18
No. of pupils: 516 VIth236
Fees: Day £18,480 WB
£22,377 FB £24,705

Friends' School
Mount Pleasant Road, Saffron
Walden, Essex CB11 3EB
Tel: 01799 525351
Head: Ms Anna Chaudhri MA
Age range: 3–18
No. of pupils: 390 VIth50
Fees: Day £2,375–£5,305 WB
£6,615–£7,690 FB £7,190–£8,590

Gosfield School
Cut Hedge Park, Halstead Road,
Gosfield, Halstead, Essex CO9 1PF
Tel: 01787 474040
Principal: Dr Sarah Welch
Age range: 4–18
No. of pupils: VIth21
Fees: Day £4,740–£13,695 WB
£15,465–£17,310 FB £17,985–£23,130

New Hall School
The Avenue, Boreham,
Chelmsford, Essex CM3 3HS
Tel: 01245 467588
Principal: Mrs Katherine Jeffrey MA,
BA, PGCE, MA(Ed Mg), NPQH
Age range: Coed 3-11,
Single 11-16, Coed 16–18
No. of pupils: 1175 VIth197
Fees: Day £8,742–£18,042 WB
£17,670–£25,815 FB £19,521–£27,099

Hampshire

Bedales School
Church Road, Steep, Petersfield,
Hampshire GU32 2DG
Tel: 01730 711733
Head: Keith Budge MA
Age range: 13–18
No. of pupils: 463 VIth192
Fees: Day £8,825 FB £11,230

Brockwood Park & Inwoods School
Brockwood Park, Bramdean,
Hampshire SO24 0LQ
Tel: +44 (0)1962 771744
Co-Principals: Mr Adrian Sydenham
& Dr Gopal Krishnamurthy
Age range: 4–19
No. of pupils: 92
Fees: Day £3,150 FB £17,270

GEMS Sherfield School
Sherfield-on-Loddon, Hook,
Hampshire RG27 0HU
Tel: +44 (0)1256 884 800
Headmaster: Mr Dick Jaine
Age range: 3 months–18 years
No. of pupils: 445 VIth16
Fees: Day £7,350–£13,890 FB £20,946

Hampshire Collegiate School
Embley Park, Romsey,
Hampshire SO51 6ZE
Tel: 01794 512206
Principal: Mrs Emma-Kate Henry
Age range: 2–18
No. of pupils: 683

Lord Wandsworth College
Long Sutton, Hook,
Hampshire RG29 1TB
Tel: 01256 862201
Head of School: Mr Adam Williams
Age range: 11–18 years
No. of pupils: 550
Fees: Day £19,110–£20,940
WB £25,350–£28,350 FB
£26,100–£29,700

Moyles Court School
Moyles Court, Ringwood,
Hampshire BH24 3NF
Tel: 01425 472856
Headmaster: Mr Dean
Age range: 3–16
Fees: Day £3,285–£4,650
FB £6,690–£7,740

Rookwood School
Weyhill Road, Andover,
Hampshire SP10 3AL
Tel: 01264 325900
Headmistress: Mrs L Whetstone MA
Age range: 3–16
Fees: Day £7,770–£12,780
FB £19,545–£22,875

St John's College
Grove Road South, Southsea,
Portsmouth, Hampshire PO5 3QW
Tel: 023 9281 5118
Headmaster: Mr Timothy Bayley
Age range: 2–18
No. of pupils: 600 VIth86
Fees: Day £8,460–£11,100
FB £23,970–£25,770

St Swithun's School
Alresford Road, Winchester,
Hampshire SO21 1HA
Tel: 01962 835700
Headmistress: Jane Gandee
MA(Cantab)
Age range: G11–18
No. of pupils: G525 VIth85
Fees: Day £17,640 FB £28,290

The Portsmouth Grammar School
High Street, Portsmouth,
Hampshire PO1 2LN
Tel: +44 (0)23 9236 0036
Headmaster: J E Priory MA
Age range: 2–18
No. of pupils: 1645 VIth298
Fees: Day £8,379–£13,059

Winchester College
College Street, Winchester,
Hampshire SO23 9NA
Tel: 01962 621247
Headmaster: R D Townsend MA,
DPhil
Age range: B13–18
No. of pupils: 690 VIth280
Fees: FB £35,610

Hertfordshire

Aldenham School
Elstree, Hertfordshire WD6 3AJ
Tel: 01923 858122
Headmaster: James C Fowler MA
Age range: 3–18
No. of pupils: 700 VIth158
Fees: Day £13,626–£19,500
FB £18,768–£28,410

Berkhamsted School
Overton House, 131 High Street,
Berkhamsted, Hertfordshire HP4 2DJ
Tel: 01442 358001
Principal: Mr Richard Backhouse
MA(Cantab)
Age range: 3–18 years
No. of pupils: 1680 VIth361
Fees: Day £10,065–£19,095
WB £25,565 FB £30,415

Bishop's Stortford College
10 Maze Green Road, Bishop's
Stortford, Hertfordshire CM23 2PJ
Tel: 01279 838575
Headmaster: Mr Jeremy Gladwin
Age range: 13–18
No. of pupils: VIth249
Fees: Day £17,496–£17,655 WB
£25,950–£26,109 FB £26,208–£27,405

Bishop's Stortford College Prep School
Maze Green Road, Bishop's
Stortford, Hertfordshire CM23 2PH
Tel: 01279 838607
Head of Prep School: Mr Bill
Toleman
Age range: 4–13
Fees: Day £8,088–£12,489 WB
£18,114–£19,671 FB £18,312–£20,691

HAILEYBURY
For further details see p. 92
Haileybury, Hertford,
Hertfordshire SG13 7NU
Tel: +44 (0)1992 706353
Email: registrar@haileybury.com
Website: www.haileybury.com
The Master: J S Davies
MA(Cantab)
Age range: 11–18
No. of pupils: 759 VIth301
Fees: Day £15,435–£23,220
FB £19,605–£30,900

Princess Helena College
Preston, Hitchin,
Hertfordshire SG4 7RT
Tel: 01462 443888
Headmistress: Mrs Sue Wallace-
Woodroffe
Age range: G11–18
No. of pupils: 194 VIth35
Fees: Day £15,225–£18,585
FB £21,705–£26,985

St Christopher School
Barrington Road, Letchworth,
Hertfordshire SG6 3JZ
Tel: 01462 650 850
Head: Richard Palmer
Age range: 3–18
No. of pupils: 511 VIth78
Fees: Day £3,375–£14,505
FB £15,600–£25,470

St Edmund's College & Prep School
Old Hall Green, Nr Ware,
Hertfordshire SG11 1DS
Tel: 01920 824247
Head: Paulo Durán BA MA
Age range: 3–18
No. of pupils: 799 VIth135
Fees: Day £9,465–£14,955 WB
£19,830–£22,575 FB £21,855–£24,990

St Francis' College
Broadway, Letchworth Garden
City, Hertfordshire SG6 3PJ
Tel: 01462 670511
Headmistress: Mrs B Goulding
Age range: G3–18
No. of pupils: 460 VIth75
Fees: Day £8,670–£13,830 WB
£19,425–£22,875 FB £24,195–£27,645

St Margaret's School, Bushey
Merry Hill Road, Bushey,
Hertfordshire WD23 1DT
Tel: 020 8416 4400
Head: Mrs Rose Hardy MA(Oxon),
MEd, FRSA
Age range: G4–18 years
No. of pupils: 450 VIth100
Fees: Day £14,730 WB
£20,220–£23,670 FB £27,600

Stanborough School
Stanborough Park, Garston,
Watford, Hertfordshire WD25 9JT
Tel: 01923 673268
Head Teacher: Ms Lorraine Dixon
Age range: 3–19
No. of pupils: 300 VIth20
Fees: Day £3,660–£5,500
WB £12,834–£15,846

The Purcell School, London
Aldenham Road, Bushey,
Hertfordshire WD23 2TS
Tel: 01923 331100
Headteacher: Mr. Stephen Yeo
Age range: 8–18
No. of pupils: 167 VIth70
Fees: WB £22,452 FB £28,716

The Royal Masonic School for Girls
Rickmansworth Park,
Rickmansworth,
Hertfordshire WD3 4HF
Tel: 01923 773168
Headmistress: Mrs Diana Rose
MA(Cantab)
Age range: G4–18
No. of pupils: 917 VIth188
Fees: Day £9,000–£14,700 WB
£15,750–£23,760 FB £16,050–£25,050

Tring Park School for the Performing Arts
Tring Park, Tring,
Hertfordshire HP23 5LX
Tel: 01442 824255
Principal: Mr Stefan Anderson MA,
ARCM, ARCT
Age range: 8–19
No. of pupils: 340 VIth217
Fees: Day £13,785–£21,960
FB £23,250–£32,880

Kent

Ashford School
East Hill, Ashford, Kent TN24 8PB
Tel: 01233 739030
Head: Mr M R Buchanan BSc(Hons),
CertEd, NPQH, CPhys
Age range: 3 months–18 years
No. of pupils: 835 VIth170
Fees: Day £8,400–£16,200
WB £28,500 FB £32,400

Ashgrove School
116 Widmore Road,
Bromley, Kent BR1 3BE
Tel: 020 8460 4143
Principal: Patricia Ash CertEd,
BSc(Hons), PhD, CMath, FIMA
Age range: 4–11
Fees: Day £8,460

Benenden School
Cranbrook, Kent TN17 4AA
Tel: 01580 240592
Headmistress: Mrs S Price
Age range: G11–18
No. of pupils: 543
Fees: FB £31,410

Bethany School
Curtisden Green, Goudhurst,
Cranbrook, Kent TN17 1LB
Tel: 01580 211273
Headmaster: Mr Francie Healy BSc,
HDipEd, NPQH
Age range: 11–18 years
No. of pupils: 345 VIth112
Fees: Day £15,483–£16,986 WB
£23,967–£26,283 FB £25,842–£28,917

CATS College Canterbury
68 New Dover Road,
Canterbury, Kent CT1 3LQ
Tel: +44 (0)1227866540
Principal: Jonathan Ullmer MBE,
MA, LRAM, FCollP, ACP, Dip Arts,
NPQH
Age range: 14–18
No. of pupils: 400

Cobham Hall School
Cobham, Kent DA12 3BL
Tel: 01474 823371
Headmaster: Mr Paul Mitchell BSc
Age range: G11–18
No. of pupils: 180

Dover College
Effingham Crescent,
Dover, Kent CT17 9RH
Tel: 01304 205969 Ext:201
Headmaster: Gerry Holden
Age range: 3–18
No. of pupils: 340 VIth100
Fees: Day £6,750–£14,250 WB
£18,900–£22,200 FB £20,700–£27,900

Farringtons School
Perry Street, Chislehurst,
Kent BR7 6LR
Tel: 020 8467 0256
Head: Mrs Dorothy Nancekievill
Age range: 3–18
No. of pupils: 681 VIth94
Fees: Day £10,680–£13,560
WB £25,530 FB £27,120

Kent College
Whitstable Road, Canterbury,
Kent CT2 9DT
Tel: 01227 763231
Head Master: Dr D J Lamper
Age range: 3–18
No. of pupils: 702
Fees: Day £15,669–£17,259
FB £23,529–£32,316

Kent College Pembury
Old Church Road, Pembury,
Tunbridge Wells, Kent TN2 4AX
Tel: +44 (0)1892 822006
Headmistress: Mrs Sally-Anne
Huang MA(Oxon), MSc, PGCE
Age range: G3–18
No. of pupils: 650 VIth102
Fees: Day £7,887–£17,322
FB £21,471–£27,924

King's School, Rochester
Satis House, Boley Hill,
Rochester, Kent ME1 1TE
Tel: 01634 888555
Headmaster: Dr I R Walker BA, PhD,
LTh, ABIA, FCollP, FRSA
Age range: 13–18
No. of pupils: 688 VIth113
Fees: Day £7,655–£14,400
FB £17,145–£24,210

Rochester Independent College
Star Hill, Rochester,
Medway, Kent ME1 1XF
Tel: 01634 828115
Principals: Alistair Brownlow, Brian
Pain, Pauline Bailey
Age range: 11–19
No. of pupils: 306 VIth233
Fees: Day £12,000–£16,500 WB
£25,650–£27,300 FB £27,450–£29,100

Sevenoaks School
High Street, Sevenoaks,
Kent TN13 1HU
Tel: +44 (0)1732 455133
Head: Dr Katy Ricks MA, DPhil
Age range: 11–18
No. of pupils: 1054 VIth423
Fees: Day £20,763–£23,571
FB £33,156–£35,964

St Edmund's School
St Thomas\' Hill, Canterbury,
Kent CT2 8HU
Tel: 01227 475601
Head: Louise Moelwyn-Hughes
Age range: 3–18
No. of pupils: 535
Fees: Day £18,651 FB £29,781

St Lawrence College
Ramsgate, Kent CT11 7AE
Tel: 01843 572931
Principal: Mr Antony Spencer
Age range: 3–18
No. of pupils: VIth140
Fees: Day £7,047–£17,436
FB £23,640–£31,452

Sutton Valence School
North Street, Sutton
Valence, Kent ME17 3HL
Tel: 01622 845200
Headmaster: Mr B C W Grindlay
MA(Cantab), MusB, FRCO, CHM
Age range: 11–18
No. of pupils: 170
Fees: Day £5,020–£6,660 WB
£7,930–£10,310 FB £7,930–£10,310

THE KING'S SCHOOL, CANTERBURY
For further details see p. 100
The Precincts, Canterbury,
Kent CT1 2ES
Tel: 01227 595501
Email: info@kings-school.co.uk
Website:
www.kings-school.co.uk
Head: Mr P Roberts
Age range: 13–18
No. of pupils: 824 VIth380
Fees: Day £26,055 FB £34,440

TONBRIDGE SCHOOL
For further details see p. 103
Tonbridge, Kent TN9 1JP
Tel: 01732 365555
Email: admissions@
tonbridge-school.org
Website:
www.tonbridge-school.co.uk
Headmaster: T H P Haynes
Age range: B13–18
No. of pupils: 778 VIth317
Fees: Day £27,216 FB £36,288

Middlesex

ACS Hillingdon International School
Hillingdon Court, 108 Vine Lane, Hillingdon, Uxbridge, Middlesex UB10 0BE
Tel: +44 (0) 1895 259 771
Head of School: Linda LaPine
Age range: 4–18
No. of pupils: 520
Fees: Day £17,090–£22,550

North London Collegiate School
Canons, Canons Drive, Edgware, Middlesex HA8 7RJ
Tel: +44 (0)20 8952 0912
Headmistress: Mrs Bernice McCabe
Age range: G4–18
No. of pupils: 1080
Fees: Day £5,214–£6,169

Radnor House
Pope's Villa, Cross Deep, Twickenham, Middlesex TW1 4QG
Tel: 020 8891 6264
Head of School: Mr. David Paton MA

ST HELEN'S SCHOOL
For further details see p. 84
Eastbury Road, Northwood, Middlesex HA6 3AS
Tel: +44 (0)1923 843210
Email: admissions@sthelens.london
Website: www.sthelens.london
Headmistress: Dr Mary Short BA, PhD
Age range: G3–18
No. of pupils: 1145 VIth165

Surrey

ACS Cobham International School
Heywood, Portsmouth Road, Cobham, Surrey KT11 1BL
Tel: +44 (0) 1932 867251
Head of School: Mr A Eysele
Age range: 2–18
No. of pupils: 1460
Fees: Day £10,690–£25,050 FB £36,240–£43,730

ACS Egham International School
Woodlee, London Road, Egham, Surrey TW20 0HS
Tel: +44 (0) 1784 430 800
Head of School: Jeremy Lewis
Age range: 3–18
No. of pupils: 620
Fees: Day £7,010–£23,430

Box Hill School
Old London Road, Mickleham, Dorking, Surrey RH5 6EA
Tel: 01372 373382
Headmaster: Mr Corydon Lowde
Age range: 11–18
No. of pupils: 425 VIth96
Fees: Day £16,140–£17,170 WB £24,600–£25,800 FB £29,970–£35,850

Caterham School
Harestone Valley, Caterham, Surrey CR3 6YA
Tel: 01883 343028
Head: Mr C. W. Jones MA(Cantab)
Age range: 11–18
No. of pupils: VIth321

Charterhouse
Godalming, Surrey GU7 2DX
Tel: 01483 291500
Headmaster: Mr Richard Pleming MA
Age range: B13–18 G16–18
No. of pupils: 803 VIth422
Fees: Day £29,361 FB £35,529

City of London Freemen's School
Ashtead Park, Ashtead, Surrey KT21 1ET
Tel: 01372 277933
Headmaster: Mr Philip MacDonald MA(Oxon)
Age range: 7–18
No. of pupils: 877 VIth213
Fees: Day £10,872–£14,598 FB £23,238

Cranleigh School
Horseshoe Lane, Cranleigh, Surrey GU6 8QQ
Tel: +44 (0) 1483 273666
Headmaster: Mr Martin Reader MA, MPhil, MBA
Age range: 7–18 (including Prep School)
No. of pupils: 631 VIth253
Fees: Day £27,855 FB £34,170

Duke of Kent School
Peaslake Road, Ewhurst, Surrey GU6 7NS
Tel: 01483 277313
Head: Mrs Judith Fremont-Barnes
Age range: 3–16
No. of pupils: 234
Fees: Day £4,860–£14,130 WB £13,350–£16,770 FB £15,735–£18,855

Epsom College
Epsom, Surrey KT17 4JQ
Tel: 01372 821234
Headmaster: Mr Jay A Piggot MA
Age range: 13–18
No. of pupils: 730
Fees: Day £21,255 FB £31,098

Frensham Heights
Rowledge, Farnham, Surrey GU10 4EA
Tel: 01252 792561
Headmaster: Mr Andrew Fisher BA, MEd, FRSA
Age range: 3–18
No. of pupils: 497 VIth105
Fees: Day £5,205–£15,300 FB £19,485–£22,680

International School of London (ISL) Surrey
Old Woking Road, Woking, Surrey GU22 8HY
Tel: +44 (0)1483 750409
Campus Principal & Head of Secondary: Richard Parker
Age range: 2–18 years
No. of pupils: 252
Fees: Day £17,700–£21,900

King Edward's Witley
Godalming, Surrey GU8 5SG
Tel: +44 (0)1428 686700
Acting Headmaster: Paul Crissell MA
Age range: 2–18
Fees: Day £19,950 FB £29,145

MARYMOUNT INTERNATIONAL SCHOOL LONDON
For further details see p. 83
George Road, Kingston upon Thames, Surrey KT2 7PE
Tel: +44 (0)20 8949 0571
Email: admissions@marymountlondon.com
Website: www.marymountlondon.com
Headmistress: Ms Sarah Gallagher MA, HDip in Ed
Age range: G11–18
No. of pupils: 252 VIth115
Fees: Day £19,250–£22,035 WB £33,020–£35,765 FB £34,615–£37,360

Prior's Field
Priorsfield Road, Godalming, Surrey GU7 2RH
Tel: 01483 810551
Head of School: Mrs T Kirnig
Age range: G11–18
No. of pupils: 450
Fees: Day £15,855 FB £25,575

Reed's School
Sandy Lane, Cobham, Surrey KT11 2ES
Tel: 01932 869001
Headmaster: Mr Mark Hoskins BA MA MSc
Age range: B11–18 G16–18
No. of pupils: 650 VIth230
Fees: Day £16,938–£21,184 FB £22,582–£28,023

Royal Russell School
Coombe Lane, Croydon, Surrey CR9 5BX
Tel: 020 8657 3669
Headmaster: Christopher Hutchinson
Age range: 11–18
No. of pupils: 590 VIth180
Fees: Day £15,285 FB £22,365–£30,240

St Catherine's School
Bramley, Guildford, Surrey GU5 0DF
Tel: 01483 893363
Headmistress: Mrs A M Phillips MA(Cantab)
Age range: G4–18
No. of pupils: 900
Fees: Day £7,695–£15,660 FB £25,770

St James Senior Boys School
Church Road, Ashford, Surrey TW15 3DZ
Tel: 01784 266930
Headmaster: Mr David Brazier
Age range: B11–18
No. of pupils: B385 VIth65
Fees: Day £16,320

St John's School
Epsom Road, Leatherhead, Surrey KT22 8SP
Tel: 01372 373000
Headmaster: Martin A R Collier
Age range: 13 (11 in 2016)–18
No. of pupils: 656
Fees: Day £22,275 WB £28,125

International schools

St Teresa's Effingham (Senior School)
Beech Avenue, Effingham,
Surrey RH5 6ST
Tel: 01372 452037
Head: Mr Michael Farmer
Age range: G2–18
No. of pupils: 450 VIth90
Fees: Day £14,190–£14,730
WB £22,800–£23,340 FB
£22,800–£23,340

TASIS The American School in England
Coldharbour Lane, Thorpe,
Surrey TW20 8TE
Tel: +44 (0)1932 582316
Head: Dr Mindy Hong
Age range: 3–18
No. of pupils: 740
Fees: Day £6,810–£22,070
FB £38,350

The Royal School, Haslemere
Farnham Lane, Haslemere,
Surrey GU27 1BE
Tel: 01428 603052
Principal: Mrs Anne Lynch BEd,
PGCE, FRSA
Age range: B6 weeks–16
years G6 weeks–18 years
No. of pupils: 500
Fees: Day £3,026–£5,619 WB
£7,741–£8,290 FB £8,893–£9,442

Whitgift School
Haling Park, South Croydon,
Surrey CR2 6YT
Tel: +44 (0)20 8633 9935
Headmaster: Dr Christopher Barnett
Age range: B10–18
No. of pupils: 1464
Fees: Day £17,340 WB
£27,924 FB £33,396

Woldingham School
Marden Park, Woldingham,
Surrey CR3 7YA
Tel: 01883 349431
Headmistress: Mrs Jayne Triffitt MA(Oxon)
Age range: G11–18
No. of pupils: 530 VIth150
Fees: Day £23,700 FB £28,410

Yehudi Menuhin School
Stoke Road, Stoke d'Abernon,
Cobham, Surrey KT11 3QQ
Tel: 01932 864739
Headmaster: Dr. Richard J Hillier
MA(Cantab), PhD
Age range: 7–19
No. of pupils: 80 VIth36
Fees: FB £41,928

West Sussex

ARDINGLY COLLEGE
For further details see p. 90
College Road, Ardingly,
Haywards Heath, West
Sussex RH17 6SQ
Tel: +44 (0)1444 893000
Email: registrar@ardingly.com
Website: www.ardingly.com
Headmaster: Mr Ben Figgis
Age range: 13–18
No. of pupils: 548
Fees: Day £21,960–£23,160
FB £29,715–£31,425

Burgess Hill Girls
Keymer Road, Burgess Hill,
West Sussex RH15 0EG
Tel: 01444 241050
Head: Mrs Kathryn Bell BSc (Hons),
PGCE
Age range: B2.5–4 G2.5–18
No. of pupils: 550 VIth87
Fees: Day £7,200–£16,200
FB £25,500–£28,200

Christ's Hospital
Horsham, West Sussex RH13 0YP
Tel: 01403 211293
Head Master: John R Franklin BA,
MEd(Admin)
Age range: 11–18
No. of pupils: 870
Fees: Day £15,750–
£19,800 FB £32,100

Farlington School
Strood Park, Horsham,
West Sussex RH12 3PN
Tel: 01403 254967
Headmistress: Ms Louise Higson
BSc, PGCE
Age range: G3–18
No. of pupils: 345 VIth53
Fees: Day £7,050–£16,470 WB
£21,585–£26,310 FB £22,785–£27,510

Hurstpierpoint College
College Lane, Hurstpierpoint,
West Sussex BN6 9JS
Tel: 01273 833636
Headmaster: Mr. T J Manly BA, MSc
Age range: 4–18
No. of pupils: 1083
Fees: Day £20,925 WB £26,385
FB £29,520–£31,125

Lancing College
Lancing, West Sussex BN15 0RW
Tel: 01273 465805
Head Master: Mr Dominic T Oliver
MPhil
Age range: 13–18
No. of pupils: 550 VIth255
Fees: Day £7,710 WB
£10,970 FB £10,970

Lavant House
West Lavant, Chichester,
West Sussex PO18 9AB
Tel: 01243 527211
Headteacher: Mrs Nicola Walker
BSC (Hons), MEdm NPQH, MBA,
PGCE
Age range: G4–18
No. of pupils: VIth20

Rikkyo School in England
Guildford Road, Rudgwick,
Horsham, West Sussex RH12 3BE
Tel: 01403 822107
Headmaster: Mr Roger Munechika
Age range: 10–18
No. of pupils: 116
Fees: FB £15,000–£21,600

Seaford College
Lavington Park, Petworth,
West Sussex GU28 0NB
Tel: 01798 867392
Headmaster: J P Green MA BA
Age range: 6–18
No. of pupils: 690 VIth173
Fees: Day £9,930–£19,380 WB
£19,320–£26,130 FB £29,985

Slindon College
Slindon House, Slindon, Arundel,
West Sussex BN18 0RH
Tel: 01243 814320
Headmaster: Mr D Quick
Age range: B8–18
No. of pupils: 80 VIth17
Fees: Day £6,900 WB
£9,845 FB £9,845

The Towers Convent School
Convent of the Blessed Sacrement,
Henfield Road, Upper Beeding,
Steyning, West Sussex BN44 3TF
Tel: 01903 812185
Headmistress: Mrs Clare Trelfa
Age range: B2–8 G2–16
No. of pupils: 320
Fees: Day £7,320–£10,200

Worth School
Paddockhurst Road, Turners Hill,
Crawley, West Sussex RH10 4SD
Tel: +44 (0)1342 710200
Head Master: Gino Carminati MA,
FRSA
Age range: 11–18
No. of pupils: 580 VIth222
Fees: Day £20,235 FB £27,849

Specialist schools and sixth form colleges

London

Central London

CATS College London
43-45 Bloomsbury Square,
London WC1A 2RA
Tel: 02078 411580
Principal: Mr Mark Love
Age range: 14–20
No. of pupils: VIth235
Fees: Day £16,460–£35,740
FB £33,560–£52,840

CITY OF LONDON SCHOOL
For further details see p. 46
Queen Victoria Street,
London EC4V 3AL
Tel: 020 7489 0291
Email: admissions@clsb.org.uk
Website: www.clsb.org.uk
Head: Mrs S Fletcher MA
Age range: B10–18
No. of pupils: 940 VIth250
Fees: Day £15,633

City of London School for Girls
St Giles' Terrace, Barbican,
London EC2Y 8BB
Tel: 020 7847 5500
Headmistress: Mrs E Harrop
Age range: G7–18
Fees: Day £14,409

Italia Conti Academy of Theatre Arts
Italia Conti House, 23 Goswell
Road, London EC1M 7AJ
Tel: 020 7608 0047
Principal: Anne Sheward
Age range: 10–21

The College of Central London
Frazer House, 32-38 Leman
Street, London E1 8EW
Tel: +44 (0) 20 7173 6054
Principal: Nicolas Kailides
Fees: Day £3,300

East London

Al-Mizan School
46 Whitechapel Road,
London E1 1JX
Tel: 020 7650 3070
Head: Mr Ziaurr Ahman
Age range: B7–18
No. of pupils: 200 VIth13
Fees: Day £2,400

Forest School
College Place, Snaresbrook,
London E17 3PY
Tel: 020 8520 1744
Warden: Mr Anthony Faccinello
Age range: 4–18
No. of pupils: 1355 VIth260
Fees: Day £11,049–£16,335

North London

Channing School
The Bank, Highgate, London N6 5HF
Tel: 020 8340 2328
Head: Mrs B M Elliott
Age range: G4–18
No. of pupils: 746 VIth108
Fees: Day £14,085–£15,255

DWIGHT SCHOOL LONDON
For further details see p. 52
6 Friern Barnet Lane,
London N11 3LX
Tel: +44 (0)20 8920 0600
Email: admissions@dwightlondon.org
Website: www.dwightlondon.org
Head: Mrs Alison Cobbin BA, Dip Ed, MBA
Age range: 2–18+

Greek Secondary School of London
Avenue Lodge, Bounds Green
Road, London N22 7EU
Tel: 020 8881 9320
Headteacher: Antonia Valavani
Age range: 13–18
No. of pupils: 200

Highgate
North Road, Highgate,
London N6 4AY
Tel: 020 8340 1524
Head Master: Mr A S Pettitt MA
Age range: 3–18
No. of pupils: 1541 VIth312
Fees: Day £15,135–£17,475

North-West London

Fine Arts College, Hampstead
24 Lambolle Place, Belsize
Park, London NW3 4PG
Tel: 020 7586 0312
Co Principals: Candida Cave & Nicholas Cochrane
Age range: 13–19
No. of pupils: 115
Fees: Day £6,000–£15,600

Francis Holland School, Regent's Park, NW1
Clarence Gate, Ivor Place,
Regent's Park, London NW1 6XR
Tel: 020 7723 0176
Head: Mrs Vivienne Durham MA(Oxon)
Age range: G11–18
No. of pupils: 464 VIth120
Fees: Day £17,700

INTERNATIONAL COMMUNITY SCHOOL
For further details see p. 57
4 York Terrace East, Regents
Park, London NW1 4PT
Tel: +44 20 7935 1206
Email: admissions@ics.uk.net
Website: www.icschool.co.uk
Head of School: Ms Rose Threlfall
Age range: 3–18
No. of pupils: 260
Fees: Day £16,650–£22,100

Lakefield Catering & Educational Centre
Maresfield Gardens,
Hampstead, London NW3 5RY
Tel: 020 7794 5669
Course Director: Mrs Maria Brown
Age range: G16–24
No. of pupils: 16
Fees: FB £1,160

London Academy of Dressmaking and Design
18 Dobree Avenue, Willesden,
London NW10 2AE
Tel: 020 8451 7174
Principal: Mrs P A Parkinson MA
Age range: 13+
Fees: Day £2,650

Mill Hill School
The Ridgeway, Mill Hill
Village, London NW7 1QS
Tel: 020 8959 1176
Head: Dr Dominic Luckett
Age range: 13–18
No. of pupils: 689 VIth259
Fees: Day £13,860 FB £21,900

NW5 Theatre School
14 Fortess Road, London NW5 2EU
Tel: 020 7482 3236
Founder: George O'Gorman
Age range: 16–30
Fees: Day £3,600

South Hampstead High School GDST
3 Maresfield Gardens,
London NW3 5SS
Tel: 020 7435 2899
Headmistress: Mrs J E Stephen BSc
Age range: G4–18
No. of pupils: 852 VIth162
Fees: Day £9,342–£12,006

Swaminarayan School
260 Brentfield Road, Neasden,
London NW10 8HE
Tel: 020 8965 8381
Headteacher: Nilesh Manani
Age range: 2–18
No. of pupils: 452 VIth36
Fees: Day £7,818–£10,707

The American School in London
One Waverley Place,
London NW8 0NP
Tel: 020 7449 1221
Head: Mrs Coreen Hester
Age range: 4–18
No. of pupils: 1350
Fees: Day £21,950–£25,650

The King Alfred School
Manor Wood, North End
Road, London NW11 7HY
Tel: 020 8457 5200
Head: Mrs Dawn Moore MA(London)
Age range: 4–18
No. of pupils: 615 VIth70
Fees: Day £12,624–£15,219

University College School
Frognal, Hampstead,
London NW3 6XH
Tel: 020 7435 2215
Headmaster: Mr M J Beard MA
Age range: B11–18
No. of pupils: 850 VIth300
Fees: Day £16,005

Wentworth Tutorial College
6-10 Brentmead Place,
London NW11 9LH
Tel: 020 8458 8524/5
Principal: Alan Davies BSc, MSc
Age range: 14–19
No. of pupils: 115

South-East London

Alleyn's School
Townley Road, Dulwich,
London SE22 8SU
Tel: 020 8557 1500
Headmaster: Dr G Savage MA, PhD, FRSA
Age range: 4–18
No. of pupils: 1223 VIth291
Fees: Day £14,139–£16,587
Ⓐ Ⓔ 🖊 16⁺

BLACKHEATH HIGH SCHOOL GDST
For further details see p. 44
Vanbrugh Park, Blackheath,
London SE3 7AG
Tel: 020 8853 2929
Email: info@bla.gdst.net
Website: www.blackheath highschool.gdst.net
Head: Mrs Carol Chandler-Thompson BA (Hons) Exeter, PGCE Exeter
Age range: G3–18
No. of pupils: 780
🚶 Ⓐ Ⓔ 🖊 16⁺

Colfe's School
Horn Park Lane, Lee,
London SE12 8AW
Tel: 020 8852 2283
Head: Mr R F Russell MA(Cantab)
Age range: 3–18
No. of pupils: 1020
Ⓐ Ⓔ 🖊 16⁺

Dulwich College
London SE21 7LD
Tel: 020 8693 3601
Master: Dr J A F Spence
Age range: B7–18
No. of pupils: 1589 VIth470
Fees: Day £18,231 WB £35,679 FB £38,052
🚶 🌍 Ⓐ 🏛 Ⓔ 🖊 16⁺

Eltham College
Grove Park Road, Mottingham,
London SE9 4QF
Tel: 020 8857 1455
Headmaster: Mr P J Henderson BA, FRSA
Age range: B7–18 G16–18
No. of pupils: 830 VIth220
Fees: Day £10,800–£12,525
🚶 Ⓐ Ⓔ 🖊 16⁺

James Allen's Girls' School
East Dulwich Grove, Dulwich,
London SE22 8TE
Tel: 020 8693 1181
Headmistress: Mrs Marion Gibbs BA(Hons), PGCE, MLitt, FRSA
Age range: G4–18
No. of pupils: VIth200
Fees: Day £12,540–£14,103
🚶 Ⓐ Ⓔ 16⁺

Riverston School
63-69 Eltham Road, Lee Green, London SE12 8UF
Tel: 020 8318 4327
Headmistress: Mrs S E Salathiel
Age range: 9 months–19 years
No. of pupils: 215
Ⓔ 🖊 16⁺ 🐾

St Dunstan's College
Stanstead Road, London SE6 4TY
Tel: 020 8516 7200
Headmistress: Mrs J D Davies BSc
Age range: 3–18
No. of pupils: 870
🌍 Ⓐ Ⓔ ⒾⒹ 16⁺

Sydenham High School GDST
19 Westwood Hill, London SE26 6BL
Tel: 020 8557 7000
Headteacher: Kathryn Pullen MA
Age range: G4–18
No. of pupils: 630 VIth70
Fees: Day £11,466–£14,592
🚶 Ⓐ Ⓔ 🖊 16⁺

South-West London

Abbey College - London
22 Grosvenor Gardens, Belgravia, London SW1W 0DH
Tel: 020 7824 7300
Principal: Mr Mark Love BEd
Age range: 14–19
No. of pupils: 150 VIth150
Fees: Day £5,950–£16,400 FB £30,200
16⁺ Ⓐ 🏛 🖊 16⁺

Centre Academy London
92 St John's Hill, Battersea, London SW11 1SH
Tel: 020 7738 2344
Principal: Dr. Duncan Rollo BA, MA, PhD
Age range: 9–19
Fees: Day £27,600–£40,100
🌍 Ⓔ 🖊 16⁺

Emanuel School
Battersea Rise, London SW11 1HS
Tel: 020 8870 4171
Headmaster: Mr Mark Hanley-Browne
Age range: 10–18
No. of pupils: 840 VIth208
Fees: Day £17,019
Ⓐ Ⓔ 🖊 16⁺

Francis Holland School, Sloane Square, SW1
39 Graham Terrace, London SW1W 8JF
Tel: 020 7730 2971
Head: Mrs Lucy Elphinstone MA(Cantab)
Age range: G4–18
No. of pupils: 500 VIth70
Fees: Day £16,350–£18,450
🚶 Ⓐ Ⓔ 🖊 16⁺

Ibstock Place School
Clarence Lane, London SW15 5PY
Tel: 020 8876 9991
Head: Mrs Anna Sylvester-Johnson BA(Hons), PGCE
Age range: 4–18
No. of pupils: 970
Fees: Day £4,755–£6,130
Ⓐ Ⓔ 16⁺

King's College School
Southside, Wimbledon Common, London SW19 4TT
Tel: 020 8255 5300
Head Master: A D Halls MA
Age range: B11–18 G16–18
No. of pupils: 855 VIth396
Fees: Day £19,830
🚶 🌍 Ⓐ Ⓔ ⒾⒷ 16⁺

Lycee Francais Charles de Gaulle
35 Cromwell Road, London SW7 2DG
Tel: 020 7584 6322
Headteacher: Mr Olivier Rauch
Age range: 3–18
No. of pupils: 4007
Fees: Day £4,521–£10,791
🌍 Ⓐ Ⓔ 16⁺

MORE HOUSE SCHOOL
For further details see p. 63
22-24 Pont Street, Knightsbridge, London SW1X 0AA
Tel: 020 7235 2855
Email: office@morehouse.org.uk
Website: www.morehouse.org.uk
Headmistress: Mrs. Amanda Leach
Age range: G11–18
No. of pupils: 211
Fees: Day £17,160
🚶 Ⓐ Ⓔ 🖊 16⁺

Putney High School GDST
35 Putney Hill, London SW15 6BH
Tel: 020 8788 4886
Headmistress: Dr Denise Lodge BSc, MSc, PhD
Age range: G4–18
No. of pupils: VIth150
🚶 Ⓐ Ⓔ 🖊 16⁺

Queen's Gate School
133 Queen's Gate, London SW7 5LE
Tel: 020 7589 3587
Principal: Mrs R M Kamaryc BA, MSc, PGCE
Age range: G4–18
No. of pupils: 523 VIth90
🚶 Ⓐ Ⓔ 🖊 16⁺

Quest Business Training
5 Grosvenor Gardens, Belgravia, London SW1W 0BD
Tel: 020 7233 5957
Age range: 16–45
16⁺ 16⁺

St Paul's School
Lonsdale Road, Barnes, London SW13 9JT
Tel: 020 8748 9162
High Master: Prof Mark Bailey
Age range: B13–18
No. of pupils: 897
Fees: Day £19,674 FB £29,466
🚶 🌍 Ⓐ 🏛 Ⓔ 🖊 16⁺

Streatham & Clapham High School GDST
42 Abbotswood Road, London SW16 1AW
Tel: 020 8677 8400
Headmaster: Dr Millan Sachania
Age range: B3–5 G3–18
No. of pupils: 603 VIth70
Fees: Day £5,886–£9,810
🚶 Ⓐ Ⓔ 🖊 16⁺

Swedish School
82 Lonsdale Road, London SW13 9JS
Tel: 020 8741 1751
Head of School: Ms. Annika Simonsson Bergqvist
Age range: 3–18
No. of pupils: 242
Fees: Day £6,600
16⁺

The Harrodian School
Lonsdale Road, London SW13 9QN
Tel: 020 8748 6117
Headmaster: James R Hooke
Age range: 5–18
No. of pupils: 890 VIth95
Fees: Day £10,407–£15,219
Ⓐ 🖊 16⁺

Westminster School
17 Dean's Yard, Westminster, London SW1P 3PF
Tel: 020 7963 1003
Headmaster: Mr Patrick Derham
Age range: B13–18 G16–18
No. of pupils: 744
Fees: Day £24,276–£26,322 FB £35,058
🚶 🌍 Ⓐ 🏛 Ⓔ 🖊 16⁺

Wimbledon High School GDST
Mansel Road, Wimbledon, London SW19 4AB
Tel: 020 8971 0900
Headmistress: Mrs H Hanbury
Age range: G4–18
No. of pupils: 900 VIth155
Fees: Day £11,445–£15,024
🚶 Ⓐ Ⓔ 🖊 16⁺

West London

Alan D Education
61-62 East Castle Street, London W1W 8NQ
Tel: 020 7580 1030
Director of Education: Alan Hemmings
Fees: Day £200 FB £12,400
16⁺ 16⁺ 🐾

Ashbourne Middle School
17 Old Court Place,
Kensington, London W8 4PL
Tel: 020 7937 3858
Principal: M J Kirby MSc, BApSc
Age range: 13–16
No. of pupils: VIth150
Fees: Day £14,725 FB £21,500
(A) (£) 16+

Blake College
162 New Cavendish Street,
London W1W 6YS
Tel: 020 7636 0658
Course Director: D A J Cluckie
BA, BSc
Fees: Day £4,720–£5,310
16+ 16+

David Game College
David Game House, 69 Notting
Hill Gate, London W11 3JS
Tel: 020 7221 6665
Principal: D T P Game MA, MPhil
Age range: 14–19
No. of pupils: 200 VIth150
Fees: Day £12,000–£13,000
16+ (A) 16+

Ealing Independent College
83 New Broadway, Ealing,
London W5 5AL
Tel: 020 8579 6668
Principal: Dr Ian Moores
Age range: 13–22
No. of pupils: 100 VIth70
Fees: Day £3,865–£12,600
16+ (A) 16+

International School of London (ISL) London
139 Gunnersbury Avenue,
Ealing, London W3 8LG
Tel: +44 (0)20 8992 5823
Middle & Lower School Principal:
Andrew Mitchell
Age range: 3–18 years
No. of pupils: 480
Fees: Day £18,000–£24,600
(globe) (IB) (pen) 16+

King Fahad Academy
Bromyard Avenue, Acton,
London W3 7HD
Tel: 020 8743 0131
Acting Head of Primary School: Ms
Julie Benafif
Age range: 3–18
No. of pupils: 446
Fees: Day £3,000
(globe) (A) (£) (IB) 16+

Latymer Upper School
King Street, Hammersmith,
London W6 9LR
Tel: 0845 638 5800
Head: Mr D Goodhew MA(Oxon)
Age range: 11–18
No. of pupils: 1123 VIth354
Fees: Day £16,485
(A) (£) (pen) 16+

Notting Hill & Ealing High School GDST
2 Cleveland Road, West
Ealing, London W13 8AX
Tel: 020 8991 2165
Headmistress: Ms Lucinda Hunt
Age range: G4–18
No. of pupils: 903 VIth150
Fees: Day £12,849–£16,521
(person) (A) (£) 16+

Portland Place School
56-58 Portland Place,
London W1N 1NJ
Tel: 0207 307 8700
Head: Mr Tim Cook
Age range: 11–18
No. of pupils: 300 VIth50
Fees: Day £12,522–£16,425
(A) (£) (pen) 16+

Queen's College
43-49 Harley Street,
London W1G 8BT
Tel: 020 7291 7000
Head: Dr F M R Ramsey MA,
DPhil(Oxon)
Age range: G11–18
No. of pupils: 360 VIth90
Fees: Day £11,520–£14,550
(person) (A) (£) 16+

Ray Cochrane Beauty School
118 Baker Street, London W1U 6TT
Tel: 020 7486 6291
Principal: Miss Baljeet Suri CIDESCO,
CIBTAC, FETC
Age range: 16–50
No. of pupils: 30
Fees: Day £2,195–£8,995
16+ 16+

Southbank International School - Westminster
63-65 Portland Place,
London W1B 1QR
Tel: 020 7243 3803
Principal: Justine Oliver
Age range: 11–18/19
(globe) (IB) (pen) 16+

St Augustine's Priory
Hillcrest Road, Ealing,
London W5 2JL
Tel: 020 8997 2022
Headteacher: Mrs. Sarah Raffray
MA
Age range: G3–18
No. of pupils: 470
Fees: Day £3,180–£13,572
(person) (A) (pen) 16+

ST BENEDICT'S SCHOOL
For further details see p. 70
54 Eaton Rise, Ealing,
London W5 2ES
Tel: 020 8862 2254
Email: enquiries@
stbenedicts.org.uk
Website:
www.stbenedicts.org.uk
Headmaster: Mr C J Cleugh
BSc, MSc
Age range: 3–18
No. of pupils: 1106 VIth212
Fees: Day £11,520–£14,550
(A) (£) (pen) 16+

St James Senior Girls' School
Earsby Street, London W14 8SH
Tel: 020 7348 1777
Headmistress: Mrs Sarah Labram BA
Age range: G10–18
No. of pupils: 325 VIth61
Fees: Day £17,310
(person) (A) (£) (pen) 16+

St Paul's Girls' School
Brook Green, London W6 7BS
Tel: 020 7603 2288
High Mistress: Ms Clarissa Farr MA,
PGCE
Age range: G11–18 years
No. of pupils: 740 VIth200
Fees: Day £20,874–£22,437
(person) (A) (£) (pen) 16+

The Godolphin and Latymer School
Iffley Road, Hammersmith,
London W6 0PG
Tel: +44 (0)20 8741 1936
Head Mistress: Mrs R Mercer BA
Age range: G11–18
No. of pupils: 812
Fees: Day £19,224
(person) (globe) (A) (£) (IB) (pen) 16+

Berkshire

Bradfield College
Bradfield, Berkshire RG7 6AU
Tel: 0118 964 4516
Headmaster: Dr Christopher
Stevens
Age range: 13–18
No. of pupils: 770 VIth310
Fees: Day £27,420 FB £34,275
(globe) (A) (home) (£) (IB) (pen) 16+

Brigidine School Windsor
Queensmead, King\'s Road,
Windsor, Berkshire SL4 2AX
Tel: 01753 863779
Headmistress: Mrs Elizabeth
Robinson
Age range: B2–7 G3–18
No. of pupils: 300
Fees: Day £3,945–£11,865
(person) (A) (£) (pen) 16+

Claires Court Nursery, Girls and Sixth Form
1 College Avenue, Maidenhead,
Berkshire SL6 6AW
Tel: 01628 411480
Head: Mr Paul Bevis
Age range: B16–18 G3–18
No. of pupils: 495 VIth111
Fees: Day £5,715–£14,580
(person) (A) (£) (pen) 16+

Claires Court Senior Boys
Ray Mill Road East, Maidenhead,
Berkshire SL6 8TE
Tel: 01628 411470
Headmaster: Mr J M Rayer BSc,
PGCE
Age range: B11–16
No. of pupils: 335 VIth112
Fees: Day £13,860–£14,580
(person) (A) (£) (pen) 16+

Eton College
Windsor, Berkshire SL4 6DW
Tel: 01753 671249
Head Master: Simon Henderson MA
Age range: B13–18
No. of pupils: 1300 VIth520
Fees: FB £33,270
(person) (globe) (A) (home) (£) (pen) 16+

Heathfield School
London Road, Ascot,
Berkshire SL5 8BQ
Tel: 01344 898342
Head: Mrs Jo Heywood BSc(Hons),
PGCE
Age range: G11–18
No. of pupils: 200 VIth80
Fees: Day £22,680–£23,310
FB £32,400–£33,300
(person) (globe) (A) (home) (£) (pen) 16+

Hurst Lodge
Bagshot Road, Ascot,
Berkshire SL5 9JU
Tel: 01344 622154
Principal: Ms Victoria Smit
Age range: 3–18
No. of pupils: 202 VIth13
Fees: Day £6,420–£25,200
WB £19,905–£34,005
(globe) (A) (home) (£) (pen) 16+

Leighton Park School
Shinfield Road, Reading,
Berkshire RG2 7DE
Tel: 0118 987 9600
Head: Nigel Williams BA(Bristol),
MA(London), PGCE
Age range: 11–18
No. of pupils: 474 VIth145
Fees: Day £16,524–£20,313 WB
£22,524–£27,225 FB £25,614–£31,632
(globe) (A) (home) (£) (IB) (pen) 16+

Luckley House School
Luckley Road, Wokingham,
Berkshire RG40 3EU
Tel: 0118 978 4175
Headmistress: Mrs Jane Tudor
Age range: G11–18
No. of pupils: 300 VIth50
Fees: Day £13,476 WB
£21,858 FB £23,586

IVS ASCOT (LICENSED VICTUALLERS' SCHOOL)
For further details see p. 93
London Road, Ascot,
Berkshire SL5 8DR
Tel: 01344 882770
Email: enquiries@lvs.
ascot.sch.uk
Website: www.lvs.ascot.sch.uk
Headmistress: Mrs Christine
Cunniffe BA (Hons), MMus, MBA
Age range: 4–18
No. of pupils: 870
Fees: Day £9,528–£17,079
FB £24,384–£30,006

Padworth College
Padworth, Reading,
Berkshire RG7 4NR
Tel: 0118 983 2644
Principal: Mr John Aguilar
Age range: 13–19
No. of pupils: 116 VIth50
Fees: Day £14,250 FB £28,392

PANGBOURNE COLLEGE
For further details see p. 96
Pangbourne, Reading,
Berkshire RG8 8LA
Tel: 0118 984 2101
Email: registrar@
pangbourne.com
Website:
www.pangbourne.com
Headmaster: Thomas J C
Garnier
Age range: 11–18
No. of pupils: 420 VIth148
Fees: Day £15,999–£22,548
FB £22,533–£31,890

Queen Anne's School
6 Henley Road, Caversham,
Reading, Berkshire RG4 6DX
Tel: 0118 918 7300
Headmistress: Mrs Julia Harrington
BA(Hons), PGCE, NPQH
Age range: G11–18
No. of pupils: 336 VIth100
Fees: Day £5,695 WB
£7,545–£7,975 FB £8,395

Reading Blue Coat School
Holme Park, Sonning Lane, Sonning,
Reading, Berkshire RG4 6SU
Tel: 0118 944 1005
Headmaster: M J Windsor
Age range: B11–18 G16–18
No. of pupils: 710 VIth230
Fees: Day £13,470

Reddam House Bearwood
Bearwood Road, Wokingham,
Berkshire RG41 5BG
Tel: 0118 974 8300
Headmaster: Mr Donald Wilkinson
Age range: 0–18
No. of pupils: 487 VIth80
Fees: Day £13,890–£16,365
FB £24,360–£28,080

Redroofs School for the Performing Arts (Redroofs Theatre School)
26 Bath Road, Maidenhead,
Berkshire SL6 4JT
Tel: 01628 674092
Principal: June Rose
Age range: 8–18
No. of pupils: 100
Fees: Day £4,000

St George's Ascot
Wells Lane, Ascot, Berkshire SL5 7DZ
Tel: 01344 629920
Headmistress: Mrs Rachel Owens
MA(Hons) (Oxon) PGCE NPQH
Age range: G11–18
No. of pupils: 280 VIth85
Fees: Day £29,325–£30,375 FB £31,125

St Joseph's College
Upper Redlands Road,
Reading, Berkshire RG1 5JT
Tel: 0118 966 1000
Head of College (Senior School):
Mr Andrew Colpus
Age range: 3–18
No. of pupils: VIth46
Fees: Day £5,634–£9,630

St Mary's School Ascot
St Mary's Road, Ascot,
Berkshire SL5 9JF
Tel: 01344 296614
Headmistress: Mrs Mary Breen
BSc, MSc
Age range: G11–18
No. of pupils: 390 VIth120
Fees: Day £23,400 FB £32,850

Teikyo School UK
Framewood Road, Wexham,
Slough, Berkshire SL2 4QS
Tel: 01753 663711
Headmaster: A Watanabe BA
Age range: 16–18

The Abbey School
Kendrick Road, Reading,
Berkshire RG1 5DZ
Tel: 0118 987 2256
Head: Mrs Rachel S E Dent
Age range: G3–18
No. of pupils: 1070
Fees: Day £15,090

The Marist Schools
King's Road, Sunninghill,
Ascot, Berkshire SL5 7PS
Tel: 01344 624291
Head of Secondary School: Mr K
McCloskey
Age range: G2–18
No. of pupils: 550 VIth60
Fees: Day £7,845–£10,695

The Oratory School
Woodcote, Reading,
Berkshire RG8 0PJ
Tel: 01491 683500
Head Master: Mr A J Wyles
BSc(Hons), MFd, PGCE. FRGS
Age range: B11–18
No. of pupils: 380 VIth120
Fees: Day £23,250 FB
£21,540–£31,950

Wellington College
Duke's Ride, Crowthorne,
Berkshire RG45 7PU
Tel: +44 (0)1344 444000
Master: Mr Julian Thomas
Age range: 13–18
No. of pupils: 1045 VIth470
Fees: Day £26,130–
£30,030 FB £35,775

Buckinghamshire

Akeley Wood School
Akeley Wood, Buckingham,
Buckinghamshire MK18 5AE
Tel: 01280 814110
Headmaster: Dr Jerry Grundy BA,
PhD
Age range: 12 months–18 years
No. of pupils: 833 VIth119
Fees: Day £7,185–£10,575

Pipers Corner School
Pipers Lane, Great
Kingshill, High Wycombe,
Buckinghamshire HP15 6LP
Tel: 01494 718 255
Headmistress: Mrs H J Ness-Gifford
BA(Hons), PGCE
Age range: G4–18
No. of pupils: VIth72
Fees: Day £7,230–£14,010
WB £18,750–£222,845 FB
£18,990–£23,085

St Mary's School
94 Packhorse Road, Gerrards
Cross, Buckinghamshire SL9 8JQ
Tel: 01753 883370
Headmistress: Mrs J A Ross
BA(Hons), NPQH
Age range: G3–18
No. of pupils: 320 VIth38
Fees: Day £3,420–£12,155

Stowe School
Buckingham, Buckinghamshire
MK18 5EH
Tel: 01280 818000
Headmaster: Dr Anthony
Wallersteiner
Age range: 13–18
No. of pupils: 769 VIth318
Fees: Day £22,500 FB £30,975

The Webber Independent School
Soskin Drive, Stantonbury
Fields, Milton Keynes,
Buckinghamshire MK14 6DP
Tel: 01908 574740
Principal: Hilary Marsden
Age range: 3–18
No. of pupils: 300 VIth15
Fees: Day £3,894–£10,371

Wycombe Abbey
High Wycombe,
Buckinghamshire HP11 1PE
Tel: +44 (0)1494 897008
Headmistress: Mrs Rhiannon J
Wilkinson MA (Oxon) MEd
Age range: G11–18
No. of pupils: 554
Fees: Day £26,775 FB £35,700

East Sussex

Battle Abbey School
Battle, East Sussex TN33 0AD
Tel: 01424 772385
Headmaster: Mr R C Clark
BA(Hons), MA(Ed)
Age range: 2–18
No. of pupils: 286 VIth48
Fees: Day £6,630–£13,390 FB £23,190
Ⓐ Ⓐ ⓐ Ⓔ ⦸ 16·

Bede's School
The Dicker, Upper Dicker,
Hailsham, East Sussex BN27 3QH
Tel: +44 (0)1323843252
Head: Dr Richard Maloney
Age range: 12–18+
No. of pupils: 800 VIth295
Fees: Day £15,450 FB £25,725
Ⓐ Ⓐ ⓐ Ⓔ ⦸ 16· ✿

Brighton & Hove High School GDST
Montpelier Road, Brighton,
East Sussex BN1 3AT
Tel: 01273 280280
Head: Mrs Lorna Duggleby
Age range: G3–18
No. of pupils: 680 VIth70
Fees: Day £5,028–£8,898
Ⓐ Ⓐ Ⓔ ⦸ 16·

Brighton College
Eastern Road, Brighton,
East Sussex BN2 0AL
Tel: 01273 704200
Head Master: Richard Cairns MA
Age range: 3–18
No. of pupils: 945 VIth340
Fees: Day £4,890–£18,675 WB
£24,729–£25,884 FB £28,575–£30,141
Ⓐ Ⓐ ⓐ Ⓔ ⦸ 16·

Buckswood School
Broomham Hall, Rye
Road, Guestling, Hastings,
East Sussex TN35 4LT
Tel: 01424 813 813
Headteacher: Mr Mark Redsell
Age range: 10–19
No. of pupils: 420
Ⓐ Ⓐ ⓐ Ⓔ ⓘ ⦸ 16·

Buckswood St George's
Westwood House, 7-9
Holmesdale Gardens, Hastings,
East Sussex TN34 1LY
Tel: 01424 813696
College Director: Ian Godfrey
Age range: B16–19 G16–20
No. of pupils: VIth50
16· Ⓐ ⓐ Ⓔ ⓘ 16·

Eastbourne College
Old Wish Road, Eastbourne,
East Sussex BN21 4JX
Tel: 01323 452323 (Admissions)
Headmaster: Mr S P Davies MA
Age range: 13–18
No. of pupils: 630 VIth273
Fees: Day £20,940–£21,300
FB £31,965–£32,325
Ⓐ Ⓐ ⓐ Ⓔ ⦸ 16·

Greenfields School
Priory Road, Forest Row,
East Sussex RH18 5JD
Tel: 01342 822189
Headteacher: Mr G Hudson
Age range: 2–19
No. of pupils: 125
Fees: Day £500–£10,800
FB £19,170–£20,850
Ⓐ Ⓐ Ⓔ 16·

K-BIS Theatre School
Clermont Hall, Cumberland Road,
Brighton, East Sussex BN1 6SL
Tel: 01273 566739
Principal: Mrs Marcia King LGSM
Age range: 5–18
No. of pupils: VIth7
Fees: Day £5,980
Ⓐ Ⓔ ⦸ 16· ✿

Lewes Old Grammar School
High Street, Lewes, East
Sussex BN7 1XS
Tel: 01273 472634
Headmaster: Mr Robert Blewitt
Age range: 3–18
No. of pupils: 463 VIth50
Fees: Day £5,550–£10,815
Ⓐ Ⓔ ⦸ 16·

MAYFIELD SCHOOL
For further details see p. 94
The Old Palace, Mayfield,
East Sussex TN20 6PH
Tel: +44 (0)1435 874600
Email: registrar@
mayfieldgirls.org
Website: www.mayfieldgirls.org
Head: Ms Antonia Beary MA,
Mphil(Cantab), PGCE
Age range: G11–18
No. of pupils: 356 VIth100
Fees: Day £19,125 WB
£30,900 FB £30,900
Ⓐ Ⓐ Ⓐ ⓐ Ⓔ ⦸ 16·

MICHAEL HALL SCHOOL
For further details see p. 98
Kidbrooke Park, Priory Road,
Forest Row, East Sussex RH18 5BG
Tel: 01342 822275
Email: info@michaelhall.co.uk
Website: www.michaelhall.co.uk
Age range: 3–19
Fees: Day £8,840–£12,120
FB £5,400–£7,610
Ⓐ Ⓐ ⓐ ⦸ 16·

Moira House Girls School
Upper Carlisle Road, Eastbourne,
East Sussex BN20 7TE
Tel: 01323 644144
Principal: Mrs L A Watson MA(Ed),
MInstD
Age range: G2–18
No. of pupils: 360 VIth105
Fees: Day £6,300–£14,655 WB
£19,260–£24,060 FB £20,715–£26,550
Ⓐ Ⓐ Ⓐ ⓐ Ⓔ ⦸ 16·

ROEDEAN SCHOOL
For further details see p. 99
Roedean Way, Brighton,
East Sussex BN2 5RQ
Tel: 01273 667500
Email: info@roedean.co.uk
Website: www.roedean.co.uk
Headmaster: Mr. Oliver Bond
BA(Essex), PGCE, NPQH
Age range: G11–18
No. of pupils: 440 VIth177
Fees: Day £14,970–£19,470
WB £26,730–£29,820 FB
£28,860–£34,950
Ⓐ Ⓐ Ⓐ ⓐ Ⓔ ⦸ 16·

Essex

BANCROFT'S SCHOOL
For further details see p. 78
High Road, Woodford
Green, Essex IG8 0RF
Tel: 020 8505 4821
Email: office@bancrofts.org
Website: www.bancrofts.org
Head: Mrs Mary Ireland BSc,
DipEd, CBiol, MBS
Age range: 7–18
No. of pupils: 1123 VIth240
Ⓐ Ⓔ ⦸ 16·

Brentwood School
Middleton Hall Lane,
Brentwood, Essex CM15 8EE
Tel: 01277 243243
Headmaster: Mr Ian Davies
Age range: 3–18
No. of pupils: 1550
Fees: Day £16,635 FB £32,649
Ⓐ Ⓐ ⓐ Ⓔ ⓘ ⦸ 16·

Chigwell School
High Road, Chigwell, Essex IG7 6QF
Tel: 020 8501 5700
Headmaster: Mr M E Punt MA, MSc
Age range: 4–18
No. of pupils: 915 VIth185
Fees: Day £10,200–£16,020
FB £26,730–£26,730
Ⓐ Ⓐ ⓐ Ⓔ ⦸ 16·

Felsted School
Felsted, Great Dunmow,
Essex CM6 3LL
Tel: +44 (0) 1371 822605
Headmaster: Dr Michael Walker
Age range: 13–18
No. of pupils: 516 VIth236
Fees: Day £18,480 WB
£22,377 FB £24,705
Ⓐ Ⓐ ⓐ Ⓔ ⓘ ⦸ 16·

Friends' School
Mount Pleasant Road, Saffron
Walden, Essex CB11 3EB
Tel: 01799 525351
Head: Ms Anna Chaudhri MA
Age range: 3–18
No. of pupils: 390 VIth50
Fees: Day £2,375–£5,305 WB
£6,615–£7,690 FB £7,190–£8,590
Ⓐ Ⓐ ⓐ Ⓔ ⦸ 16·

Gosfield School
Cut Hedge Park, Halstead Road,
Gosfield, Halstead, Essex CO9 1PF
Tel: 01787 474040
Principal: Dr Sarah Welch
Age range: 4–18
No. of pupils: VIth21
Fees: Day £4,740–£13,695 WB
£15,465–£17,310 FB £17,985–£23,130
Ⓐ Ⓐ ⓐ Ⓔ ⦸ 16·

New Hall School
The Avenue, Boreham,
Chelmsford, Essex CM3 3HS
Tel: 01245 467588
Principal: Mrs Katherine Jeffrey MA,
BA, PGCE, MA(Ed Mg), NPQH
Age range: Coed 3-11,
Single 11-16, Coed 16–18
No. of pupils: 1175 VIth197
Fees: Day £8,742–£18,042 WB
£17,670–£25,815 FB £19,521–£27,099
Ⓐ Ⓐ ⓐ Ⓔ ⦸ 16·

Park School for Girls
20 Park Avenue, Ilford, Essex IG1 4RS
Tel: 020 8554 2466
Headmistress: Mrs N O'Brien BA
Age range: G7–18
No. of pupils: 230 VIth19
Fees: Day £4,755–£6,285
Ⓐ Ⓐ 16·

Hampshire

Allbrook School
The Old School, Pitmore
Road, Allbrook, Eastleigh,
Hampshire SO50 4LW
Tel: 023 8061 6316
Head of Studies: Mrs Hilary Laider
Age range: 11–16
No. of pupils: 79

Alton Convent School
Anstey Lane, Alton,
Hampshire GU34 2NG
Tel: 01420 82070
Head: Graham Maher
Age range: B0–11 G0–18
No. of pupils: 563 VIth53
Fees: Day £8,655–£12,285

Bedales School
Church Road, Steep, Petersfield,
Hampshire GU32 2DG
Tel: 01730 711733
Head: Keith Budge MA
Age range: 13–18
No. of pupils: 463 VIth192
Fees: Day £8,825 FB £11,230

Brockwood Park & Inwoods School
Brockwood Park, Bramdean,
Hampshire SO24 0LQ
Tel: +44 (0)1962 771744
Co-Principals: Mr Adrian Sydenham
& Dr Gopal Krishnamurthy
Age range: 4–19
No. of pupils: 92
Fees: Day £3,150 FB £17,270

Churcher's College
Petersfield, Hampshire GU31 4AS
Tel: 01730 263033
Headmaster: Mr Simon Williams
MA, BSc
Age range: 4–18
No. of pupils: 1067 VIth224
Fees: Day £7,605–£11,955

Farnborough Hill
Farnborough Road, Farnborough,
Hampshire GU14 8AT
Tel: 01252 545197
Headmistress: Mrs S Buckle BSc,
MA, PGCE, NPQH
Age range: G11–18
No. of pupils: 563 VIth80
Fees: Day £12,120

GEMS Sherfield School
Sherfield-on-Loddon, Hook,
Hampshire RG27 0HU
Tel: +44 (0)1256 884 800
Headmaster: Mr Dick Jaine
Age range: 3 months–18 years
No. of pupils: 445 VIth16
Fees: Day £7,350–£13,890 FB £20,946

Hampshire Collegiate School
Embley Park, Romsey,
Hampshire SO51 6ZE
Tel: 01794 512206
Principal: Mrs Emma-Kate Henry
Age range: 2–18
No. of pupils: 683

King Edward VI School
Wilton Road, Southampton,
Hampshire SO15 5UQ
Tel: 023 8070 4561
Head Master: Mr A J Thould
MA(Oxon)
Age range: 11–18
No. of pupils: 975 VIth260
Fees: Day £14,355

Lord Wandsworth College
Long Sutton, Hook,
Hampshire RG29 1TB
Tel: 01256 862201
Head of School: Mr Adam Williams
Age range: 11–18 years
No. of pupils: 550
Fees: Day £19,110–£20,940
WB £25,350–£28,350 FB
£26,100–£29,700

Portsmouth High School GDST
Kent Road, Southsea, Portsmouth,
Hampshire PO5 3EQ
Tel: 023 9282 6714
Headmistress: Mrs Jane Prescott
BSc NPQH
Age range: G3–18
No. of pupils: 421
Fees: Day £2,542–£4,248

Salesian College
Reading Road, Farnborough,
Hampshire GU14 6PA
Tel: 01252 893000
Headmaster: Mr P A Wilson
BA(Hons), MA, CertEd
Age range: B11–18 G16–18
No. of pupils: 650 VIth140
Fees: Day £9,000

St John's College
Grove Road South, Southsea,
Portsmouth, Hampshire PO5 3QW
Tel: 023 9281 5118
Headmaster: Mr Timothy Bayley
Age range: 2–18
No. of pupils: 600 VIth86
Fees: Day £8,460–£11,100
FB £23,970–£25,770

St Swithun's School
Alresford Road, Winchester,
Hampshire SO21 1HA
Tel: 01962 835700
Headmistress: Jane Gandee
MA(Cantab)
Age range: G11–18
No. of pupils: G525 VIth85
Fees: Day £17,640 FB £28,290

The Portsmouth Grammar School
High Street, Portsmouth,
Hampshire PO1 2LN
Tel: +44 (0)23 9236 0036
Headmaster: J E Priory MA
Age range: 2–18
No. of pupils: 1645 VIth298
Fees: Day £8,379–£13,059

Winchester College
College Street, Winchester,
Hampshire SO23 9NA
Tel: 01962 621247
Headmaster: R D Townsend MA,
DPhil
Age range: B13–18
No. of pupils: 690 VIth280
Fees: FB £35,610

Hertfordshire

Aldenham School
Elstree, Hertfordshire WD6 3AJ
Tel: 01923 858122
Headmaster: James C Fowler MA
Age range: 3–18
No. of pupils: 700 VIth158
Fees: Day £13,626–£19,500
FB £18,768–£28,410

Berkhamsted School
Overton House, 131 High Street,
Berkhamsted, Hertfordshire HP4 2DJ
Tel: 01442 358001
Principal: Mr Richard Backhouse
MA(Cantab)
Age range: 3–18 years
No. of pupils: 1680 VIth361
Fees: Day £10,065–£19,095
WB £25,565 FB £30,415

Bishop's Stortford College
10 Maze Green Road, Bishop's
Stortford, Hertfordshire CM23 2PJ
Tel: 01279 838575
Headmaster: Mr Jeremy Gladwin
Age range: 13–18
No. of pupils: VIth249
Fees: Day £17,496–£17,655 WB
£25,950–£26,109 FB £26,208–£27,405

Champneys International College of Health & Beauty
Chesham Road, Wigginton,
Tring, Hertfordshire HP23 6HY
Tel: 01442 291333
College Principal: Ms Pam Clegg
Age range: 16+
No. of pupils: 61
Fees: Day £3,000–£9,050

Haberdashers' Aske's School
Butterfly Lane, Elstree,
Borehamwood,
Hertfordshire WD6 3AF
Tel: 020 8266 1700
Headmaster: Mr P B Hamilton MA
Age range: B5–18
No. of pupils: 1402 VIth310
Fees: Day £10,641–£14,103

Haberdashers' Aske's School for Girls
Aldenham Road,
Elstree, Borehamwood,
Hertfordshire WD6 3BT
Tel: 020 8266 2300
Headmistress: Miss Biddie A
O'Connor MA (Oxon)
Age range: G4–18
No. of pupils: 1185
Fees: Day £13,269–£15,516

HAILEYBURY
For further details see p. 92
Haileybury, Hertford,
Hertfordshire SG13 7NU
Tel: +44 (0)1992 706353
Email: registrar@haileybury.com
Website: www.haileybury.com
The Master: J S Davies
MA(Cantab)
Age range: 11–18
No. of pupils: 759 VIth301
Fees: Day £15,435–£23,220
FB £19,605–£30,900

Immanuel College
87/91 Elstree Road, Bushey,
Hertfordshire WD23 4EB
Tel: 020 8950 0604
Headmaster: Mr Philip Skelker MA
Age range: 11–18
No. of pupils: 520 VIth127
Fees: Day £10,995

Princess Helena College
Preston, Hitchin,
Hertfordshire SG4 7RT
Tel: 01462 443888
Headmistress: Mrs Sue Wallace-
Woodroffe
Age range: G11–18
No. of pupils: 194 VIth35
Fees: Day £15,225–£18,585
FB £21,705–£26,985

Queenswood
Shepherd's Way, Brookmans Park,
Hatfield, Hertfordshire AL9 6NS
Tel: 01707 602500
Principal: Mrs P C Edgar BA(Hons)
London, PGCE
Age range: G11–18
No. of pupils: 400 VIth120
Fees: Day £19,485–£21,825
FB £26,295–£28,665

Rudolf Steiner School
Langley Hill, Kings Langley,
Hertfordshire WD4 9HG
Tel: 01923 262505
Age range: 3–19
No. of pupils: 405
Fees: Day £2,985–£7,800

Sherrardswood School
Lockleys, Welwyn,
Hertfordshire AL6 0BJ
Tel: 01438 714282
Headmistress: Mrs L Corry
Age range: 2–18
No. of pupils: 357
Fees: Day £6,720–£12,750

St Albans High School for Girls
Townsend Avenue, St Albans,
Hertfordshire AL1 3SJ
Tel: 01727 853800
Headmistress: Mrs Jenny Brown
MA (Oxon)
Age range: G4–18
No. of pupils: 940 VIth170

St Albans School
Abbey Gateway, St Albans,
Hertfordshire AL3 4HB
Tel: 01727 855521
Headmaster: Mr JWJ Gillespie
MA(Cantab), FRSA
Age range: B11–18 G16–18
No. of pupils: 870
Fees: Day £16,818

St Christopher School
Barrington Road, Letchworth,
Hertfordshire SG6 3JZ
Tel: 01462 650 850
Head: Richard Palmer
Age range: 3–18
No. of pupils: 511 VIth78
Fees: Day £3,375–£14,505
FB £15,600–£25,470

St Columba's College
King Harry Lane, St Albans,
Hertfordshire AL3 4AW
Tel: 01727 855185
Headmaster: David R Buxton
Age range: B4–18
No. of pupils: 860 VIth150
Fees: Day £8,235–£10,416

St Edmund's College & Prep School
Old Hall Green, Nr Ware,
Hertfordshire SG11 1DS
Tel: 01920 824247
Head: Paulo Durán BA MA
Age range: 3–18
No. of pupils: 799 VIth135
Fees: Day £9,465–£14,955 WB
£19,830–£22,575 FB £21,855–£24,990

St Francis' College
Broadway, Letchworth Garden
City, Hertfordshire SG6 3PJ
Tel: 01462 670511
Headmistress: Mrs B Goulding
Age range: G3–18
No. of pupils: 460 VIth75
Fees: Day £8,670–£13,830 WB
£19,425–£22,875 FB £24,195–£27,645

St Margaret's School, Bushey
Merry Hill Road, Bushey,
Hertfordshire WD23 1DT
Tel: 020 8416 4400
Head: Mrs Rose Hardy MA(Oxon),
MEd, FRSA
Age range: G4–18 years
No. of pupils: 450 VIth100
Fees: Day £14,730 WB
£20,220–£23,670 FB £27,600

St Martha's School
Camlet Way, Hadley Wood,
Barnet, Hertfordshire EN4 0NJ
Tel: 020 8449 6889
Headmaster: Mr Matthew Burke
Age range: G11–18
No. of pupils: 220 VIth40
Fees: Day £4,625

Stanborough School
Stanborough Park, Garston,
Watford, Hertfordshire WD25 9JT
Tel: 01923 673268
Head Teacher: Ms Lorraine Dixon
Age range: 3–19
No. of pupils: 300 VIth20
Fees: Day £3,660–£5,500
WB £12,834–£15,846

The Purcell School, London
Aldenham Road, Bushey,
Hertfordshire WD23 2TS
Tel: 01923 331100
Headteacher: Mr. Stephen Yeo
Age range: 8–18
No. of pupils: 167 VIth70
Fees: WB £22,452 FB £28,716

The Royal Masonic School for Girls
Rickmansworth Park,
Rickmansworth,
Hertfordshire WD3 4HF
Tel: 01923 773168
Headmistress: Mrs Diana Rose
MA(Cantab)
Age range: G4–18
No. of pupils: 917 VIth188
Fees: Day £9,000–£14,700 WB
£15,750–£23,760 FB £16,050–£25,050

Tring Park School for the Performing Arts
Tring Park, Tring,
Hertfordshire HP23 5LX
Tel: 01442 824255
Principal: Mr Stefan Anderson MA,
ARCM, ARCT
Age range: 8–19
No. of pupils: 340 VIth217
Fees: Day £13,785–£21,960
FB £23,250–£32,880

Kent

Ashford School
East Hill, Ashford, Kent TN24 8PB
Tel: 01233 739030
Head: Mr M R Buchanan BSc(Hons),
CertEd, NPQH, CPhys
Age range: 3 months–18 years
No. of pupils: 835 VIth170
Fees: Day £8,400–£16,200
WB £28,500 FB £32,400

Beckenham College
The Clockhouse Business Centre,
Unit 2, Thayers Farm Road,
Beckenham, Kent BR3 4LZ
Tel: 020 8650 3321
Principal: Mrs E Wakeling
Age range: 16+
Fees: Day £100–£3,500

Beechwood Sacred Heart
12 Pembury Road, Tunbridge
Wells, Kent TN2 3QD
Tel: 01892 532747
Headmaster: Mr Aaron Lennon
BA(Hons)
Age range: 3–18
No. of pupils: 400 VIth70
Fees: Day £9,060–£15,936
WB £23,460 FB £26,460

Benenden School
Cranbrook, Kent TN17 4AA
Tel: 01580 240592
Headmistress: Mrs S Price
Age range: G11–18
No. of pupils: 543
Fees: FB £31,410

Bethany School
Curtisden Green, Goudhurst,
Cranbrook, Kent TN17 1LB
Tel: 01580 211273
Headmaster: Mr Francie Healy BSc,
HDipEd, NPQH
Age range: 11–18 years
No. of pupils: 345 VIth112
Fees: Day £15,483–£16,986 WB
£23,967–£26,283 FB £25,842–£28,917

Bishop Challoner School
228 Bromley Road, Shortlands,
Bromley, Kent BR2 0BS
Tel: 020 8460 3546
Headteacher: Ms Paula Anderson
Age range: 3–18
No. of pupils: 412 VIth32
Fees: Day £6,441–£9,036

BROMLEY HIGH SCHOOL GDST
For further details see p. 81
Blackbrook Lane, Bickley,
Bromley, Kent BR1 2TW
Tel: 020 8781 7000/1
Email: bhs@bro.gdst.net
Website:
www.bromleyhigh.gdst.net
Head: Mrs A M Drew BA(Hons),
MBA (Dunelm)
Age range: G4–18
No. of pupils: 912 VIth125
Fees: Day £12,423–£15,405

Canterbury Steiner School
Garlinge Green, Chartham,
Canterbury, Kent CT4 5RU
Tel: 01227 738285
Age range: 3–18
Fees: Day £3,246–£4,405.50

CATS College Canterbury

68 New Dover Road,
Canterbury, Kent CT1 3LQ
Tel: +44 (0)1227866540
Principal: Jonathan Ullmer MBE,
MA, LRAM, FCollP, ACP, Dip Arts,
NPQH
Age range: 14–18
No. of pupils: 400
🌐 16⁺ Ⓐ ⚑ ⒾⒷ 16⁺

Cobham Hall School

Cobham, Kent DA12 3BL
Tel: 01474 823371
Headmaster: Mr Paul Mitchell BSc
Age range: G11–18
No. of pupils: 180
⚑ 🏃 ⚑ £ ⒾⒷ ✎ 16⁺

COMBE BANK SCHOOL
For further details see p. 91
Combe Bank Drive,
Sevenoaks, Kent TN14 6AE
Tel: 01959 563720
Email: enquiries@
combebank.co.uk
Website:
www.combebank.co.uk
Head: Mr David Paton BComm
(Hons) PGCE MA
Age range: 2.5–18
No. of pupils: 250
Ⓐ £ ✎ 16⁺

Darul Uloom London

Foxbury Avenue, Perry Street,
Chislehurst, Kent BR7 6SD
Tel: 020 8295 0637
Principal: Mufti Mustafa
Age range: B11–18
No. of pupils: 160
Fees: FB £2,400
🏃 Ⓐ ⚑ 16⁺

Dover College

Effingham Crescent,
Dover, Kent CT17 9RH
Tel: 01304 205969 Ext:201
Headmaster: Gerry Holden
Age range: 3–18
No. of pupils: 340 VIth100
Fees: Day £6,750–£14,250 WB
£18,900–£22,200 FB £20,700–£27,900
🌐 Ⓐ ⚑ £ ✎ 16⁺

Farringtons School

Perry Street, Chislehurst,
Kent BR7 6LR
Tel: 020 8467 0256
Head: Mrs Dorothy Nancekievill
Age range: 3–18
No. of pupils: 681 VIth94
Fees: Day £10,680–£13,560
WB £25,530 FB £27,120
🌐 Ⓐ ⚑ £ ✎ 16⁺

Kent College

Whitstable Road, Canterbury,
Kent CT2 9DT
Tel: 01227 763231
Head Master: Dr D J Lamper
Age range: 3–18
No. of pupils: 702
Fees: Day £15,669–£17,259
FB £23,529–£32,316
🌐 Ⓐ ⚑ £ ⒾⒷ ✎ 16⁺

Kent College Pembury

Old Church Road, Pembury,
Tunbridge Wells, Kent TN2 4AX
Tel: +44 (0)1892 822006
Headmistress: Mrs Sally-Anne
Huang MA(Oxon), MSc, PGCE
Age range: G3–18
No. of pupils: 650 VIth102
Fees: Day £7,887–£17,322
FB £21,471–£27,924
🏃 🌐 Ⓐ ⚑ £ ✎ 16⁺

King's School, Rochester

Satis House, Boley Hill,
Rochester, Kent ME1 1TE
Tel: 01634 888555
Headmaster: Dr I R Walker BA, PhD,
LTh, ABIA, FCollP, FRSA
Age range: 13–18
No. of pupils: 688 VIth113
Fees: Day £7,655–£14,400
FB £17,145–£24,210
🌐 Ⓐ ⚑ £ ✎ 16⁺

Rochester Independent College

Star Hill, Rochester,
Medway, Kent ME1 1XF
Tel: 01634 828115
Principals: Alistair Brownlow, Brian
Pain, Pauline Bailey
Age range: 11–19
No. of pupils: 306 VIth233
Fees: Day £12,000–£16,500 WB
£25,650–£27,300 FB £27,450–£29,100
🌐 16⁺ Ⓐ ⚑ £ ✎ 16⁺

Sackville School

Tonbridge Rd. Hildenborough,
Tonbridge, Kent TN11 9HN
Tel: 01732 838888
Headteacher: Mr John Hewitt BA
MBA
Age range: 11–18
No. of pupils: 184 VIth35
Fees: Day £13,620
Ⓐ £ ✎ 16⁺

Sevenoaks School

High Street, Sevenoaks,
Kent TN13 1HU
Tel: +44 (0)1732 455133
Head: Dr Katy Ricks MA, DPhil
Age range: 11–18
No. of pupils: 1054 VIth423
Fees: Day £20,763–£23,571
FB £33,156–£35,964
🌐 ⚑ £ ⒾⒷ ✎ 16⁺

St Edmund's School

St Thomas\' Hill, Canterbury,
Kent CT2 8HU
Tel: 01227 475601
Head: Louise Moelwyn-Hughes
Age range: 3–18
No. of pupils: 535
Fees: Day £18,651 FB £29,781
🌐 Ⓐ ⚑ £ ✎ 16⁺

St Lawrence College

Ramsgate, Kent CT11 7AE
Tel: 01843 572931
Principal: Mr Antony Spencer
Age range: 3–18
No. of pupils: VIth140
Fees: Day £7,047–£17,436
FB £23,640–£31,452
🌐 Ⓐ ⚑ £ ✎ 16⁺

Sutton Valence School

North Street, Sutton
Valence, Kent ME17 3HL
Tel: 01622 845200
Headmaster: Mr B C W Grindlay
MA(Cantab), MusB, FRCO, CHM
Age range: 11–18
No. of pupils: VIth170
Fees: Day £5,020–£6,660 WB
£7,930–£10,310 FB £7,930–£10,310
🌐 Ⓐ ⚑ £ ✎ 16⁺

THE KING'S SCHOOL, CANTERBURY
For further details see p. 100
The Precincts, Canterbury,
Kent CT1 2ES
Tel: 01227 595501
Email: info@kings-school.co.uk
Website:
www.kings-school.co.uk
Head: Mr P Roberts
Age range: 13–18
No. of pupils: 824 VIth380
Fees: Day £26,055 FB £34,440
🌐 Ⓐ ⚑ £ ✎ 16⁺

TONBRIDGE SCHOOL
For further details see p. 103
Tonbridge, Kent TN9 1JP
Tel: 01732 365555
Email: admissions@
tonbridge-school.org
Website:
www.tonbridge-school.co.uk
Headmaster: T H P Haynes
Age range: B13–18
No. of pupils: 778 VIth317
Fees: Day £27,216 FB £36,288
🏃 🌐 Ⓐ ⚑ £ ✎ 16⁺

Walthamstow Hall School

Sevenoaks, Kent TN13 3UL
Tel: 01732 451334
Headmistress: Mrs J Milner
MA(Oxford)
Age range: G2–18
No. of pupils: 500 VIth80
Fees: Day £8,070–£13,710
🏃 Ⓐ £ ✎ 16⁺

Middlesex

ACS Hillingdon International School

Hillingdon Court, 108 Vine
Lane, Hillingdon, Uxbridge,
Middlesex UB10 0BE
Tel: +44 (0) 1895 259 771
Head of School: Linda LaPine
Age range: 4–18
No. of pupils: 520
Fees: Day £17,090–£22,550
🌐 £ ⒾⒷ ✎ 16⁺

Halliford School

Russell Road, Shepperton,
Middlesex TW17 9HX
Tel: 01932 223593
Headmaster: Mr Simon G Wilson
BSc LRAM
Age range: B11–18 G16–18
No. of pupils: 426
Fees: Day £13,800
🏃 Ⓐ £ ✎ 16⁺

Hampton School

Hanworth Road, Hampton,
Middlesex TW12 3HD
Tel: 020 8979 5526
Headmaster: Mr Kevin Knibbs MA
(Oxon)
Age range: B11–18
No. of pupils: 1130 VIth330
Fees: Day £12,870
🏃 Ⓐ £ ✎ 16⁺

Harrow School

5 High Street, Harrow on the
Hill, Middlesex HA1 3HT
Tel: 020 8872 8000
Head Master: Mr Jim Hawkins
Age range: B13–18
No. of pupils: 830 VIth320
Fees: FB £33,285
🏃 Ⓐ ⚑ £ ✎ 16⁺

Harrow Secretarial College & Computer Training Centre
68 Station Road, Harrow,
Middlesex HA1 2SQ
Tel: 020 8424 9900
Fees: Day £0

Kew House School
Kew House, 6 Capital Interchange
Way, London, Middlesex TW8 0EX
Tel: 0208 742 2038
Headmaster: Mr Mark Hudson
Age range: 11–18
Fees: Day £18,924

Merchant Taylors' School
Sandy Lodge, Northwood,
Middlesex HA6 2HT
Tel: 01923 820644
Head: Mr S J Everson MA (Cantab)
Age range: B11–18
No. of pupils: 865 VIth282
Fees: Day £16,660

North London Collegiate School
Canons, Canons Drive,
Edgware, Middlesex HA8 7RJ
Tel: +44 (0)20 8952 0912
Headmistress: Mrs Bernice McCabe
Age range: G4–18
No. of pupils: 1080
Fees: Day £5,214–£6,169

Northwood College for Girls GDST
Maxwell Road, Northwood,
Middlesex HA6 2YE
Tel: 01923 825446
Head Mistress: Miss Jacqualyn Pain
MA, MA, MBA
Age range: G3–18
No. of pupils: 750 VIth100
Fees: Day £8,400–£13,800

Regent College
Sai House, 167 Imperial Drive,
Harrow, Middlesex HA2 7HD
Tel: 020 8966 9900
Principal: Mr Selva Pankaj MBA,
FCMA
Age range: 11–19
No. of pupils: 167
Fees: Day £2,745–£12,995

St Catherine's School
Cross Deep, Twickenham,
Middlesex TW1 4QJ
Tel: 020 8891 2898
Headmistress: Sister Paula Thomas
BEd(Hons), MA
Age range: G3–18
No. of pupils: 430
Fees: Day £9,915–£13,680

ST HELEN'S SCHOOL
For further details see p. 84
Eastbury Road, Northwood,
Middlesex HA6 3AS
Tel: +44 (0)1923 843210
Email: admissions@
sthelens.london
Website: www.sthelens.london
Headmistress: Dr Mary Short
BA, PhD
Age range: G3–18
No. of pupils: 1145 VIth165

St John's Senior School
North Lodge, The Ridgeway,
Enfield, Middlesex EN2 8BE
Tel: 020 8366 0035
Headmaster: Mr Andrew Tardios
LLB(Hons), BA(Hons), CertEd
Age range: 11–18 years
No. of pupils: 262 VIth72
Fees: Day £12,060

The John Lyon School
Middle Road, Harrow on the
Hill, Middlesex HA2 0HN
Tel: 020 8515 9400
Head: Miss Katherine Haynes BA,
MEd, NPQH
Age range: B11–18
No. of pupils: 579

The Lady Eleanor Holles School
Hanworth Road, Hampton,
Middlesex TW12 3HF
Tel: 020 8979 1601
Head Mistress: Mrs Heather Hanbury
Age range: G7–18
No. of pupils: 875 VIth170
Fees: Day £13,050–£16,200

Surrey

ACS Cobham International School
Heywood, Portsmouth Road,
Cobham, Surrey KT11 1BL
Tel: +44 (0) 1932 867251
Head of School: Mr A Eysele
Age range: 2–18
No. of pupils: 1460
Fees: Day £10,690–£25,050
FB £36,240–£43,730

ACS Egham International School
Woodlee, London Road,
Egham, Surrey TW20 0HS
Tel: +44 (0) 1784 430 800
Head of School: Jeremy Lewis
Age range: 3–18
No. of pupils: 620
Fees: Day £7,010–£23,430

Box Hill School
Old London Road, Mickleham,
Dorking, Surrey RH5 6EA
Tel: 01372 373382
Headmaster: Mr Corydon Lowde
Age range: 11–18
No. of pupils: 425 VIth96
Fees: Day £16,140–£17,170
WB £24,600–£25,800 FB
£29,970–£35,850

Cambridge Tutors College
Water Tower Hill, Croydon,
Surrey CR0 5SX
Tel: 020 8688 5284/7363
Principal: Mr M Eagers
Age range: 15–19
No. of pupils: 215 VIth200
Fees: Day £19,800

Caterham School
Harestone Valley, Caterham,
Surrey CR3 6YA
Tel: 01883 343028
Head: Mr C. W. Jones MA(Cantab)
Age range: 11–18
No. of pupils: VIth321

Charterhouse
Godalming, Surrey GU7 2DX
Tel: 01483 291500
Headmaster: Mr Richard Pleming
MA
Age range: B13–18 G16–18
No. of pupils: 803 VIth422
Fees: Day £29,361 FB £35,529

City of London Freemen's School
Ashtead Park, Ashtead,
Surrey KT21 1ET
Tel: 01372 277933
Headmaster: Mr Philip MacDonald
MA(Oxon)
Age range: 7–18
No. of pupils: 877 VIth213
Fees: Day £10,872–
£14,598 FB £23,238

Claremont Fan Court School
Claremont Drive, Esher,
Surrey KT10 9LY
Tel: 01372 467841
Head of Senior School: Mr
Jonathan Insall-Reid
Age range: 2–18
No. of pupils: 736 VIth90
Fees: Day £4,845–£16,035

Cranleigh School
Horseshoe Lane, Cranleigh,
Surrey GU6 8QQ
Tel: +44 (0) 1483 273666
Headmaster: Mr Martin Reader MA,
MPhil, MBA
Age range: 7–18 (including
Prep School)
No. of pupils: 631 VIth253
Fees: Day £27,855 FB £34,170

Croydon High School GDST
Old Farleigh Road, Selsdon,
South Croydon, Surrey CR2 8YB
Tel: 020 8260 7500
Head of Junior School: Mrs Sophie
Bradshaw
Age range: G3–18
No. of pupils: 600 VIth110

Dunottar School
High Trees Road, Reigate,
Surrey RH2 7EL
Tel: 01737 761945
Head: Mrs Rowena Cole
Age range: 11–18
No. of pupils: 200 VIth40
Fees: Day £14,700

Epsom College
Epsom, Surrey KT17 4JQ
Tel: 01372 821234
Headmaster: Mr Jay A Piggot MA
Age range: 13–18
No. of pupils: 730
Fees: Day £21,255 FB £31,098

Ewell Castle School
Church Street, Ewell, Epsom,
Surrey KT17 2AW
Tel: 020 8393 1413
Principal: Peter Harris
Age range: B3–18 G3-11-16-18
No. of pupils: 531
Fees: Day £6,750–£13,020

Frensham Heights
Rowledge, Farnham,
Surrey GU10 4EA
Tel: 01252 792561
Headmaster: Mr Andrew Fisher BA,
MEd, FRSA
Age range: 3–18
No. of pupils: 497 VIth105
Fees: Day £5,205–£15,300
FB £19,485–£22,680

Greenacre School for Girls
Sutton Lane, Banstead,
Surrey SM7 3RA
Tel: 01737 352114
Headmistress: Mrs L E Redding
Age range: G3–18
No. of pupils: 320 VIth30
Fees: Day £8,898–£15,282

Guildford High School
London Road, Guildford,
Surrey GU1 1SJ
Tel: 01483 561440
Headmistress: Mrs F J Boulton BSc,
MA
Age range: G4–18
No. of pupils: 980 VIth160
Fees: Day £9,591–£15,564

King Edward's Witley
Godalming, Surrey GU8 5SG
Tel: +44 (0)1428 686700
Acting Headmaster: Paul Crissell
MA
Age range: 2–18
Fees: Day £19,950 FB £29,145

Kingston Grammar School
70 London Rd, Kingston upon
Thames, Surrey KT2 6PY
Tel: 020 8456 5875
Head Master: Mr Stephen Lehec
Age range: 11–18
No. of pupils: 820
Fees: Day £17,430

Lingfield Notre Dame School
Lingfield, Surrey RH7 6PH
Tel: 01342 833176
Headmaster: Mr R Bool
Age range: 2–18
No. of pupils: 886 VIth120
Fees: Day £8,900–£12,000

MARYMOUNT INTERNATIONAL SCHOOL LONDON
For further details see p. 83
George Road, Kingston upon
Thames, Surrey KT2 7PE
Tel: +44 (0)20 8949 0571
Email: admissions@
marymountlondon.com
Website:
www.marymountlondon.com
Headmistress: Ms Sarah
Gallagher MA, HDip in Ed
Age range: G11–18
No. of pupils: 252 VIth115
Fees: Day £19,260–£22,035
WB £33,020–£35,765 FB
£34,615–£37,360

Notre Dame School
Cobham, Surrey KT11 1HA
Tel: 01932 869990
Principal: Mr David Plummer B.Ed.
(Hons.), Dip HE, FRSA
Age range: 2–18
No. of pupils: 600

OLD PALACE OF JOHN WHITGIFT SCHOOL
For further details see p. 86
Old Palace Road, Croydon,
Surrey CR0 1AX
Tel: 020 8686 7347
Email: info@oldpalace.
croydon.sch.uk
Website:
www.oldpalace.croydon.sch.uk
Head: Mrs. C Jewell
Age range: B3 months–4
years G3 months–19 years
No. of pupils: 740 VIth120
Fees: Day £10,086–£13,497

Prior's Field
Priorsfield Road, Godalming,
Surrey GU7 2RH
Tel: 01483 810551
Head of School: Mrs T Kirnig
Age range: G11–18
No. of pupils: 450
Fees: Day £15,855 FB £25,575

Reed's School
Sandy Lane, Cobham,
Surrey KT11 2ES
Tel: 01932 869001
Headmaster: Mr Mark Hoskins BA
MA MSc
Age range: B11–18 G16–18
No. of pupils: 650 VIth230
Fees: Day £16,938–£21,184
FB £22,582–£28,023

Reigate Grammar School
Reigate Road, Reigate,
Surrey RH2 0QS
Tel: 01737 222231
Headmaster: Mr Shaun Fenton MA
(Oxon) M Ed (Oxon)
Age range: 11–18
No. of pupils: 947 VIth246
Fees: Day £16,590

Royal Grammar School, Guildford
High Street, Guildford,
Surrey GU1 3BB
Tel: 01483 880600
Headmaster: Dr J M Cox BSc, PhD
Age range: B11–18
No. of pupils: 900
Fees: Day £15,300–£16,050

Royal Russell School
Coombe Lane, Croydon,
Surrey CR9 5BX
Tel: 020 8657 3669
Headmaster: Christopher
Hutchinson
Age range: 11–18
No. of pupils: 590 VIth180
Fees: Day £15,285 FB
£22,365–£30,240

Sir William Perkins's School
Guildford Road, Chertsey,
Surrey KT16 9BN
Tel: 01932 574900
Head: Mr C Muller
Age range: G11–18 years
No. of pupils: 605 VIth140
Fees: Day £14,163

St Catherine's School
Bramley, Guildford, Surrey GU5 0DF
Tel: 01483 893363
Headmistress: Mrs A M Phillips
MA(Cantab)
Age range: G4–18
No. of pupils: 900
Fees: Day £7,695–£15,660 FB £25,770

St George's College
Weybridge Road, Addlestone,
Weybridge, Surrey KT15 2QS
Tel: 01932 839300
Headmistress: Mrs Rachel Owens
Age range: 11–18
No. of pupils: 909 VIth250
Fees: Day £15,120–£17,235

St James Senior Boys School
Church Road, Ashford,
Surrey TW15 3DZ
Tel: 01784 266930
Headmaster: Mr David Brazier
Age range: B11–18
No. of pupils: B385 VIth65
Fees: Day £16,320

St John's School
Epsom Road, Leatherhead,
Surrey KT22 8SP
Tel: 01372 373000
Headmaster: Martin A R Collier
Age range: 13 (11 in 2016)–18
No. of pupils: 656
Fees: Day £22,275 WB £28,125

St Teresa's Effingham (Senior School)
Beech Avenue, Effingham,
Surrey RH5 6ST
Tel: 01372 452037
Head: Mr Michael Farmer
Age range: G2–18
No. of pupils: 450 VIth90
Fees: Day £14,190–£14,730
WB £22,800–£23,340 FB
£22,800–£23,340

Surbiton High School
13-15 Surbiton Crescent, Kingston
upon Thames, Surrey KT1 2JT
Tel: 020 8546 5245
Principal: Ann Haydon BSc(Hons)
Age range: G4–18
No. of pupils: 1210 VIth186
Fees: Day £6,390–£10,857

Sutton High School GDST
55 Cheam Road, Sutton,
Surrey SM1 2AX
Tel: 020 8642 0594
Headmistress: Mrs Katharine
Crouch
Age range: G3–18
No. of pupils: 600 VIth60
Fees: Day £9,153–£15,450

Tante Marie Culinary Academy
Woodham House, Carlton Road,
Woking, Surrey GU21 4HF
Tel: 01483 726957
Principal: Mr Andrew Maxwell
Age range: 16–60
No. of pupils: 72
Fees: Day £20,750

TASIS The American School in England
Coldharbour Lane, Thorpe,
Surrey TW20 8TE
Tel: +44 (0)1932 582316
Head: Dr Mindy Hong
Age range: 3–18
No. of pupils: 740
Fees: Day £6,810–£22,070
FB £38,350

The Royal Ballet School
White Lodge, Richmond,
Surrey TW10 5HR
Tel: 020 7836 8899
Director: Ms Gailene Stock AM
Age range: 11–19
No. of pupils: VIth80
Fees: Day £14,394–£18,946
FB £17,709–£25,588

The Royal School, Haslemere
Farnham Lane, Haslemere,
Surrey GU27 1BE
Tel: 01428 603052
Principal: Mrs Anne Lynch BEd,
PGCE, FRSA
Age range: B6 weeks–16
years G6 weeks–18 years
No. of pupils: 500
Fees: Day £3,026–£5,619 WB
£7,741–£8,290 FB £8,893–£9,442
(🏃)(A)(🏛)(£)(✎)(16·)

Tormead School
27 Cranley Road, Guildford,
Surrey GU1 2JD
Tel: 01483 575101
Headmistress: Mrs Christina Foord
Age range: G4–18
No. of pupils: 760 VIth120
Fees: Day £5,520–£11,565
(🏃)(A)(£)(✎)(16·)

Trinity School
Shirley Park, Croydon,
Surrey CR9 7AT
Tel: 020 8656 9541
Headmaster: M J Bishop MA, MBA
Age range: B10–18 G16–18
No. of pupils: VIth220
Fees: Day £14,460
(🏃)(A)(£)(✎)(16·)

Whitgift School
Haling Park, South Croydon,
Surrey CR2 6YT
Tel: +44 (0)20 8633 9935
Headmaster: Dr Christopher
Barnett
Age range: B10–18
No. of pupils: 1464
Fees: Day £17,340 WB
£27,924 FB £33,396
(🏃)(🌐)(A)(🏛)(£)(IB)(✎)(16·)

Woldingham School
Marden Park, Woldingham,
Surrey CR3 7YA
Tel: 01883 349431
Headmistress: Mrs Jayne Triffitt
MA(Oxon)
Age range: G11–18
No. of pupils: 530 VIth150
Fees: Day £23,700 FB £28,410
(🏃)(🌐)(A)(🏛)(£)(✎)(16·)

Yehudi Menuhin School
Stoke Road, Stoke d'Abernon,
Cobham, Surrey KT11 3QQ
Tel: 01932 864739
Headmaster: Dr. Richard J Hillier
MA(Cantab), PhD
Age range: 7–19
No. of pupils: 80 VIth36
Fees: FB £41,928
(🌐)(A)(🏛)(£)(✎)(16·)

West Sussex

ARDINGLY COLLEGE
For further details see p. 90
College Road, Ardingly,
Haywards Heath, West
Sussex RH17 6SQ
Tel: +44 (0)1444 893000
Email: registrar@ardingly.com
Website: www.ardingly.com
Headmaster: Mr Ben Figgis
Age range: 13–18
No. of pupils: 548
Fees: Day £21,960–£23,160
FB £29,715–£31,425
(🌐)(A)(🏛)(£)(IB)(✎)(16·)

Burgess Hill Girls
Keymer Road, Burgess Hill,
West Sussex RH15 0EG
Tel: 01444 241050
Head: Mrs Kathryn Bell BSc (Hons),
PGCE
Age range: B2.5–4 G2.5–18
No. of pupils: 550 VIth87
Fees: Day £7,200–£16,200
FB £25,500–£28,200
(🏃)(🌐)(A)(🏛)(£)(✎)(16·)

Christ's Hospital
Horsham, West Sussex RH13 0YP
Tel: 01403 211293
Head Master: John R Franklin BA,
MEd(Admin)
Age range: 11–18
No. of pupils: 870
Fees: Day £15,750–
£19,800 FB £32,100
(🌐)(A)(🏛)(£)(IB)(16·)

Farlington School
Strood Park, Horsham,
West Sussex RH12 3PN
Tel: 01403 254967
Headmistress: Ms Louise Higson
BSc, PGCE
Age range: G3–18
No. of pupils: 345 VIth53
Fees: Day £7,050–£16,470 WB
£21,585–£26,310 FB £22,785–£27,510
(🏃)(🌐)(A)(🏛)(£)(✎)(16·)

Hurstpierpoint College
College Lane, Hurstpierpoint,
West Sussex BN6 9JS
Tel: 01273 833636
Headmaster: Mr. T J Manly BA, MSc
Age range: 4–18
No. of pupils: 1083
Fees: Day £20,925 WB £26,385
FB £29,520–£31,125
(🌐)(A)(🏛)(£)(IB)(16·)

Lancing College
Lancing, West Sussex BN15 0RW
Tel: 01273 465805
Head Master: Mr Dominic T Oliver
MPhil
Age range: 13–18
No. of pupils: 550 VIth255
Fees: Day £7,710 WB
£10,970 FB £10,970
(🌐)(A)(🏛)(£)(✎)(16·)

Lavant House
West Lavant, Chichester,
West Sussex PO18 9AB
Tel: 01243 527211
Headteacher: Mrs Nicola Walker
BSC (Hons), MEdm NPQH, MBA,
PGCE
Age range: G4–18
No. of pupils: VIth20
(🏃)(🌐)(A)(🏛)(£)(✎)(16·)

Our Lady of Sion School
Gratwicke Road, Worthing,
West Sussex BN11 4BL
Tel: 01903 204063
Headmaster: Mr M Scullion MA, BEd
Age range: 2–18
No. of pupils: 528 VIth55
Fees: Day £5,715–£9,150
(A)(£)(16·)

Seaford College
Lavington Park, Petworth,
West Sussex GU28 0NB
Tel: 01798 867392
Headmaster: J P Green MA BA
Age range: 6–18
No. of pupils: 690 VIth173
Fees: Day £9,930–£19,380 WB
£19,320–£26,130 FB £29,985
(🌐)(A)(🏛)(£)(✎)(16·)

Worth School
Paddockhurst Road, Turners Hill,
Crawley, West Sussex RH10 4SD
Tel: +44 (0)1342 710200
Head Master: Gino Carminati MA,
FRSA
Age range: 11–18
No. of pupils: 580 VIth222
Fees: Day £20,235 FB £27,849
(🌐)(A)(🏛)(£)(IB)(✎)(16·)

Examinations and qualifications

Qualifications

Qualifications

Common Entrance

What Is Common Entrance?

The Common Entrance examinations are used in UK Independent schools (and some independent schools overseas) for transfer from junior to senior schools at the ages of 11+ and 13+. They were first introduced in 1904 and are internationally recognised as being a rigorous form of assessment following a thorough course of study. The examinations are produced by the Independent Schools Examinations Board and backed by HMC (Headmasters' and Headmistresses' Conference), GSA (Girls' Schools Association), and IAPS (Independent Association of Prep Schools) which together represent the leading independent schools in the UK, and many overseas.

Common Entrance is not a public examination as, for example, GCSE, and candidates may normally be entered only in one of the following circumstances:

a) they have been offered a place at a senior school subject to their passing the examination, or

b) they are required to take the examination as a preliminary to sitting the scholarship examination, or

c) they are entered as a 'trial run', in which case the papers are marked by the junior school concerned

Candidates normally take the examination in their own junior or preparatory schools, either in the UK or overseas.

How does Common Entrance fit into the progression to GCSEs?

Rapid changes in education nationally and internationally have resulted in regular reviews of the syllabuses for all the examinations. Reviews of the National Curriculum, in particular, have brought about a number of changes, with the Board wishing to ensure that it continues to set high standards. It is also a guiding principle that Common Entrance should be part of the natural progression from 11-16, and not a diversion from it.

Common Entrance at 11+

At 11+, the examination consists of English, mathematics and science. It is designed so that it can be taken by candidates either from independent preparatory schools or by candidates from schools in the maintained sector or overseas who have had no special preparation. The examination is normally taken in January for entrance to senior schools the following September.

Common Entrance at 13+

At 13+, most candidates come from independent preparatory schools. The compulsory subjects are English, mathematics and science. Papers in French, geography, German, Classical Greek, history, Latin, Mandarin Chinese, religious studies and Spanish are also available and candidates usually offer as many subjects as they can. In most subjects, papers are available at more than one level to cater for candidates of different abilities. Mandarin Chinese is offered as an online test. There are three examination sessions each year, with the majority of candidates sitting in the summer prior to entry to their senior schools in September.

Marking and grading

The papers are set centrally but the answers are marked by the senior school for which a candidate is entered. Mark schemes are provided by the Board but senior schools are free to set their own grade boundaries. Results are available within two weeks of the examinations taking place.

Pre-Testing and the ISEB Common Pre-Tests

A number of senior independent schools 'pre-test' pupils for entry, prior to them taking their main entrance examinations at a later date. Usually, these pre-tests take place when a pupil is in Year 6 or Year 7 of his or her junior school and will then be going on to sit Common Entrance in Year 8. The tests are designed to assess a pupil's academic potential and suitability for a particular senior school so that the child, the parents and the school know well in advance whether he/she is going to be offered a place at the school, subject to a satisfactory performance in the entrance examinations. It enables senior schools which are heavily oversubscribed to manage their lists and helps to ensure that pupils are not entered for examinations which they are unlikely to pass. In short, it reduces uncertainty for all concerned.

Pre-tests may be written specifically for the senior school for which the candidate is entered but a growing number of schools are choosing to use the Common Pre-Tests provided by the Independent Schools Examinations Board. These online tests are usually taken in the candidate's own prep school and one of their main advantages is that a pupil need sit the tests only once, with the results then made available to any senior school which wishes to use them. The multiple-choice tests cover verbal reasoning, non-verbal reasoning, English and mathematics, with the results standardised according to the child's age when they are taken. Further information is available on the ISEB website at www.iseb.co.uk

Parents are advised to check the entrance requirements for senior schools to see if their child will be required to sit a pre-test. Generally, though, practice tests are not made available and no special preparation is required.

Further information
Details of the Common Entrance examinations and how to register candidates are obtainable from the Chief Administrator at the address below. Copies of past papers and a wide range of textbooks and other resources can be purchased from Galore Park Publishing Ltd at www.galorepark.co.uk. Support materials are also available from Hodder Education and other publishers; see the Resources section of the ISEB website for details.

Independent Schools Examinations Board
Suite 3, Endeavour House,
Crow Arch Lane,
Ringwood, Hampshire BH24 1HP

Telephone: 01425 470555
Email: enquiries@iseb.co.uk
Web: www.iseb.co.uk

General Certificate of Secondary Education (GCSE)

What are the GCSE qualifications?
GCSE qualifications were first introduced in 1986 and are the principal means of assessment at Key Stage 4 across a range of academic subject areas. They command respect and have status not only in the UK but worldwide.

Main features of the GCSE
There are three unitary awarding organisations for GCSEs in England (see 'Awarding organisations and examination dates' section, p401). WJEC and CCEA also offer GCSE qualifications in Wales and Northern Ireland as well as England. Each examining group designs its own specifications but they are required to conform to set criteria. The award of a grade is intended to indicate that a candidate has met the required level of skills, knowledge and understanding.

From September 2015 new GCSEs in English literature, English language and maths will be taught in schools in England. Assessment in these reformed GCSEs will consist primarily of formal examinations taken at the end of the student's two year course. Assessment not by written exam will be limited to a few subjects only.

Current GCSEs taught in subjects other than English literature, English language and maths will continue to incorporate a flexible approach to assessment. Many specifications will continue to give credit for assignments set and marked by the teacher, with some external moderation, and the marks awarded form a contribution towards the final grade achieved. This is in addition to more traditional examinations at the end of the course. The proportion of credit obtained from controlled assessment is subject to limits laid down by the regulatory authorities. New GCSEs in these subjects will be introduced in September 2016 and September 2017.

Grading
Candidate performance at GCSE is currently graded from A* to G.

There are 'differentiated' examination papers in many subjects. The scheme of GCSE assessment may involve two papers targeted at either grades A*-D or grades C-G. The higher tiered paper (graded A*-D) will also provide for an exceptional grade E on the higher tier, so that candidates who just miss a D grade are not disadvantaged. Mathematics uses two tiers; some subjects – such as history and art – use one.

The reformed GCSEs introduced from September 2015 will have a new 9 to 1 grading scale, where 9 is the top level. Exams will also no longer be 'differentiated' unless one paper is not appropriate for all students' knowledge and abilities.

Can anyone take GCSE qualifications?
GCSEs are intended mainly for 16-year-old pupils, but are open to anyone of any age, whether studying full-time or part-time at a school, college or privately. There are no formal entry requirements.

GCSEs are available in a wide range of subjects. Students normally study up to ten subjects over a two-year period. Short course GCSEs are available in some subjects (including ICT and religious studies) – these include half the content of a full GCSE, so two short course GCSEs are equivalent to one full GCSE.

The reformed GCSEs that are introduced from September 2015 will have a new 9 to 1 grading scale, where 9 is the top level, replacing A* to C. The new GCSEs will be assessed by exams taken at the end of the two year course. Assessment not by written exam will be limited to a few subjects only. New GCSEs in other subjects will be introduced in September 2016 and September 2017.

General Qualifications at Advanced level, General Certificate of Education (GCE), General Certificate of Education (GCE) in applied subjects

Typically, A level qualifications are studied over a two-year period. There are no lower or upper age limits. Schools and colleges usually expect students aged 16-18 to have obtained grades A*-C in five subjects at GCSE level before taking an advanced level course. This requirement may vary between centres and according to which specific subjects are to be studied. Mature students may be assessed on different criteria as to their suitability to embark on the course. All these qualifications consist of a number of units. They can be assessed in stages or at the end of the course.

GCE Qualifications

GCE qualifications are available at two levels. The Advanced Subsidiary (AS) is the two- or three-unit General Certificate of Education (GCE). It provides progression between GCSE at level 2 and the full A level. It is both the first half of an A level and a qualification in its own right. All A level specifications include an AS. There are currently five free-standing AS qualifications that do not lead to a full A level, namely critical thinking, European studies, science for public understanding, social science: citizenship, and world development.

The A level is the four- or six-unit GCE. It consists of the AS and a further three units called the A2, usually studied in the second year. Nearly 70 titles are available, covering a wide range of subject areas, including humanities, sciences, language, business, arts, mathematics and technology.

Some GCE AS and A levels, particularly the practical ones, contain a proportion of coursework. All GCE A levels contain in one or more of the A2 units an assessment that tests students' understanding of the whole specification (synoptic assessment). GCE AS are graded A-E and A levels are graded A*-E. Students generally take four or

five subjects at AS level in the first year of advanced level study. In the second year, they generally study A2 units in two or three subjects, thereby completing A levels in those subjects.

Revised A level specifications were introduced in September 2008, with a new A* grade awarded from 2010 to those students who have achieved both of the following:

- Grade A overall (that is 80% of the maximum uniform marks for the whole A level qualification)

- 90% of the maximum uniform marks on the aggregate of the A2 unit scores

The A* grade is awarded for the A level qualification only and not for the AS qualification or for individual units.

Over 30 A level subjects are available for study in the following fields: English, ICT, maths, science, business, arts, technology, physical education, languages and humanities.

New AS and A levels in certain subjects will come into effect from September 2015, with further subjects being introduced according to this new format over the following two years. Like the new GCSEs, all the exams for the new A levels will be at the end of two years of study. The amount of coursework at A Level has also been reduced. In some subjects, such as the Sciences, practical work will not contribute to the final A level but will be reported separately in a certificate of endorsement. The new AS Levels that come into schools from September 2015 will no longer count towards the final grade of an A level. They are separate qualifications in their own right.

GCEs in applied subjects

Formerly known as Vocational Certificates of Education (VCEs), GCE/A levels in applied subjects have an AS/A2 structure, comparable to existing GCEs.

Please note that all AQA's applied A-levels have been withdrawn, except for Business and Science which are being withdrawn with final certification in 2017. AQA is planning on introducing new applied generals for some of these subjects and is replacing A-levels in Applied Business and Applied Science with new Level 3 Certificates and Extended Certificates in these subjects from 2016.

Edexcel's applied GCEs allow the grade of A* to be awarded where needed. These qualifications allow for a nine-unit GCE for the double award qualifications. This is the advanced GCE with advanced subsidiary (additional), which allows students to 'top up' from a six-unit award to achieve this. It also allows students unable to complete the full 12-unit award to go for the nine-unit award.

However, applieds will no longer be available as an alternative GCE is redeveloped. For example, Applied Business will have a final certification is in 2016, as the new GCE in Business is available for first teaching in 2015.

Cambridge International AS and A level

Cambridge International AS and A Level is an internationally benchmarked qualification, taught in over 125 countries worldwide. It is typically for learners aged 16 to 19 years who need advanced study to prepare for university. It was created specifically for an international audience and the content has been devised to suit the wide variety of schools worldwide and avoid any cultural bias.

Cambridge International A Level is typically a two-year course, and Cambridge International AS Level is typically one year. Some subjects can be started as a Cambridge International AS Level and extended to a Cambridge International A Level. Students can either follow a broad course of study, or specialise in one particular subject area.

Learners use Cambridge International AS and A Levels to gain places at leading universities worldwide, including the UK, Ireland, USA, Canada, Australia, New Zealand, India, Singapore, Egypt, Jordan, South Africa, the Netherlands, Germany and Spain. In places such as the US and Canada, good grades in carefully chosen Cambridge International A Level subjects can result in up to one year of university course credit.

Assessment options:
Option 1: take Cambridge International AS levels only – the Cambridge International syllabus content is half a Cambridge International A level.
Option 2: staged assessment, which means taking the Cambridge International AS Level in one exam session and the Cambridge International A Level at a later session. However, this route is not possible in all subjects.
Option 3: take all Cambridge International A Level papers in the same examination session, usually at the end of the course.

Grades and subjects
Cambridge International A Levels are graded from A* to E. Cambridge International AS Levels are graded from A to E.

Subjects: available in 55 subjects including accounting, Afrikaans, Afrikaans – first language (AS only),

Afrikaans language (AS only), applied information and communication technology, Arabic, Arabic language (AS only), art and design, biology, business studies, chemistry, Chinese, Chinese language (AS only), classical studies, computing, design and technology, design and textiles, divinity, economics, English language, English literature, environmental management, food studies, French, French language (AS only), French literature (AS only), general paper 8001, general paper 8004, geography, German, German language (AS only), Global Perspectives & Research, Hindi, Hindi language (AS only), Hindi literature (AS only), Hinduism, history, Islamic studies, Japanese language (AS only), English language and literature (AS only), law, Marathi, Marathi language (AS only), marine science, mathematics, further mathematics, media studies, music, physical education, physical science, physics, Portuguese, Portuguese language (AS only), Portuguese literature (AS only), psychology, sociology, Spanish, Spanish first language (AS only), Spanish language (AS only), Spanish literature (AS only), Tamil, Tamil language (AS only), Telugu, Telugu language (AS only), thinking skills, travel and tourism, Urdu, Urdu language (AS only), Urdu Pakistan.

Website: www.cie.org.uk/alevel

Cambridge International General Certificate of Secondary Education (IGCSE)

Cambridge IGCSE is the world's most popular international qualification for 14 to16 year olds. It develops skills in creative thinking, enquiry and problem solving, in preparation for the next stage in a student's education. Cambridge IGCSE is taken in over 140 countries, and is widely recognised by employers and higher education institutions worldwide.

Cambridge IGCSE is graded from A*-G. In the UK, Cambridge IGCSE is accepted as equivalent to the GCSE. It can be used as preparation for Cambridge International A and AS Levels, UK A and AS levels, IB or AP and in some instances entry into university. Cambridge IGCSE First Language English and Cambridge IGCSE English as a Second Language are recognised by a significant number of UK universities as evidence of competence in the language for university entrance.

Subjects: available in over 70 subjects including accounting, Afrikaans – first language, Afrikaans –

second language, agriculture, Arabic – first language, Arabic – foreign language, art and design, Baha Indonesia, Bangladesh studies, biology, business studies, chemistry, child development, Chinese – first language, Chinese – second language, Chinese (Mandarin) – foreign language, computer studies, Czech – first language, design and technology, development studies, drama, Dutch – first language, Dutch – foreign language, economics, English – first language, English – literature, English – second language, enterprise, environmental management, food and nutrition, French – first language, French – foreign language, geography, German – first language, German – foreign language, global perspectives, Greek – foreign language, Hindi as a second language, Italian – foreign language, history, India studies, Indonesian – foreign language, information and communication technology, IsiZulu as a second language, Japanese – first language, Japanese – foreign language, Kazakh as a second language, Korean (first language), Latin, Malay – foreign language, mathematics, mathematics – additional, international mathematics, music, Pakistan studies, physical education, physical science, physics, Portuguese – first language, Portuguese – foreign language, religious studies, Russian – first language, science – combined, sciences – co-ordinated (double), sociology, Spanish – first language, Spanish – foreign language, Spanish – literature, Thai – first language, travel and tourism, Turkish – first language, Urdu – second language, world literature.

Website: www.cie.org.uk/igcse

Cambridge Pre-U

Cambridge Pre-U is a post-16 qualification that equips students with the skills they need to succeed at university. Developed with universities, it was first introduced in UK schools in September 2008. It is now taught in 170 schools, including some schools outside the UK.

Cambridge Pre-U is a linear course, with exams taken at the end of two years. It encourages the development of well-informed, open and independent-minded individuals; promotes deep understanding through subject specialisation, with a depth and rigour appropriate to progression to higher education; and develops skills in independent research valued by universities.

Assessment
Cambridge Pre-U Principal Subjects are examined at the end of two years. Cambridge Pre-U Short Courses are

typically examined at the end of one year. Students can study a combination of A Levels and Principal Subjects.

In order to gain the Cambridge Pre U Diploma, students must study at least three Cambridge Pre-U Principal Subjects (up to two A Levels can be substituted for Principal Subjects) and Cambridge Pre-U Global Perspectives and Research (GPR). Cambridge Pre-U GPR includes an extended project in the second year, developing skills in research and critical thinking.

Subjects: available in 26 subjects including art and design, biology, business and management, chemistry, drama and theatre, economics, literature in English, French, further mathematics, geography, German, global perspectives and research, classical Greek, history, Italian, art history, Latin, Mandarin Chinese, mathematics, music, philosophy and theology, physics, psychology, Russian, Spanish.

Website: www.cie.org.uk/cambridgepreu

Edexcel International GCSEs

Pearson's Edexcel International GCSEs are academic qualifications aimed at learners aged 14 to 16. They're equivalent to a UK General Certificate of Secondary Education (GCSE), and are the main requirement for Level 3 studies, including progression to GCE AS or A levels, BTECs or employment. International GCSEs are linear qualifications, meaning that students take all of the exams at the end of the course. They are available at Level 1 (grades D-G) and Level 2 (grades A*-C). There are currently more than 100,000 learners studying Edexcel International GCSEs, in countries throughout Asia, Africa, Europe, the Middle East and Latin America. Developed by subject specialists and reviewed regularly, many of Pearson's Edexcel International GCSEs include specific international content to make them relevant to students worldwide.

Pearson's Edexcel International GCSEs were initially developed for international schools. They have since become popular among independent schools in the UK, but are not approved for use in UK state schools. If you're a UK state school, you may be interested in offering Pearson's Edexcel Level 1/Level 2 Certificates. These qualifications are based on the Edexcel International GCSE specifications but currently count towards national performance measures and are eligible for funding in UK state schools until 2016.

International GCSEs are offered in over 40 subjects. Subject areas include: Art and Design, Business &

Economics, **English, Humanities**, Information and Communication Technology, **Languages, Mathematics, Sciences**. *Note that the subject areas highlighted in bold are also available as part of the Edexcel Certificate qualification suite.*

Free Standing Maths Qualifications (FSMQ)

Aimed at those students wishing to acquire further qualifications in maths, specifically additional mathematics and foundations of advanced mathematics (MEI).

Further UCAS points can be earned upon completion of the advanced FSMQ in additional mathematics, whereas the higher FSMQ in foundations of advanced mathematics is designed for those not yet ready to take AS/A level GCE mathematics.

New foundation and higher level FSMQs were introduced in 2011, with first exams in 2012. For further details see the AQA or OCR website.

AQA Certificate in Mathematical Studies (Core Maths)

This new Level 3 qualification is available from September 2015. It is designed for students who achieved a Grade C or above at GCSE and want to continue studying Maths. The qualification carries UCAS points

Additional and Alternative

AQA Baccalaureate

The AQA Baccalaureate is awarded to students studying at least three A levels. This is a complete curriculum programme, which adds a broader range of study, and includes the Extended Project Qualification (EPQ).

This qualification is built on familiar subjects, so it can be tailored to fit in with existing curricula. It includes extracurricular activities and encourages a series of 'enrichment activities' covering personal qualities, perseverance, leadership, independence, time management, commitment and communication.

The AQA Bacc is awarded to students who achieve at least three A levels (minimum grade E), a broader study AS level subject and the EPQ, plus they must undertake a minimum of 100 hours of 'enrichment activities'.

The AQA Bacc is accepted by universities; offers are based on the component parts of the diploma, with students receiving their AQA certificate alongside their A level, AS level and EPQ certificates.

Cambridge Primary

Cambridge Primary is typically for learners aged 5 to 11 years. It develops learner skills and understanding through the primary years in English, mathematics and science. The flexible curriculum frameworks include optional assessment tools to help schools monitor learners' progress and give detailed feedback to parents. At the end of Cambridge Primary, schools can enter students for Cambridge Primary Checkpoint tests which are marked in Cambridge.

Website: www.cie.org.uk/primary

Cambridge Secondary 1

Cambridge Secondary 1 is typically for learners aged 11 to 14 years. It develops learner skills and understanding in English, English as a second language, mathematics and science for the first three years of secondary education, and includes assessment tools. At the end of Cambridge Secondary 1, schools can enter students for Cambridge Secondary 1 Checkpoint tests which are marked in

Cambridge and provide an external international benchmark for student performance.

Website: www.cie.org.uk/cambridgesecondary1

European Baccalaureate (EB)

Not to be confused with the International Baccalaureate (IB), this certificate is available in European schools and recognised in all EU countries.

To obtain the baccalaureate, a student must obtain a minimum score of 60%, which is made up from: coursework, oral participation in class and tests (40%); five written examinations (36%) – mother-tongue, first foreign language and maths are compulsory for all candidates; four oral examinations (24%) – mother tongue and first foreign language are compulsory (history or geography may also be compulsory here, dependant on whether the candidate has taken a written examination in these subjects).

Throughout the EU the syllabus and examinations necessary to achieve the EB are identical. The only exception to this rule is the syllabus for the mother tongue language. The EB has been specifically designed to meet, at the very least, the minimum qualification requirements of each member state. Study for the EB begins at nursery stage (age four) and progresses through primary (age six) and on into secondary school (age 12).

The International Baccalaureate (IB)

Information supplied by the IB

The International Baccalaureate (IB) offers four challenging and high quality educational programmes for a worldwide community of schools, aiming to develop internationally minded people who, recognizing their common humanity and shared guardianship of the planet, help to create a better, more peaceful world.

The IB works with schools around the world (both state and privately funded) that share the commitment to international education to deliver these programmes.

Schools that have achieved the high standards required for authorization to offer one or more of the IB programmes are known as IB World Schools. There are over half a million students attending more than 3500 IB World Schools in 139 countries and this number is growing annually.

The Primary Years, Middle Years and Diploma Programmes share a common philosophy and common characteristics. They develop the whole student, helping students to grow intellectually, socially, aesthetically and culturally. They provide a broad and balanced education that includes science and the humanities, languages and mathematics, technology and the arts. The programmes teach students to think critically, and encourage them to draw connections between areas of knowledge and to use problem-solving techniques and concepts from many disciplines. They instil in students a sense of responsibility towards others and towards the environment. Lastly, and perhaps most importantly, the programmes give students an awareness and understanding of their own culture and of other cultures, values and ways of life.

A fourth programme called the IB Career-related Programme (IBCP) became available to IB World Schools from September 2012.

The IBCP incorporates the educational principles, vision and learner profile of the IB into a unique offering that specifically addresses the needs of students who wish to engage in career-related education. The IBCP encourages these students to benefit from elements of an IB education, through a selection of two or more Diploma Programme courses in addition to a unique IBCP core, comprised of an approaches to learning (ATL) course, language development, a reflective project, and community and service.

The IBCP is designed to provide a 'value added' qualification to schools that already offer the IB Diploma Programme and are also delivering career-related studies to their students. The IBCP enables schools to widen participation to an IB education. Schools retain the ability to choose the career-related courses that are most suited to local conditions and the needs of their students. Schools gain the added flexibility in direct curriculum development as well as the IBCP core to create an educational pathway that puts a strong focus on individual student needs. All IB programmes include:

- a written curriculum or curriculum framework;
- student assessment appropriate to the age range;
- professional development and networking opportunities for teachers;
- support, authorization and programme evaluation for the school.

The IB Primary Years Programme

The IB Primary Years Programme (PYP), for students aged three to 12, focuses on the development of the whole child as an inquirer, both in the classroom and in the world outside. It is a framework consisting of five essential elements (concepts, knowledge, skills, attitude, action) and guided by six trans-disciplinary themes of global significance, explored using knowledge and skills derived from six subject areas (language, social studies, mathematics, science and technology, arts, personal, social and physical education) with a powerful emphasis on inquiry-based learning.

The most significant and distinctive feature of the PYP is the six trans-disciplinary themes. These themes are about issues that have meaning for, and are important to, all of us. The programme offers a balance between learning about or through the subject areas, and learning beyond them. The six themes of global significance create a trans-disciplinary framework that allows students to 'step up' beyond the confines of learning within subject areas:

- Who we are.
- Where we are in place and time.
- How we express ourselves
- How the world works
- How we organize ourselves
- Sharing the planet

The PYP exhibition is the culminating activity of the programme. It requires students to analyse and propose solutions to real-world issues, drawing on what they have learned through the programme. Evidence of student development and records of PYP exhibitions are reviewed by the IB as part of the programme evaluation process.

Assessment is an important part of each unit of inquiry as it both enhances learning and provides opportunities for students to reflect on what they know, understand and can do. The teacher's feedback to the students provides the guidance, the tools and the incentive for them to become more competent, more skilful and better at understanding how to learn.

The IB Middle Years Programme (MYP)

The MYP is designed for students aged 11 to 16. It provides a framework of learning that encourages students to become creative, critical and reflective thinkers. The MYP emphasizes intellectual challenge, encouraging students to make connections between their studies in traditional subjects and the real world. It fosters the development of skills for communication, intercultural understanding and global engagement – essential qualities for young people who are becoming global leaders.

The Middle Years Programme:

- addresses holistically students' intellectual, social, emotional and physical well-being.
- provides students opportunities to develop the knowledge, attitudes and skills they need in order to manage complexity and take responsible action for the future.
- ensures breadth and depth of understanding through study in eight subject groups.
- requires the study of at least two languages (language of instruction and additional language of choice) to support students in understanding their own cultures and those of others.
- empowers students to participate in service within the community.
- helps to prepare students for further education, the workplace.

The MYP has recently undergone the biggest review in its history and the newly-revised version was introduced for first teaching in September 2014.

New features include stronger connections with the IB continuum of international education for students aged 3–19 and optional external assessments.

The new MYP offers:

- greater flexibility for schools to combine the MYP with the requirements of national and state educational systems
- closer alignment across the IB continuum, offering an ideal preparation for students going on to study the IB Diploma Programme or the IB Career-related Certificate.

The IB Diploma Programme (IBDP)

The IB Diploma Programme, for students aged 16 to 19, is an academically challenging and balanced programme of education with final examinations, which prepares students for success at university and life beyond.

IBDP students study six courses at higher level or standard level. Students must choose one subject from each of groups 1 to 5, thus ensuring breadth of experience in languages, social studies, the experimental sciences and mathematics. The sixth subject may be an arts subject chosen from group 6, or the student may choose another subject from groups 1 to 5. At least three and not more than four subjects are taken at higher level (recommended 240 teaching hours), the others at standard level (150 teaching hours). Students can study these subjects, and be examined, in English, French or Spanish.

In addition, three core elements – the extended essay, theory of knowledge and creativity, action, service – are compulsory and central to the philosophy of the programme.

Students take written examinations at the end of the programme, which are marked by external IB examiners. Students also complete assessment tasks in the school, which are either initially marked by teachers and then moderated by external moderators or sent directly to external examiners.

The marks awarded for each course range from one (lowest) to seven (highest). Students can also be awarded up to three additional points for their combined results on theory of knowledge and the extended essay. The diploma is awarded to students who gain at least 24 points, subject to certain minimum levels of performance across the whole programme and to satisfactory participation in the creativity, action, and service requirement. The highest total that a Diploma Programme student can be awarded is 45 points.

The IB Career-related Programme (IBCP)

The IB Career-related Programme, for students aged 16 to 19, accentuates and enhances skill development and the attainment of the competencies relevant to today's challenging work place. Students are able to develop a specific pathway into higher education in consultation with their school. A specially-designed IBCP core recognizes and emphasizes IB values, missions and the needs of career-related students.

IBCP students study a specialized IBCP core and a minimum of two Diploma Programme courses. The IBCP core consists of the following:

Community and Service: This element of the IBCP core is based on the principle of service learning, which uses community service as a vehicle for new learning that has academic value. The service learning model in the IBCP emphasises knowledge development, civic development, social development and personal development.

Approaches to learning (ATL): This course is designed to introduce students to life skills. At the heart of the ATL model is the learner who uses a range of skills to make sense of the world around them and develops skills with an emphasis on critical and ethical thinking and effective communication.

Language development: Language development ensures that all students have access to, and are exposed to, a second language that will assist and further their understanding of the wider world. Students are encouraged to extend or begin a second language that suits their needs, background and context.

Reflective project: Through a reflective project students identify, analyse, critically discuss and evaluate an ethical issue arising from their career-related studies. The project can be submitted in a variety of formats including an essay, web page or short film. This work allows the student to engage in personal inquiry, action and reflection and to develop strong research and communications skills.

The Diploma Programme courses are assessed in accordance with the standard Diploma Programme assessment process. However, the career-related courses are assessed by the career-related course provider, not the IB. Approaches to learning, community and service and language development are internally assessed by the school, while the reflective project is moderated by the IB.

For more information on IB programmes, visit: www.ibo.org

Africa, Europe, Middle East Global Centre, Churchillplein 6, The Hague, 2517JW, The Netherlands

Tel: +31 (0)70 352 6233
Email: communications@ibo.org

Pearson Edexcel Mathematics Awards

Pearson's Edexcel Mathematics Awards are small, stand-alone qualifications designed to help students to develop and demonstrate proficiency in different areas of mathematics. These Awards enable students to focus on understanding key concepts and techniques, and are available across three subjects, including: Number and Measure (Levels 1 and 2), Algebra (Levels 2 and 3) and Statistical Methods (Levels 1, 2 and 3). The level 1 Award in Number and Measure is now also an approved stepping stone qualification for the 16-18 maths condition of funding

Designed to build students' confidence and fluency; the Awards can fit into the existing programme of delivery for mathematics in schools and colleges, prepare students for GCSE and/or GCE Mathematics, and to support further study in other subjects, training or the workplace. They offer a choice of levels to match students' abilities, with clear progression between the levels. These small, 60-70 guided learning hour qualifications are assessed through one written paper per level. Each qualification is funded and approved for pre-16 and 16-18 year old students in England and in schools and colleges in Wales.

Projects

Extended Project Qualification (EPQ)

AQA, OCR, Pearson and WJEC offer the Extended Project Qualification, which is a qualification aimed at developing a student's research and independent learning skills. The EPQ can be taken as a stand-alone qualification, and it is equivalent to half an A level. It is also possible to take the EPQ as part of the AQA Baccalaureate.

Entry level, basic and key skills

Awards and Certificates in Education, Training and Skills (ACETS)

A range of qualifications offered by CCEA aimed at students who want to acquire qualifications relevant to the world of work. Subjects available:

- Business enterprise
- Classroom assistant
- Creative craft
- Drug awareness studies
- Drug awareness studies and their applications
- Employability
- Essential skills: application of number
- Essential skills: communication
- Key skills: application of number
- Key skills: communication
- Key skills: ICT
- Key skills: improving own learning and performance
- Key skills: problem solving
- Key skills: working with others
- Occupational studies
- Performance skills
- Personal effectiveness
- Personal money management
- Substance misuse awareness

Cambridge Progression

OCR has developed qualifications in maths and English to meet the needs of adult learners, as replacements for Key and Basic Skills. Available from Entry Level to Level 2, the qualifications can be stand alone or enable progression to other programmes such as GCSEs.

Entry Level Qualifications

If you want to take GCSE or NVQ level 1 but have not yet reached the standard required, then entry level qualifications are for you as they are designed to get you started on the qualifications ladder.

Entry level qualifications are available in a wide range of areas. You can take an entry level certificate in most subjects where a similar GCSE exists. There are also vocational entry level qualifications – some in specific areas like retail or catering and others where you can take units in different work-related subjects to get a taster of a number of career areas. There are also entry level certificates in life skills and the basic skills of literacy and numeracy.

Anyone can take an entry level qualification – your school or college will help you decide which qualification is right for you.

Entry level qualifications are flexible programmes so the time it takes to complete will vary according to where you study and how long you need to take the qualification.

Subjects available: art and design; business studies; catering; child development; citizenship studies; design and technology; drama; English; essential skills: adult literacy; essential skills: adult numeracy; French; geography; German; graphical and material studies; hairdressing; history; home economics; ICT; job-seeking skills; learning for life and work; leisure and tourism; manufacturing; mathematics; occupational studies; office practice; physical education; preparation for employment; religious studies; retail; science; Spanish; and technology and design.

Functional Skills

Functional Skills are qualifications in English, maths and ICT that equip learners with the basic practical skills required in everyday life, education and the workplace. They are available at Entry 1 through to Level 2. Functional Skills are identified as funded 'stepping stone' qualifications to English and maths GCSE for post-16 learners who haven't previously achieved a grade D in these subjects. There are part of apprenticeship completion requirements.

Vocational qualifications

AQA Tech-levels

AQA Tech-levels are level 3 technical qualifications and are on a par with A-levels. They are aimed at post-16 learners who want to specialise in or focus on a specific industry, sector or occupation. They are developed in collaboration with employers and professional bodies, so the content is up-to-date and relevant and designed to equip learners with highly-valued specialist skills and knowledge.

Studying Tech-levels gives learners a number of options on where to go or what to do next. They prepare and enable you to go on to a higher level apprenticeship or directly into work; they also carry UCAS points should you wish to go on to university instead.

There aren't any formal entry requirements, but if you have GCSEs in several subjects then Tech-levels can be a natural next step for you.

AQA Tech-levels count towards the Technical Baccalaureate (TechBacc). BTECs

BTEC Level 2 First qualifications
ie BTEC Level 2 Diplomas, BTEC Level 2 Extended Certificates, BTEC Level 2 Certificates and BTEC Level 2 Award.

BTEC Firsts are Level 2 introductory work-related programmes covering a wide range of vocational areas including business, engineering, information technology, health and social care, media, travel and tourism, and public services.

Programmes may be taken full or part-time. They are practical programmes that provide a foundation for the knowledge and skills you will need in work. Alternatively, you can progress onto a BTEC National qualification, Applied GCE A level or equivalent.

There are no formal entry requirements and they can be studied alongside GCSEs. Subjects available: agriculture; animal care; applied science; art and design; business; children's care, learning and development; construction; countryside and the environment; engineering; fish husbandry; floristry; health and social care; horse care; horticulture; hospitality; IT; land-based technology; business; creative media production; music; performing arts; public services; sport; travel and tourism; and vehicle technology.

BTEC Foundation Diploma in Art and Design (QCF)
For those students preparing to go on to higher education within the field of art and design. This diploma is recognised as one of the best courses of its type in the UK, and is used in preparation for degree programmes.

BTEC Nationals
ie BTEC Level 3 Extended Diplomas (QCF), BTEC Level 3 Diplomas (QCF), BTEC Level 3 Subsidiary Diplomas (QCF), BTEC Level 3 Certificates (QCF)

BTEC National programmes are long-established vocational programmes. They are practical programmes that are highly valued by employers. They enable you to gain the knowledge and skills that you will need in work, or give you the choice to progress on to a BTEC Higher National, a Foundation Degree or a degree programme.

BTEC Nationals cover a range of vocationally specialist sectors including child care, children's play, learning and development, construction, art and design, aeronautical engineering, electrical/electronic engineering, IT, business, creative and media production, performing arts, public services, sport, sport and exercise sciences and applied science. The programmes may be taken full- or part-time, and can be taken in conjunction with NVQs and/or functional skills units at an appropriate level.

There are no formal entry requirements, but if you have any of the following you are likely to be at the right level to study a BTEC national qualification.

- a BTEC Level 2 First qualification
- GCSEs – at grades A* to C in several subjects
- Relevant work experience

There are also very specialist BTEC Nationals, such as pharmaceutical science and blacksmithing and metalworking.

BTEC Higher Nationals
Known as HNDs and HNCs – ie BTEC Level 5 HND Diplomas (QCF) and BTEC Level 4 HNC Diplomas (QCF)

BTEC HNDs and HNCs are further and higher education qualifications that offer a balance of education and vocational training. They are available in a wide range of work-related areas such as graphic design, business, health and social care, computing and systems development, manufacturing engineering, hospitality management, and public services.

BTEC higher national courses combine study with

hands-on work experience during your course. Once completed, you can use the skills you learn to begin your career, or continue on to a related degree course.

HNDs are often taken as a full-time course over two years but can also be followed part-time in some cases.

HNCs are often for people who are working and take two years to complete on a part-time study basis by day release, evenings, or a combination of the two. Some HNC courses are done on a full time basis.

There are no formal entry requirements, but if you have any of the following you are likely to be at the right academic level:

- at least one A level
- a BTEC Level 3 National qualification
- level 3 NVQ

BTEC specialist and professional qualifications
These qualifications are designed to prepare students for specific and specialist work activities. In September 2010 they were split into two distinct groups:

- Specialist qualifications (entry to level 3)
- Professional qualifications (levels 4 to 7)

Cambridge Nationals

Cambridge Nationals, the updated version of OCR Nationals, are vocationally-related qualifications that take an engaging, practical and inspiring approach to learning and assessment.

They are industry-relevant, geared to key sector requirements and very popular with schools and colleges because they suit such a broad range of learning styles and abilities.

Cambridge Nationals are available in business, engineering, health and social care, ICT, science, sport, art and design, media and performing arts. Available as joint Level 1 and 2 qualifications, the updated Nationals are aimed at students aged 14 to 16 in full-time study.

Cambridge Technicals
See the OCR website for further details.

OCR's Cambridge Technicals are practical and flexible vocationally-related qualifications, offering students in-depth study in a wide range of subjects, including business, health and social care, IT, sport, art and design, media, science, performing arts and engineering.

Cambridge Technicals are aimed at young people aged 16 to 19 who have completed Key Stage 4 of their education and want to study in a more practical, work-related way.

Cambridge Technicals are available at Level 2 and Level 3, and carry UCAS points at Level 3.

NVQs (NQF)

NVQs reward those who demonstrate skills gained at work. They relate to particular jobs and are usefully taken while you are working. Within reason, NVQs do not have to be completed in a specified amount of time. They can be taken by full-time employees or by school and college students with a work placement or part-time job that enables them to develop the appropriate skills. There are no age limits and no special entry requirements.

NVQs are organised into five levels, based on the competencies required. Levels 1-3 are the levels most applicable to learners within the 14-19 phase. Achievement of level 4 within this age group will be rare. See the OCR website for further information.

QCF and Vocationally-related Certificates

There are three levels: award, certificate and diploma.

Vocationally-Related Certificates are assessed according to each individual specification, but may include practical assessments and/or marked assessments. They are designed to provide evidence of a student's relevant skills and knowledge in their chosen subject. These qualifications can be used for employment or as a path towards further education.

Language qualifications

Asset Languages
Asset languages recognise the four skills of language learning – reading, writing, speaking and listening – separately. Developed by OCR, these languages recognise skills in a range of languages from Breakthrough (Entry Level) up to Intermediate (Level 2).

Awarding organisations and examination dates

Awarding organisations and examination dates

In England there are three awarding organisations, each offering GCSE, including Applied GCSEs, A level and Applied A levels. There are separate awarding organisations in Wales (WJEC) and Northern Ireland (CCEA). The awarding organisation in Scotland (SQA) offers equivalent qualifications.

This information was supplied by the awarding bodies and was accurate at the time of going to press. It is intended as a general guide only for candidates in the United Kingdom. Dates are subject to variation and should be confirmed with the awarding organisation concerned.

Contact:
Email: mailbox@aqa.org.uk
Website: www.aqa.org.uk
Tel: 0800 197 7162

Devas Street, Manchester M15 6EX

Stag Hill House, Guildford, Surrey GU2 7XJ
Tel: 01483 506506

31-33 Springfield Avenue, Harrogate, North Yorkshire HG1 2HW

AQA

Qualifications offered:
GCSE
AS and A level
Tech-levels
FCSE
FSMQ
Entry Level Certificate (ELC)
Foundation and Higher Projects
Extended Project Qualification (EPQ)
AQA Baccalaureate
AQA Level 1/2 Certificates
AQA Level 3 Certificates
Functional Skills
Adult literacy and numeracy
Preparation for Working Life
Enterprise and employability
QCF in Personal and Social Education
Foundation learning in the qualification and credit framework
Other assessment schemes:
Unit Award Scheme (UAS)

Examination dates for summer 2016: 13 May – 29 June

CCEA – Council for the Curriculum, Examinations and Assessment

Qualifications offered:
GCSE
GCE AS/A2 level
Key Skills (Levels 1-4)
Entry Level Qualifications
Essential Skills (Levels 1,2 & Entry Level)
Occupational Studies (Levels 1 & 2)
QCF Qualifications
CCEA is currently expanding its portfolio of Applied GCSE, GCE and QCF Level 1 and 2 qualifications to help meet the requirements of the Entitlement Framework.

Examination dates for summer 2016: 4 May – 29 June

Contact:
Email: info@ccea.org.uk
Website: www.ccea.org.uk

29 Clarendon Road, Clarendon Dock, Belfast, BT1 3BG
Tel: (028) 9026 1200

IB – International Baccalaureate

Qualification offered:
IB Diploma
IB Career-related Programme

Contact:
www.ibo.org

Examination dates for summer 2016: 2 – 20 May

IB Global Centre, The Hague, Churchillplein 6, 2517 JW, The Hague, The Netherlands

Tel: +31 70 352 60 00

OCR – Oxford Cambridge and RSA Examinations

Qualifications offered by OCR or sister awarding organisation Cambridge International Examinations, include:
GCSE
GCE AS/A level
IGCSE
Extended Project
Cambridge Pre-U
Cambridge Nationals
Cambridge Technicals
Functional Skills
FSMQ - Free Standing Maths Qualification
Cambridge Progression
NVQ
Plus 'own brand' qualifications, *eg* in IT, business, languages and administration.

Examination dates for summer 2016: 16 May to 29 June (provisional)

Contact:
Website: www.ocr.org.uk (or www.cie.org.uk)

OCR Head Office, 1 Hills Road, Cambridge CB1 2EU
Tel: 01223 553998

Pearson

Qualifications offered:
Pearson's qualifications are offered in the UK but are also available through their international centres across the world. They include:
DiDA, CiDA, AiDA
GCE A levels (AS/A2)
Applied GCEs
GCSEs
Applied GCSEs
Adult Literacy and Numeracy
Functional Skills
Foundation Learning
International GCSEs
Key Skills
ESOL (Skills for Life)
BTEC Customised Qualifications
BTEC Foundation Diploma in Art & Design
BTEC Nationals
BTEC Higher National Certificates and Higher National Diplomas (HNC/HND)
BTEC Firsts
BTEC Specialist qualifications
BTEC Professional qualifications
BTEC WorkSkills
NVQs
Project qualifications

Examination dates for summer 2016: 16 May – 29 June

Contact:
190 High Holborn, London WC1V 7BH

See website for specific contact details: www.edexcel.com

Educational organisations

Educational organisations

The Allied Schools (AS)

Providers of financial and administrative support services and advice to member schools, and is also secretariat to their governing bodies (registered charity No. 1051729).
Member schools:
Canford School
Harrogate Ladies' College
Highfield School
The Old Hall School
Stowe School
Westonbirt Prep
Westonbirt School
Wrekin College
Membership is open to other schools.
The Allied Schools Agency Ltd
Rectory Barn, 6 The Moat, Kingham
Nr Chipping Norton, Oxfordshire OX7 6XZ
Tel: 01608 658197; Fax: 01280 848876.
Email: admin@alliedschools.org.uk
Website: www.alliedschools.org.uk

Artsmark

Arts Council England's Artsmark was set up in 2001, and rounds are held annually.
All schools in England can apply for an Artsmark – primary, middle, secondary, special and pupil referral units, maintained and independent – on a voluntary basis. An Artsmark award is made to schools showing commitment to the full range of arts – music, dance, drama and art and design.
14 Great Peter Street, Westminster, London SW1P 3NQ
Tel: 0845 300 6200.
Email: artsmark@artscouncil.org.uk
Website: www.artsmark.org.uk

Association for the Education and Guardianship of International Students (AEGIS)

AEGIS brings together schools and guardianship organisations to promote the welfare of international students. AEGIS provides accreditation for all reputable guardianship organisations.
Secretary: Janet Bowman, AEGIS, The Wheelhouse, Bond's Mill Estate, Bristol Road, Stonehouse, Gloucestershire GL10 3RF.
Tel/Fax: 01453 821293
Email: janet@aegisuk.net
Website: www.aegisuk.net

The Association of American Study Abroad Programmes (AASAP)

Established in 1991 to represent American study programmes in the UK.
Contact: Amanda Milburn, University of Maryland in London, Connaught Hall, 36-45 Tavistock Square, London WC1H 9EX
Tel: 020 7756 8350
Email: info@aasapuk.org
Website: www.aasapuk.org

The Association of British Riding Schools (ABRS)

An independent body of proprietors and principals of riding establishments, aiming to look after their interests and those of the riding public and to raise standards of management, instruction and animal welfare.
Unit 8, Bramble Hill Farm, Five Oaes Road, Slinfold, Horsham, Sussex RH13 0RL. Tel: 01403 790294
Email: office@abrs-info.org
Website: www.abrs-info.org

Association of Colleges (AOC)

Created in 1996 to promote the interest of further education colleges in England and Wales.
2-5 Stedham Place, London WC1A 1HU
Tel: 0207 034 9900
Fax: 0207 034 9950
Email: enquiries@aoc.co.uk
Website: www.aoc.co.uk

Association of Governing Bodies of Independent Schools (AGBIS)

AGBIS supports and advises governing bodies of schools in the independent sector on all aspects of governance. (Registered charity No. 1108756)
Enquiries should be addressed to: AGBIS General Secretary, Stuart Westley, AGBIS, 3 Codicote Road, Welwyn, Hertfordshire AL6 9LY
Tel: 01438 840730
Fax: 0560 3432632
Email: admin@agbis.org.uk
Website: www.agbis.org.uk

Association of Employment and Learning Providers (AELP)

AELP's purpose is to influence the education and training agenda. They are the voice of independent learning providers throughout England.
Colenso House, 46 Bath Hill, Keynsham, Bristol BS31 1HG
Tel: 0117 986 5389
Email: enquiries@aelp.org.uk
Website: www.aelp.org.uk

The Association of School and Colleges Leaders (ASCL)

Formerly the Secondary Heads Association, the ASCL is a professional association for secondary school and college leaders.
130 Regent Road, Leicester LE1 7PG
Tel: 0116 299 1122
Fax: 0116 299 1123
Email: info@ascl.org.uk
Website: www.ascl.org.uk

Boarding Schools' Association (BSA)

For information on the BSA see editorial on page 33

The British Accreditation Council for Independent Further and Higher Education (BAC)

The British Accreditation Council (BAC) has now been the principal accrediting body for the independent further and higher education and training sector for nearly 30 years. BAC-accredited institutions in the UK now number more than 300, offering everything from website design to yoga to equine dentistry, as well as more standard qualifications in subjects such as business, IT, management and law. As well as our accreditation of institutions offering traditional teaching, BAC has developed a new accreditation scheme for providers offering online, distance and blended learning. Some students may also look to study outside UK at one of the institutions holding BAC international accreditation.
Ground Floor, 14 Devonshire Square, London, EC2M 4YTTel: 0300 330 1400
Email: info@the-bac.org
Website: www.the-bac.org

The British Association for Early Childhood Education (BAECE)

Promotes quality provision for all children from birth to eight in whatever setting they are placed. Publishes booklets and organises conferences for those interested in early years education and care. (Registered charity Nos. 313082; SCO39472)
136 Cavell Street, London E1 2JA
Tel: 020 7539 5400
Fax: 020 7539 5409
Email: office@early-education.org.uk
Website: www.early-education.org.uk

The Choir Schools' Association (CSA)

Represents 44 schools attached to cathedrals, churches and college chapels, which educate cathedral and collegiate choristers.
The Information Officer, Village Farm, The Street, Market Weston, Diss, Norfolk IP22 2NZ
Tel: 01359 221333
Email: info@choirschools.org.uk
Website: www.choirschools.org.uk

The Council for Independent Education (CIFE)

CIFE is the professional association for independent sixth form and tutorial colleges accredited by the British Accreditation Council for Independent Further and Higher Education (BAC), the Independent Schools Council or the DfE (Ofsted). Member colleges specialise in preparing students for GCSE and A level (AS and A2) in particular and university entrance in general.
The aim of the association is to provide a forum for the exchange of information and ideas, and for the promotion of best practice, and to safeguard adherence to strict standards of professional conduct and ethical propriety. Further information can be obtained from CIFE:
Tel: 0208 767 8666
Email: enquiries@cife.org.uk
Website: www.cife.org.uk

Council of British International Schools (COBIS)

COBIS is a membership association of British schools of quality worldwide and is committed to a stringent process of quality assurance for all its member schools. COBIS is a member of the Independent Schools Council (ISC) of the United Kingdom.
55-56 Russell Square, Bloomsbury, London WC1B 4HP
Tel: 020 3826 7190
Email: executive.director@cobis.org.uk
Website: www.cobis.org.uk

Council of International Schools (CIS)

CIS is a not-for-profit organisation committed to supporting its member schools and colleges in achieving and delivering the highest standards of international education. CIS provides accreditation to schools, teacher and leader recruitment and best practice development. CIS Higher Education assists member colleges and universities in recruiting a diverse profile of qualified international students.
Schipholweg 113, 2316 XC Leiden, The Netherlands.
Tel: +31 71 524 3300
Email: info@cois.org
Website: www.cois.org

Dyslexia Action (DA)

A registered, educational charity (No. 268502), which has established teaching and assessment centres and conducts teacher-training throughout the UK. The aim of the institute is to help people with dyslexia of all ages to overcome their difficulties in learning to read, write and spell and to achieve their potential.
Dyslexia Action House, 10 High Street, Egham, Surrey TW20 9EA
Tel: 0300 303 8357
Email: hello@dyslexiaaction.org.uk
Website: www.dyslexiaaction.org.uk

European Association for International Education (EAIE)

A not-for-profit organisation aiming for internationalisation in higher education in Europe. It has a membership of over 1800.
PO Box 11189, 1001 GD Amsterdam, The Netherlands
Tel: +31 20 344 5100
Fax: +31 20 344 5119
Email: info@eaie.org
Website: www.eaie.org

ECIS

ECIS is a membership organisation which provides services to support professional development, good governance and leadership in international schools.
Fourth Floor, 146 Buckingham Palace Road, London, SW1W 9TR
Tel: 020 7824 7040
Email: ecis@ecis.org
Website: www.ecis.org

The Girls' Day School Trust (GDST)

The Girls' Day School Trust (GDST) is one of the largest, longest-established and most successful groups of independent schools in the UK, with 4000 staff and over 20,000 students between the ages of three and 18.
As a charity that owns and runs a family of 26 schools in England and Wales, it reinvests all its income into its schools for the benefit of the pupils. With a long history of pioneering innovation in the education of girls, the GDST now also educates boys in some of its schools, and has two coeducational sixth form colleges. (Registered charity No. 306983)
100 Rochester Row, London SW1P 1JP
Tel: 020 7393 6666
Fax: 020 7393 6789
Email: info@wes.gdst.net
Website: www.gdst.net

Girls' Schools Association (GSA)

For information on the GSA see editorial on page 34

The Headmasters' and Headmistresses' Conference (HMC)

For information on the HMC see editorial on page 34

Human Scale Education (HSE)

An educational reform movement aiming for small education communities based on democracy, fairness and respect. (Registered charity No. 1000400)
Unit 8, Fairseat Farm, Chew Stoke, Bristol BS40 8XF
Tel/Fax: 01275 332516
Email: info@hse.org.uk
Website: www.hse.org.uk

The Independent Association of Prep Schools (IAPS)

For further information about IAPS see editorial on page 36

The Independent Schools Association (ISA)

For further information about ISA see editorial on page 36

The Independent Schools' Bursars Association (ISBA)

Exists to support and advance financial and operational performance in independent schools. The ISBA is a charitable company limited by guarantee. (Company No. 6410037; registered charity No. 1121757.)
Bluett House, Unit 11-12 Manor Farm, Cliddesden, Basingstoke, Hampshire RG25 2JB
Tel: 01256 330369
Fax: 01256 330376
Email: office@theisba.org.uk
Website: www.theisba.org.uk

The Independent Schools Council (ISC)

The Independent Schools Council exists to promote choice, diversity and excellence in education; the development of talent at all levels of ability; and the widening of opportunity for children from all backgrounds to achieve their potential. Its 1280 member schools educate more than 500,000 children at all levels of ability and from all socio-economic classes. Nearly a third of children in ISC schools receive help with fees. The Governing Council of ISC contains representatives from each of the eight ISC constituent associations listed below.
See also page 40.

Members:
Association of Governing Bodies of Independent Schools (AGBIS)
Council of British International Schools (COBIS)
Girls' Schools Association (GSA)
Headmasters' and Headmistresses' Conference (HMC)
Independent Association of Prep Schools (IAPS)
Independent Schools Association (ISA)
Independent Schools Bursars' Association (ISBA)
The Society of Heads
The council also has close relations with the BSA and the SCIS.
First Floor, 27 Queen Anne's Gate, London, SW1H 9BU
Tel: 020 7766 7070
Fax: 020 7766 7071
Email: research@isc.co.uk
Website: www.isc.co.uk

The Independent Schools Examinations Board (ISEB)

Details of the Common Entrance examinations are obtainable from:
Suite 3, Endeavour House, Crow Arch Lane, Ringwood BH24 1HP
Tel: 01425 470555
Email: enquiries@iseb.co.uk
Website: www.iseb.co.uk
Copies of past papers can be purchased from Galore Publishing Ltd: www.galorepark.co.uk

The Inspiring Futures Foundation (IFF)

The IFF provides careers education and guidance to schools and students. Professional support and training is available to school staff and our Futurewise programme provides individual, web-based, support for students and their parents. Career/subject insight courses, gap-year fairs and an information service are additional elements of the service.
St George's House, Knoll Road, Camberley, Surrey GU15 3SY
Tel: 01276 687500
Fax: 01276 28258
Email: helpline@inspiringfutures.org.uk
Website: www.inspiringfutures.org.uk

International Baccalaureate (IB)

For full information about the IB see full entry on page 187

International Schools Theatre Association (ISTA)

International body of teachers and students of theatre, run by teachers for teachers. Registered charity No. 1050103.
3 Omega Offices, 14 Coinagehall St, Helston, Cornwall TR13 8EB
Tel: 01326 560398
Email: office@ista.co.uk
Website: www.ista.co.uk

Maria Montessori Institute (MMI)

Authorised by the Association Montessori Internationale (AMI) to run their training course in the UK. Further information is available from:
26 Lyndhurst Gardens, Hampstead, London NW3 5NW
Tel: 020 7435 3646
Fax: 020 7431 8096
Email: info@mariamontessori.org
Website: www.mariamontessori.org

The National Association of Independent Schools & Non-Maintained Schools (NASS)

A membership organisation working with and for special schools in the voluntary and private sectors within the UK. Registered charity No. 1083632.
PO Box 705, York YO30 6WW
Tel/Fax: 01904 624446
Email: krippon@nasschools.org.uk
Website: www.nasschools.org.uk

National Day Nurseries Association (NDNA)

A national charity (No. 1078275) that aims to promote quality in early years.
NDNA, National Early Years Enterprise Centre, Longbow Close, Huddersfield, West Yorkshire HD2 1GQ
Tel: 01484 407070
Fax: 01484 407060
Email: info@ndna.org.uk
Website: www.ndna.org.uk

NDNA Cymru, Office 2, Crown House, 11 Well Street, Ruthin, Denbighshire LL15 1AE
Tel: 01824 707823;
Fax: 01824 707824;
Email: wales@ndna.org.uk

NDNA Scotland, The Mansfield Traquair Centre, 15 Mansfield Place, Edinburgh EH3 6BB
Tel: 0131 516 6967;
Email: scotland@ndna.org.uk

National Foundation for Educational Research (NFER)

NFER is the UK's largest independent provider of research, assessment and information services for education, training and children's services. Its clients include UK government departments and agencies at both national and local levels. NFER is a not-for-profit organisation and a registered charity No. 313392.
Head Office, The Mere, Upton Park, Slough, Berkshire SL1 2DQ
Tel: 01753 574123
Fax: 01753 691632
Email: enquiries@nfer.ac.uk
Website: www.nfer.ac.uk

Potential Plus UK

Potential Plus UK is an independent charity that supports the social, emotional and learning needs of children with high learning potential of all ages and backgrounds. Registered charity No. 313182.
Suite 1.2, Challenge House, Sherwood Drive, Bletchley, Milton Keynes, Buckinghamshire MK3 6DP
Tel: 01908 646433
Fax: 0870 770 3219
Email: amazingchildren@potentialplusuk.org
Website: www.potentialplusuk.org

The Round Square Schools (RSIS)

An international group of schools formed in 1967 following the principles of Dr Kurt Hahn, the founder of Salem School in Germany, and Gordonstoun in Scotland. The Round Square, named after Gordonstoun's 17th century circular building in the centre of the school, now has more than 100 member schools. Registered charity No. 327117.
The Secretary, The Round Square, Swan House, Madeira Walk, Windsor SL41EU
Tel: 01474 709843
Website: www.roundsquare.org

Royal National Children's Foundation

In December 2010, Joint Educational Trust and the Royal Wanstead Children's Foundation merged to form this new Foundation. For further information contact:
Sandy Lane, Cobham, Surrey KT11 2ES
Tel: 01932 868622
Fax: 01932 866420
Email: admin@rncf.org.uk
Website: www.rncf.org.uk

Schools Music Association of Great Britain (SMA)

The SMA is a national 'voice' for music in education. It is now part of the Incorporated Society of Musicians (Registered charity No. 313646)
4-5 Inverness Mews, London W2 3JQ
Tel: 020 7221 3499
Fax: 020 7243 3437
Email: membership@ism.org
Website: www.schoolsmusic.org.uk

Scottish Council of Independent Schools (SCIS)

Representing more than 70 independent, fee-paying schools in Scotland, the Scottish Council of Independent Schools (SCIS) is the foremost authority on independent schools in Scotland and offers impartial information, advice and guidance to parents. Registered charity No. SC01803. They can be contacted at:
61 Dublin Street, Edinburgh EH3 6NL
Tel: 0131 556 2316
Email: info@scis.org.uk
Website: www.scis.org.uk

Society of Education Consultants (SEC)

The Society is a professional membership organisation that supports management consultants who specialise in education and children's services. The society's membership includes consultants who work as individuals, in partnerships or in association with larger consultancies.
SEC Administrator, Bellamy House,
13 West Street, Cromer NR27 9HZ
Email: administration@sec.org.uk
Website: www.sec.org.uk

The Society of Heads

For full information see editorial on page 37

The State Boarding Schools' Association (SBSA)

For full information about the SBSA see editorial on page 33

Support and Training in Prep Schools (SATIPS)

SATIPS aims to support teachers in the independent and maintained sectors of education. (Registered charity No. 313699)
5 McMichaels Way, Hurst Green,
Etchingham, East Sussex TN19 7HJ
Tel: 07584 862263
Email: support@satips.com
Website: www.satips.org

Steiner Waldorf Schools Fellowship (SWSF)

Representing Steiner education in the UK and Ireland, the SWSF has member schools and early years centres in addition to interest groups and other affiliated organisations. Member schools offer education for children within the normal range of ability, aged three to 18. (Registered charity No. 295104)
11 Church Street, Stourbridge, DY8 1LT.
Tel: 01384 374116
Fax: 01384 374142
Email: admin@steinerwaldorf.org
Website: www.steinerwaldorf.org.uk

The Tutors' Association

Launched in 2013 to represent tutoring and the supplementary education sector.
15 Bencombe Road, Marlow, Buckinghamshire, SL7 3NX
Tel: 01628 890130
Fax: +44 (0)1628 890131
Email: clenton@thetutorsassociation.org.uk
Website: www.thetutorsassociation.org.uk

UCAS (Universities and Colleges Admissions Service)

UCAS is the organisation responsible for managing applications to higher education courses in England, Scotland, Wales and Northern Ireland. (Registered charity Nos. 1024741 and SCO38598)
Rose Hill, New Barn Lane,
Cheltenham, Gloucestershire GL52 3LZ
Customer Service: 0871 468 0468
Website: www.ucas.com

UKCISA – The Council for International Student Affairs

UKCISA is the UK's national advisory body serving the interests of international students and those who work with them. (Registered charity No. 1095294)
9-17 St Albans Place, London N1 0NX
Tel: 020 7288 9214
Fax: 020 7288 4360
Website: www.ukcisa.org.uk

United World Colleges (UWC)

UWC was founded in 1962 and their philosophy is based on the ideas of Dr Kurt Hahn (see Round Square Schools). Registered charity No. 313690.
The United World Colleges (International), Second Floor, 17-21 Emerald Street,
London WC1N 3QN
Tel: 020 7269 7800
Fax: 020 7405 4374
Email: uwcio@uwc.org
Website: www.uwc.org

World-Wide Education Service of CfBT Education Trust (WES)

A leading independent service which provides home education courses worldwide.
Waverley House, Penton,
Carlisle, Cumbria CA6 5QU
Tel: 01228 577123
Fax: 01228 577333
Email: office@weshome.com
Website: www.weshome.com

Glossary

Glossary

ACETS	Awards and Certificates in Education
AEA	Advanced Extension Award
AEB	Associated Examining Board for the General Certificate of Education
AEGIS	Association for the Education and Guardianship of International Students
AGBIS	Association of Governing Bodies of Independent Schools
AHIS	Association of Heads of Independent Schools
AJIS	Association of Junior Independent Schools
ALP	Association of Learning Providers
ANTC	The Association of Nursery Training Colleges
AOC	Association of Colleges
AP	Advanced Placement
ASCL	Association of School & College Leaders
ASL	Additional and Specialist Learning
ATI	The Association of Tutors Incorporated
AQA	Assessment and Qualification Alliance/ Northern Examinations and Assessment Board
BA	Bachelor of Arts
BAC	British Accreditation Council for Independent Further and Higher Education
BAECE	The British Association for Early Childhood Education
BD	Bachelor of Divinity
BEA	Boarding Educational Alliance
BEd	Bachelor of Education
BLitt	Bachelor of Letters
BPrimEd	Bachelor of Primary Education
BSA	Boarding Schools' Association
BSc	Bachelor of Science
BTEC	Range of work-related, practical programmes leading to qualifications equivalent to GCSEs and A levels awarded by Edexcel
Cantab	Cambridge University
CATSC	Catholic Association of Teachers in Schools and Colleges
CCEA	Council for the Curriculum, Examination and Assessment
CDT	Craft, Design and Technology
CE	Common Entrance Examination
CEAS	Children's Education Advisory Service
CertEd	Certificate of Education
CIE	Cambridge International Examinations
CIFE	Conference for Independent Education
CIS	Council of International Schools
CISC	Catholic Independent Schools' Conference
CLAIT	Computer Literacy and Information Technology
CNED	Centre National d'enseignement (National Centre of long distance learning)

COBIS	Council of British International)
CSA	The Choir Schools' Association
CST	The Christian Schools' Trust
DfE	Department for Education (formerly DfES and DCFS)
DipEd	Diploma of Education
DipTchng	Diploma of Teaching
EAIE	European Association for International Education
ECIS	European Council of International Schools
EdD	Doctor of Education
Edexcel	GCSE Examining group, incorporating Business and Technology Education Council (BTEC) and University of London Examinations and Assessment Council (ULEAC)
EFL	English as a Foreign Language
ELAS	Educational Law Association
EPQ	Extended Project qualification
ESL	English as a Second Language
FCoT	Fellow of the College of Teachers (TESOL)
FEFC	Further Education Funding Council
FRSA	Fellow of the Royal Society of Arts
FSMQ	Free-Standing Mathematics Qualification
GCE	General Certificate of Education
GCSE	General Certificate of Secondary Education
GDST	Girls' Day School Trust
GNVQ	General National Vocational Qualifications
GOML	Graded Objectives in Modern Languages
GSA	Girls' Schools Association
GSVQ	General Scottish Vocational Qualifications
HMC	Headmasters' and Headmistresses' Conference
HMCJ	Headmasters' and Headmistresses' Conference Junior Schools
HNC	Higher National Certificate
HND	Higher National Diploma
IAPS	Independent Association of Prep Schools
IB	International Baccalaureate
ICT	Information and Communication Technology
IFF	Inspiring Futures Foundation (formerly ISCO)
IGCSE	International General Certificate of Secondary Education
INSET	In service training
ISA	Independent Schools Association
ISBA	Independent Schools' Bursars' Association
ISCis	Independent Schools Council information service
ISC	Independent Schools Council
ISEB	Independent Schools Examination Board
ISST	International Schools Sports Tournament
ISTA	International Schools Theatre Association

ITEC	International Examination Council
JET	Joint Educational Trust
LA	Local Authority
LISA	London International Schools Association
MA	Master of Arts
MCIL	Member of the Chartered Institute of Linguists
MEd	Master of Education
MIoD	Member of the Institute of Directors
MLitt	Master of Letters
MSc	Master of Science
MusD	Doctor of Music
MYP	Middle Years Programme
NABSS	National Association of British Schools in Spain
NAGC	National Association for Gifted Children
NAHT	National Association of Head Teachers
NAIS	National Association of Independent Schools
NASS	National Association of Independent Schools & Non-maintained Special Schools
NDNA	National Day Nurseries Association
NEASC	New England Association of Schools and Colleges
NFER	National Federation of Educational Research
NPA	National Progression Award
NQ	National Qualification
NQF	National Qualifications Framework
NQT	Newly Qualified Teacher
NVQ	National Vocational Qualifications
OCR	Oxford, Cambridge and RSA Examinations
OLA	Online Language Assessment for Modern Languages
Oxon	Oxford
PGCE	Post Graduate Certificate in Education
PhD	Doctor of Philosophy
PL	Principal Learning
PNEU	Parents' National Education Union
PYP	Primary Years Programme
QCA	Qualifications and Curriculum Authority
QCF	Qualifications and Credit Framework
RSIS	The Round Square Schools
SAT	Scholastic Aptitude Test
SATIPS	Support & Training in Prep Schools/Society of Assistant Teachers in Prep Schools
SBSA	State Boarding Schools Association
SCE	Service Children's Education
SCIS	Scottish Council of Independent Schools
SCQF	Scottish Credit and Qualifications Framework
SEC	The Society of Educational Consultants
SEN	Special Educational Needs
SFCF	Sixth Form Colleges' Forum
SFIA	School Fees Insurance Agency Limited
SFIAET	SFIA Educational Trust

SMA	Schools Music Association
SoH	The Society of Heads
SQA	Scottish Qualifications Authority
STEP	Second Term Entrance Paper (Cambridge)
SVQ	Scottish Vocational Qualifications
SWSF	Steiner Waldorf Schools Fellowship
TABS	The Association of Boarding Schools
TISCA	The Independent Schools Christian Alliance
TOEFL	Test of English as a Foreign Language
UCAS	Universities and Colleges Admissions Service for the UK
UCST	United Church Schools Trust
UKLA	UK Literacy Association
UKCISA	The UK Council for International Education
UWC	United World Colleges
WISC	World International Studies Committee
WJEC	Welsh Joint Education Committee
WSSA	Welsh Secondary Schools Association

Index

Index

Index

M

N